Britain's Oil

Britain's Oil

Guy Arnold

Hamish Hamilton: *London*

First published in Great Britain 1978
by Hamish Hamilton Limited
90 Great Russell Street London WC1B 3PT

Copyright © 1978 by Guy Arnold

British Library Cataloguing in Publication Data

Arnold, Guy
  Britain's oil.
  1. Offshore oil industry–North Sea
  I. Title
  333.8'2   HD9575.N57

  ISBN 0–241–89995–8

Printed in Great Britain by
Ebenezer Baylis and Son Limited
The Trinity Press, Worcester, and London

Contents

List of illustrations

Between pages 244 and 245

Illustrations 1, 2a, 2b, 3a, 3b, 5b, 6, and 8 are reproduced by permission of British Petroleum; 4 is reproduced by permission of the *Financial Times;* 5a and 7b are Crown Copyright photographs.
The maps were drawn by Patrick Leeson, based on those published in the *Brown Book* 1978.

Acknowledgments

A great number of individuals, companies and organizations, including government departments, have given me great assistance in my research for the information upon which this book is based. They have been generous with their time and have answered long lists of what may often have seemed simple or naive questions; they have made available papers and information, made arrangements for trips and organized visits and provided me with much hospitality. I am deeply grateful to all those who have helped me in this way.

The oil companies have been generous with their help and a number of their busiest executives have taken time to explain to me aspects of this complex industry. I am especially grateful to BP, whose hospitality and help have been invaluable: in London, in Aberdeen and Shetland. I am equally indebted to Shell and Esso. The smaller oil companies, often with a very different viewpoint to that of the 'majors', have also been unfailingly helpful.

A number of companies involved in a wide range of support activities for North Sea oil have been equally ready to help, providing many insights into the effects oil is having upon British industry; they include P & O Sea Oil Services, Brown & Root and Foster Wheeler.

I am particularly grateful to Philip Algar of the Institute of Petroleum and to the staff of the Institute's library.

A number of banks in the City now have oil divisions, and talking with their personnel has enabled me to obtain an understanding of the size and complexity of the financial operations involved in North Sea developments.

The Department of Energy is the ministry responsible for all aspects of government policy on oil and gas: I am grateful to the Secretary of State for Energy, the Rt Hon Tony Benn MP, and to the Minister of State, Dr J. Dickson Mabon MP; the Department's Information Section and especially David Woods; and to a number of civil servants who answered detailed questions on policy. I am also indebted to a number of executives and officials in the state energy corporations, BNOC, BGC and NCB, and to OSO.

1*

There are many other organizations whose members have taken time to answer questions and supply information. I should particularly like to mention the Director of Robert Gordon's Institute of Technology in Aberdeen, Peter Clarke, who laid on a special session with members of his staff; John Dawes of Bain Dawes Ltd who explained the intricacies of energy insurance; T. A. Hollobone of Hollobone, Hibbert & Associates who made plain some of the problems attached to North Sea diving; and Mrs Daphne Duffy of the Institute of Petroleum (Scotland) who arranged a Scottish itinerary for me.

Members of Parliament of several persuasions were kind enough to give me their views both on the oil industry and on the controversial subject of the use of the oil wealth, and though they may not accept my conclusions, I hope I have accurately reproduced the essence of our conversations and not misrepresented their views.

In the book I have drawn quite substantially upon several books which can be regarded as authoritative texts. Of these I should mention: *The Political Economy of North Sea Oil* by D. I. MacKay and G. A. MacKay, which is the most thorough early study of the economic impact of the North Sea; *Shetland and Oil* by James Nicolson; *Labour Law and Offshore Oil* by Jonathan Kitchen. I have quoted extensively from these books and am grateful to the publishers and authors for permission to do so. I have also quoted from many other sources and would like to thank Mrs Deirdre Hunt of RGIT for making her papers and findings available to me. I should also like to thank a number of people who have checked various parts of the text for me, though I accept full responsibility for any errors or omissions. The conclusions are my own.

Finally I wish to thank the following: Bill Adams (Scottish Council, Development and Industry); G. F. Ahalt (International Energy Bank); David C. Anderson (Barclays Group of Banks); Douglas Anderson (Ivory & Sime); P. D. M. Anderson (BNOC); Bruce Andrews (*Financial Times* North Sea Letter); John Baldwin (AUEW Construction Division); Lord Balogh; Donald Bain; J. A. Beckett; John Biffen, MP; Dr Jack Birks (BP); Brenton J. Bradly (Morgan Guaranty Trust Company of New York); Michael Brown (TTO); R. Andrew Bruce (Morgan Guaranty Trust Company of New York); W. J. Cairns (W. J. Cairns & Partners); Bill Callaghan (TUC); John Carder (Esso); K. Chaplin (Bain Dawes); Ian R. Clark (BNOC); Iain M. Clubb (Thomson Oil); A. Cluff (Cluff Oil); A. L. Coleby (Bank of England); John Collins (BP); Douglas Crawford, MP; Lloyd Crump (D of E); Peter H. J. de Vink (Ivory & Sime); Mark C. Deverell (Barclays Bank International Ltd); J. Dick (ICI); Alastair M. Dunnett (TTO); Professor G. M. Dunnett

(University of Aberdeen); Bob Dyk (Hamilton Brothers); Ronald T. Edwards (Bank of Scotland); Sir Derek Ezra (NCB); Peter Fitch (BP); Tony Fox (Tricentrol); Malcolm S. Fraser (Bank of Scotland); Professor Maxwell Gaskin (University of Aberdeen); H. R. George (D of E); J. P. Gibson; D. M. Green (BP); Terry A. Green (National Westminster International); Jim Hanna (TUC); Nigel Harrison (TTO); Edward Hart (Cluff Oil); J. Henderson (BP); the Rt Hon Sir Geoffrey Howe, QC, MP; David Howell, MP; Matthew Huber (BP); G. Kear (D of E); Lord Kearton (BNOC); G. W. Kelly (Scottish Economic Planning Department); T. J. Kenny (Shell); Tom King, MP; Geoff Larmanie (BP); C. J. W. Ledger (Shell); P. O. Lewis (British Gas); J. Licence (British Gas); C. Lucas (D of E); Lucy Macdonald; Professor Donald MacKay (Heriot Watt University); Tony Mackintosh (Wood MacKenzie & Co); Stephen Maxwell; Dr Robert McIntyre; Dick Marshall (OSO); Elizabeth Marshall (Shetland Islands Council); A. E. Maule (OSO); George S. Miller (Morgan Grenfell & Co Limited); Neil Munro (BP); Roger Newstead (Esso); Mike Parker (NCB); Dr A. W. Pearce (Esso); P. Pollard (Shell); C. L. Pritchard (Church of Scotland); Professor Colin Robinson (University of Surrey); J. S. Robson (Shell); Professor H. Rose (Barclays Bank International); Dr S. H. Salter (University of Edinburgh); Geoffrey Searle (LASMO); Norman J. Smith (OSO); Sir Philip Southwell (Brown & Root); G. G. Stockwell (Iraq Petroleum); David Underdown (Inland Revenue); Arild Vollan; Commander S. A. Warner (D of E); Michael Whittall (BP); C. J. Wilkinson (Foster Wheeler Ltd); G. Williams (UKOOA); Gordon Wilson, MP; Norman Woodhouse (NCB).

Guy Arnold
1978

Introduction

Few of the public debates about Britain's oil wealth that became a feature of press activity in 1977 ever really considered the question of advantage: on whose behalf is Britain's oil being extracted, handled and sold? There has been so much lofty language expended upon the subject of North Sea oil that some elementary facts have been obscured.

The oil companies are in the business for profit. The politicians—having somewhat late in the day realized the extent of the political opportunity offered by the oil—have as their interest party advantage and personal power. The Labour Party, in its 1977 capacity as the government, produced statesmanlike papers about the options as regards using the oil wealth that are open to the country; one may be certain that the options they favour are geared to winning elections. The Tories in opposition urge upon the country those courses of action most likely to appeal to the bulk of their supporters. The Scottish National Party (SNP) sees oil as a godsend to its cause. And everyone else—unions, support companies, interest groups—lines up to enter a claim upon resources that euphoria would stretch for ever. After all the particular interest groups have made their claims one is left wondering what, if anything, the British people as a whole will get out of their oil.

North Sea oil represents an enormous new source of political and economic power: for the oil companies, of course; for the politicians; for the civil servants. And just as Aberdonians like to claim that their city has become the world's new oil capital, so a new British oil 'establishment' has sprung into being. The civil service has a vested career interest in more government control; civil servants like power and are adept at projecting themselves as working selflessly in the national interest.

There has already been much debate about the role of the companies; multinational corporations have become the foremost bogeys of our age and are likely to remain so for a long time to come. But if it is true that such companies can be ruthless and selfish and can be demonstrated to be working against the public interest, many governments can also be shown up in the same light: either by their political opponents or, more simply, because the first concern of politicians, despite what they may argue to the contrary, is to keep their jobs and maintain their parties in power—and to do this they will embark upon policies as much against the public interest as those of the oil companies. The only difference is that a political party can be voted out of office; an oil company may be 'managed' by the politicians or, ultimately, perhaps nationalized.

Three men have particularly incurred the wrath of the oilmen: the Secretary of State for Energy, Mr Wedgwood Benn, because his name—quite apart from his position as Secretary of State—is synonymous with all those left-wing policies of state intervention most abhorred by big business. Lord Kearton, the ebullient 'poacher turned gamekeeper' who heads the British National Oil Corporation (BNOC), has rapidly demonstrated that much of the so-called expertise of the oil companies is in fact a carefully fostered mystique to keep out prying eyes—especially those of government. And Professor Peter Odell, whose thesis that there is far more extractable oil under the North Sea than the companies will ever admit (he argues that they only want to cream off the most profitable oil leaving the rest and claims this to be against the national interest), is guaranteed to make oilmen apoplectic. Their roles in the story of Britain's oil, though varied, are all of significance and the fact that three men of such widely different backgrounds have all achieved a prominence in oil matters is in itself an indication of how wide the ramifications of Britain's 'oil province' have now become.

Oil has always been big business but, until recently, for Britain this meant BP and Shell operating in the Middle East or Nigeria, or the ever-rising price of petrol to the public at large. Now thousands of onshore jobs are involved: local authorities in Scotland—Aberdeen, Peterhead, Shetland and Orkney—are finding oil a source of immense new authority; and government is discovering that for Britain—as for other quite different countries elsewhere—oil can transform the economic outlook.

Thwarted in his attempt to introduce a sensible energy policy in the USA, President Carter spoke of 'The biggest rip-off in US history' in relation to the oil companies. It is worth asking how much of a 'rip-off' has taken place in the North Sea.

It is a long time since a British Prime Minister has felt able to couple the name of the deity with the doings of the British people, yet in September 1977 on the occasion of a visit to BP's Forties field Prime Minister Callaghan felt able to speak as though God—once more—was on our side.

Given the acquisitive nature of human beings—whether in terms of wealth or of power—it is quite exceptionally difficult to be fair to all the individuals, groups and organizations that have discovered an interest in Britain's oil. Extraordinary greed at many levels has been aroused by the oil discoveries. It is not simply a question of money, and money on a huge scale. It is also a question of power.

By the end of 1977 the British people as a whole had become aware of the oil and its potential. The pound was rising again, at last; the economy was on the mend; the Labour Party suddenly saw the prospect of winning the next election, something that had looked utterly remote a year earlier; and almost daily the media had something to say about oil and the wealth it would bring to the country. 1978 began with a burst of euphoria.

Britain has been lucky in the North Sea carve-up; because of her geography and long coastline she has received 46 per cent of the North Sea (for oil and other resource purposes) south of latitude 62 degrees while Norway has received 27 per cent, the Netherlands 10 per cent, Denmark 9 per cent, West Germany 7 per cent, and the remaining 1 per cent of the southern North Sea has been divided between Belgium and France.

Alastair Dunnett (a past editor of *The Scotsman* and now chairman of the Thomson Organization oil division) says there is a vast new industry with a huge output which has grown up with phenomenal speed and that on the whole Britain is coping with it. So she should. Oilmen are noted for playing things close to the chest and recently with state participation, nationalization and other government interference with their stakes and profits round the world they have, not surprisingly, become more close-mouthed and cautious still. Yet despite all their caution there is a boom in the North Sea which cannot be disguised, and the best proof of this lies in the country's economic turnround, the growing reserves, and a government making predictions about the economy which for once come right.

The speed of realization became clearer during 1977: in April the Department of Energy announced that half the country's oil needs would be met out of North Sea resources by the end of the year; eight weeks later it was admitted that that target had been passed in May. New fields have continued to be found; existing finds are being upgraded—BP upgraded the Forties field by 25 per cent to produce 500,000 barrels a day instead of 400,000 and Shell upgraded the Dunlin field by 50 per cent. Others will be upgraded and the search is moving steadily west of Shetland.

Whatever the eventual figures for offshore reserves may turn out to be, they are already not far short of total published reserves for the

USA. On current production plans it looks as though by the 1980s Britain will have passed such oil states as Venezuela, Iraq, Kuwait, Libya, Nigeria and Indonesia and as a producer will only lie behind the giants—Saudi Arabia, the USSR, the USA and Iran—and perhaps China.

There has grown up a curious mixture of public euphoria and attendant pessimism. On the one hand, more and more interest groups count what they hope will be their chickens before the oil eggs have quite hatched; on the other hand, the doom peddlers suggest that oil could turn out to be a disaster, that we will catch 'Dutch Disease'—the phrase has been applied to the inflationary public and private spending Holland has indulged since the 1959 discovery of the Groningen gas field—and warn against any suggestion that the oil amounts to anything valuable to the country at all.

Nigeria, whose oil is expected to run out in the mid 1990s, has set herself the target of creating a modern infrastructure with her oil wealth in the meantime. She faces an exceptionally hard task, for her eighty million people, despite oil, still have a *per capita* income that is among the lowest in the world. By comparison Britain has a huge industrial-commercial-technological base of the most sophisticated kind and, added to this, has more oil than Nigeria. In those terms the opportunities are great indeed.

The idea that Britain could be self-sufficient in oil was unthinkable even at the end of the 1960s. By the mid 1970s BP could say: 'UK national self-sufficiency of around two million barrels per day is expected by 1980 and thereafter a modest surplus at least throughout the '80s.' The company estimates a peak for North Sea production between 2·8 and 3·7 million barrels a day by 1985. What happens thereafter will depend upon further discoveries. But it has to be remembered that oil goes on ticking over for 100 years or more. No major oil field has ever dried up: the rate falls off, the major extraction ends and most of the equipment is removed but something continues. With steadily improving technology the possibility of extending the life of a field must increase with the years.

Energy consumption, however, is also rising and predictions all point to a yet faster rise when the mid 1970s recession comes to an end. In 1976, for example, a total of £13,500 million was spent on energy in Britain—20 per cent up on the previous year—equivalent to an expenditure of £250 a head of the population. Total energy consumption came to 325 million tons of coal equivalent.

Demand in all the industrial countries continues to rise while the developing countries are also beginning to consume a greater amount themselves as they industrialize. The next twenty years will be the oil age in energy terms; thereafter as world stocks of oil are rapidly depleted, coal is likely to come into its own again to bridge the gap into the nuclear age.

Demand forecasts are notoriously imprecise. According to a 1969 study by the National Academy of Sciences in the USA, 80 per cent of the earth's extractable gas resources will be depleted by 2000, while oil resources at the 1972 consumption level will last for 30 years, coal for 150 years. In fact things never work out in such neat fashion. A multiplicity of predictions are now being made as to when energy resources will run out. It has become fashionable to talk of a coming energy gap, probably in the 1990s. There will be no gap. There will be switches into different fuels.

Long-term planning of the energy resources that are available to us is needed on a world scale; it is in this context that talk of a gap does have relevance. It is one thing to regard energy resources such as oil as finite; it is something quite different to attempt to plan in the 1970s for the day in the 1990s when, the pundits say, the oil will run dry. Britain at least of the major industrialized powers will now be in energy surplus for some years to come, while some of her oil will be exported. What is often overlooked is the extent of Britain's North Sea gas finds, which in oil terms are worth half the total of the oil finds.

Growing public awareness of the rate at which oil is being consumed—the Yom Kippur War and subsequent OPEC price rises can claim the credit for this awareness—mean that the alternatives for the future have come into serious debate. And in a sense this represents a public 'first'. Not in living memory has there been such wide-ranging discussion about the implications of using up a particular resource as there is now about energy. Such debate represents an advance: that we seriously consider in the 1970s the programmes to be adopted *now* in relation to the energy needs and ways of satisfying those needs in the 1990s and beyond. However imperfect the result may be, it is rare indeed that governments debate policies for twenty years ahead.

The range of alternative fuels to oil is large: coal, hydro-electric power, nuclear power and the renewable resources—wave, wind and solar energy—are the most discussed, while increasingly attention is being turned to ways of conservation; saving fuel by, for example, introducing better methods of insulation into house building.

Decisions about energy production ten years in the future have to be taken today and a wrong decision will turn out to be extremely costly. Yet it is during the period 1978–85 that the groundwork must be laid in terms of the nuclear or coal power that will fuel the nation by the end of the century. North Sea oil provides Britain with a remarkable breathing space in which to plan a future energy policy—

something that has never been done in the past. At the same time the 'bonanza' of oil wealth ought to be used as a catalyst to encourage regeneration in many parts of the economy that are now stagnant. How well these two tasks will be performed must rest largely with the politicians; and they, as a breed, are usually limited in scope by the date of the next election.

In a letter to *The Times* of August 1977 Professor Bockris, a chemist at the Flinders University of South Australia, pointed out that the average real income in a population is proportional to the energy available per person; and, more important in this connexion, that 'The exhaustion (or real increase in price) phase has begun for natural gas and oil.' His basic message was that inflation and un-employment would increase until a way of getting cheap energy from inexhaustible sources had been devised, which ultimately means the renewable sources. To the present time we have had cheap energy by using up finite supplies of non-renewable resources—coal, oil, gas.

Not surprisingly against this background of dwindling world energy resources, and most especially of oil and gas, stakes in the North Sea are immensely valuable. The oil industry's operations there are among the most costly and challenging in Britain's indus-trial history. And the demands for high investment will continue for many years.

The North Sea and Alaska oil finds are the most significant non-OPEC ones in the world and both are in hostile environments on the edges of present technology. Yet the entire North Sea and Alaska resources together amount to no more than 30 to 40 billion barrels, and this has to be seen in the context of world resources now standing at 650 billion barrels. Thus, although the North Sea may be huge in British terms, it amounts to no more than between three and four per cent of oil and gas resources in world terms.

The power of the oil companies is very great. Not only do they find and extract oil; world petrochemical production is worth $100 billion a year. There is also the vast refining and tanker business and a great part of all these activities is in the hands of the oil majors. At the same time few industries have such large risks attached to them or require such enormous capital outlays. Peter Baxendell of Shell, for example, claims that the new developments of the North Sea would probably not have been viable under the old price regime—that is, pre-1973 although there is an element of *post facto* reasoning in this claim; for BP had embarked upon the massive cost of exploit-ing the huge Forties field well before 1973 and the OPEC price rises and other fields were under way by then too—apart from the gas fields in the southern North Sea.

For anyone not directly involved the scale of operations is difficult to grasp. Much of the technology being applied in the North Sea is new or untried while the timescale is altogether different to that applied onshore. BP, for example, say that discoveries not allowed for in 1976 'will not have much economic consequence before 1985 in terms of investment or before 1990 in terms of production'. BP also say in one of their studies that: 'There can be little doubt that (if the oil is there) it will be developed and the total profile represents *rapid* development.'

All this is no doubt encouraging for the future. Now everyone knows there is oil in the North Sea; talk of energy gaps and growing scarcity is commonplace; and the economic and political benefits to the country are becoming daily clearer. But such was not the case even a very few years earlier.

In the early days of opening up the North Sea, it was rather a question of tackling vast problems in emergency type conditions without any of the powers that exist during a war. At the time Britain was simply not prepared for an operation on the scale of North Sea oil. As James Nicolson, the author of *Shetland and Oil*, put it: 'her educational and training capacity was hopelessly inadequate with a grave shortage of technicians and graduate engineers trained for a marine environment.'

So far the discoveries have been made in three main areas: the gas fields in the southern North Sea; the oil fields in the middle North Sea; and then the fields in the East Shetland basin. As more and more fields have come to light so has controversy developed about government action: why did government show so little interest in the early stages of opening up the North Sea?

Sir Philip Southwell (now President of Brown and Root), a doyen of the oil world, claims that it is easy with hindsight to blame government for slowness at the start, but at the time there was the simple question of where to obtain advice. The answer, of course, was from BP or Shell and they were reluctant to be optimistic in case they proved wrong and were blamed for later failure. Inevitably, therefore, they gave conservative estimates about the possibilities.

Further, they were none too sure themselves as can be seen from Sir Eric Drake's (then Chairman of BP) gaffe of April 1970, when he told reporters that he did not rate highly the chances of commercial oil finds in the North Sea. He said: 'There won't be a major field there,' although, he continued, BP 'have an obligation' to show themselves as explorers. Six months later BP announced the Forties find and by 1977 that field had been upgraded to produce 500,000 barrels a day, equivalent to a quarter of the entire daily production of Nigeria.

Some oilmen, especially those of the smaller independent companies have argued that the rate of development once the oil had been found did not have to be as fast as it was; instead, had there been a slower approach to opening up the North Sea and the development of a chequer board system of licences, more of the small companies could have had a share in the profitable fields. Moreover, a slower approach would have prevented the huge bulge in equipment orders in the early 1970s with the result that more of these could have gone to British companies, enabling the British offshore industry to get off to a better start.

In fact, once the nature of the finds became apparent the government embarked upon a policy of fastest possible development, and this meant that the big American companies obtained far too large a share of the total both of fields and offshore business than otherwise need have been the case. A slower build-up would have meant more British companies participating at all levels in the North Sea bonanza to the ultimate benefit of the economy as a whole.

The major advances in the British and Norwegian sectors of the North Sea that had been achieved by 1976 were the result of drilling 500 exploration wells and more than 300 development-appraisal wells south of latitude 62—including gas—between 1965 and 1975. About ninety discoveries of oil and gas were made in this period, although not all of these were commercial.

The fact is that Britain—and certainly the government—was totally unprepared to deal with the North Sea bonanza. North Sea oil represents the biggest industrial development for Britain since the railway boom of early Victorian days in the 1840s. One curious result, conditioned by years in which Britain underwent one financial crisis after another, was that people were not prepared to believe that the oil was either important or likely to make much difference to the economy.

The extent of American involvement in the North Sea will cause controversy for years. Both oilmen and government argue that the American companies had to be called in—especially in the early days—because they had the experience and the finance; after all, five of the seven 'majors' are American. Opponents of this view argue simply that a slower start would have made more sense and then the Americans need not have come to dominate the field. Whatever the rights and wrongs of the argument, to which we shall return, the result is that Britain's oil policies today have to work in a context in which 68 per cent of the North Sea oil concessions are held by non-British oil companies.

Peter Baxendell of Shell says: 'Practical recovery percentages usually vary between 20 per cent and 45 per cent of the total oil in place in the reservoir.' Thus probably twice as much oil is left in the ground as is extracted; if the maximum possible amount is to be recovered from the North Sea, a great deal of secondary and tertiary recovery methods at vastly added expense will be needed; and though so far there has been much experimentation, there have been no real breakthroughs.

North Sea oil has created its own language: the leading jargon phrase is 'on the frontiers of technology' and everyone loves the image this creates. Yet though the companies push this 'frontiers of technology' image, it is perhaps worth pointing out that any major industrial enterprise ought to be working on the frontiers of technology; when they cease doing so something is wrong—which might explain a good deal about British industrial performance over the last two or three decades.

At the same time, it is certainly true that the northern North Sea is proving to be the world's major test bed for middle and deep sea technology, and what is now being learnt there could be the basis for world-wide subsequent deep-sea activity. At present the complexities of technological developments ensure a time lag between discovery and production of five to six years.

There are an extraordinary number of facets to the oil story. It is, for example, clear that just about everyone, certainly including government, is mesmerised by oil company power. The companies themselves have some of the most efficient and smoothest imaginable of public relations departments and, to do them justice, they feel they need them. On the other hand, two years after its creation the British National Oil Corporation (BNOC) did not have any PR personnel at all; BNOC's enemies said that was unnecessary as Lord Kearton was responsible for all his own publicity.

It is certainly true that in the North Sea the oil companies are enjoying one of their greatest booms ever. BP now appears to have adapted the famous General Motors motto: 'what's good for GM is good for America' has been transformed into 'what's good for BP is good for Britain'. Possibly in BP's case there is even more justification than in GM's since half the company is owned by the British government anyway.

During 1977 at a major oil occasion in Norway, an American oil mogul not noted for his reticence was remarked as being quite especially self-effacing, allowing Norway's Statoil to take all the credit for an enterprise for which his own company was more than half responsible. Asked by a top-ranking British oil figure why he behaved so differently in Norway to Britain he replied: 'It's open season in Britain, so we shoot!' It still is.

Apart from the major oil companies many new names have

appeared on the oil scene: P & O have moved into the offshore supply business; Ivory and Sime, the Edinburgh finance company, have become major activists in oil business; and two notably successful companies that have entered the North Sea arena in a big way and are now oil companies in their own right are LASMO and The Thomson Organization.

In the course of a decade the scene has been set for what could develop into a major battle during the 1980s between two schools of thought: the commercial and the nationalist. There are likely to be many and sometimes bitter arguments between government and companies over policies relating to refining, exports, the rate of depletion or the speed of development. There are many nuances to these arguments and they are by no means as simple as at first they may appear to be. Broadly, however, it is at least likely that governments will argue—sometimes—for holding back the rate of development as part of a long-term energy strategy while the companies will argue commercially: that if the oil is not produced it is lost.

As one oilman put it: if you wait twenty years for a day's flow of oil from a field when you could get it today, then in accounting terms the oil is worth nothing. Moreover, in the hectic boom conditions of the North Sea to shut a platform down for a single day means the loss of perhaps 150,000 barrels of oil selling at approximately $14 a barrel, so that the companies view such a shutdown as something only to be contemplated in a top emergency.

There is also the question of government power to intervene, and how and when this should be exercised. So far the pattern has been much the same in Britain as elsewhere (with the major exception of the USA). In the early days when little was known, the government left the companies alone. As substantial finds were made, however, the government progressively intervened more and more and tightened its control. The government has not yet gone as far as it will in terms of exercising control over the North Sea; when in the later 1980s and 1990s the decline of oil supplies becomes rapid, government control of production will almost certainly be increased.

Meanwhile the politicians face the exciting prospect of an economic upsurge for them to manage. The coming of North Sea oil has changed fundamentally the financial and, therefore, the political outlook for the next two decades. This is true despite various not very successful attempts by politicians in both major parties to play down the importance of oil to the economy. The oil also opens up industrial possibilities that are new, exciting and potentially of the greatest future impact.

As a BP briefing paper puts it: 'It is difficult to imagine any sector of the U.K. economy of comparable size which can offer such returns to the nation, or to overstate the relative importance of developing U.K. oil production in a world of "high" oil prices.' The Treasury estimates that by 1985 oil could be contributing 5 per cent of the Gross National Product.

Excitement about oil had become a fact of public life in Britain by the end of 1977; there was the consequent danger of too many expectations that could not be fulfilled. The period 1945 to 1975 has hardly been an easy one for Britain. In the former year she emerged victorious from the Second World War with her Empire intact and 4,600,000 armed forces round the world, so that at the peace conferences Britain could behave as though on a par, in power terms, with the USA and the USSR. It was to take most of the succeeding thirty years for Britain to come to terms with her true power position in a drastically altered world and those years included the ending of the Empire—a process that a whole generation found difficult to accept; the trauma of Suez; and the inability or unwillingness to deal with problems such as Rhodesia. The resentment at decline from great power status to the second rank was perhaps revealed most clearly in the long British agonizing over whether or not to consider herself a part of the European Community, since to do so signalled acceptance of a new and diminished status. Moreover, ever since more than half the population can remember, there has been at least a biennial financial crisis—sometimes an annual one and in bad years more than one—so that Balance of Payments problems have come to be accepted as part of the British way of life.

Thus, when North Sea oil was discovered, it is not surprising that on the one hand the government approach, once sure, was to go for the fastest possible exploitation in the hope that oil revenues would solve at least some of the country's perennial problems; and on the other hand, there was a strong suspicion on the part of a great many that the oil was an illusion and did not really amount to much—an attitude that only seemed to be disappearing by the end of 1977. It could also be argued that the political grasping at the North Sea oil lifeboat to save the economy is a major indictment of the performance of successive governments over many years to solve anything at all.

When the Prime Minister visited the Forties field we saw that he brought God into his speech. One has to search back to the nineteenth century for such unctuous coupling of God with the interests of the British people; yet Callaghan and his Labour colleagues must have seen the sudden reversal of British economic fortunes in the latter part of 1977 as little short of a miracle in their own political terms.

As one shrewd observer remarked with a certain malicious wit:

if you ringed the North Sea with gunships and then ordered the oil companies to go, they would refuse; and yet one senior cabinet minister was so scared of frightening the companies by too much government pressure as to argue that even if there was only one chance in a hundred of the companies pulling out, he dare not take it. That story illustrates both the power of oil and the weakness of government.

At least by 1977—because of the North Sea discoveries and the 1973 emergency following the Yom Kippur War—everyone had become aware of the finite nature of energy resources, so that talk of an energy gap towards the end of the century was accepted as part of the conventional wisdom. So for a time long-term policies will be debated. It is, however, worth recalling that prior to the North Sea discoveries and the 1973 crisis, anyone who bothered to think about it could see then the finite nature of resources just as well as they could later. But the low price of oil induced complacency and few efforts were made at conservation. Unhappily the likelihood is that by the 1980s, once Britain is both self-sufficient and enjoying the added prosperity which comes from being an oil exporter, she will forget the temporary bout of long-term thinking that she indulged in 1977 and 1978 and return to good living while she is able.

In 1976 the long years of exploration and investment began to pay off. As the *Brown Book* of the Department of Energy drily recorded, the year's progress included: the rapid build-up of oil production to a figure of half a million barrels a day by the year's end; a significant government take which began to make a substantial difference to the balance of payments; the rapid build-up of the state corporation, BNOC; the conclusion of state participation agreements with most of the companies; the fifth round of licence awards; the formation of a joint public-private sector company for gas-gathering pipelines in the area east of Shetlands. The year also saw twelve new oil and two further gas discoveries bringing the total since 1964 to seventy-three (forty-five oil and twenty-eight gas finds), while the success ratio of drilling was maintained at an incredible one in five to one in two east of Shetland, contrasted with a world average of one in twenty. Offshore investment came to a quarter of total investment for the year.

The extent of government revenue from oil was at last becoming apparent in the public mind: government take from royalties and tax is expected to come to £5·5 billion by 1980 when the oil import bill will have been eliminated (in fact before then), and thereafter the government's annual revenue from oil will be approximately £4·5 billion. This is in terms of present finds; the oil and gas search, however, will be extended to new areas of the continental shelf and into the Channel and Celtic Sea.

During 1976 Auk, Montrose, Beryl, Brent and Piper fields came on stream although each one experienced some difficulties—unsurprisingly in view of North Sea conditions—such as damage to platforms or piling problems, but, as the *Brown Book* concluded, oil should supply Britain with 20 per cent of its primary energy needs in 1977.

The oilmen and the government knew in 1976 what the impact of oil was going to be; 1977 was the year in which the message at last got across to the public. Speaking in Aberdeen at the Offshore Europe Conference and Exhibition, the Minister of State at the Department of Energy, Dr Mabon, said: 'Within three years Britain will be one of the ten largest oil producers in the world; and one of the very few industrialized countries to be self-sufficient in oil and gas. UK industry's experience and expertise gained in one of the toughest environments in the world, the North Sea, will have been exported to many other areas in the shape of the supply of UK goods and services. The world market for offshore supplies is already worth £4,000 million and forecasts suggest that it will increase to £6,000 million by 1980.'

Apart from her own oil, Britain was being told that she could capture a huge new world market or at least a very sizeable part of it. And why not? The Minister also said on that occasion: '1977 will go down on record as an important milestone in the history of UK offshore oil and gas development—the year in which Britain became a major oil producer.'

All this was sufficiently encouraging to induce euphoria in the unwary. Possibly the greatest problem associated with the oil boom will be the expectation that oil money will solve all our current problems. It will do no such thing. The fact is, however, that the oil companies, the government and the banks all have the same wish: to get the oil out as fast as possible. Set against this approach is the sober assessment of scientists in a book simply called *The North Sea* in which they look at all North Sea resources. They say:

> . . . there is a strongly held view that if the costs of the benefits of drilling for oil in the North Sea are examined objectively, the oil should be left in place until offshore drilling and control techniques are better developed. As it is . . ., it seems certain that under prevailing conditions there will be major oil spills.

What seems more and more likely is that neither companies nor politicians are going to be especially objective and the North Sea is about to be raped of the best of its oil wealth as fast as possible. There will certainly be an ever-growing series of pressures upon the government of the day to spend more on consumption and reflate the economy. The hazards in the North Sea oil province will increase markedly in the next few years; by 1980 there will be hundreds of wells in operation in the British sector of the North Sea alone, and taking these into account as well as drilling rigs, a new pattern of navigation for the sea will have to be devised.

Energy is in any case a huge vested interest; it is going to grow. As of 1977 the energy industry in Britain directly employed 650,000 people, or 3 per cent of the work force, and supported a further 200,000 jobs in process plants. The multiplier effects of North Sea oil upon the economy as a whole had only just begun to be realized at the end of 1977, when they were seen to be making some unexpected impacts upon the economy. And as the oil boom has caught the public imagination so new figures have made their impact upon us. The difficulty encountered in examining oil is that all the participants are sincere enough in their ways, and all believe that the particular views they push are the right ones. It is a question of attitudes.

In the early stages of North Sea developments successive governments were uninterested. Then when it became apparent that a major boom was on the way everyone moved—or tried to move—in on the oil scene. Attitudes have been conditioned by continuing economic malaise, the 1973 crisis and the subsequent three-day week, so that the public has developed a deep suspicion about the possible benefits of oil as well as an over-readiness to look for disasters.

The range of attitudes to oil is great; all concerned are fiercely determined that they are right. There is a major body of opinion that is deeply suspicious of businessmen and their motives; this for example comes out in the attitude of many civil servants who begin by assuming that a businessman is 'guilty' until he is proved innocent. Thus when businessmen approach government for help that has been offered as a matter of policy, they are none the less often regarded as having a selfish axe to grind.

The oil companies like to argue that everyone is working for the same ends—the good of the country and economy—but such claims can appear flimsy when companies object with such vehemence, as they do, to government policies.

Oil policies can be reviewed from two standpoints: how they affect the state and the multinational corporations; and how they affect the economy and the community.

The power of oil is very great and the ability of governments to control it and the multinational companies limited. As one oil banker happily remarked: 'Oil moves in the night.'

PART ONE
The North Sea

1
Disasters, Pollution and the Environment

Nothing concentrates the attention of the British as quickly or with as much interest as a disaster; thus, when the Ekofisk 'blow-out' occurred it might be said that North Sea oil 'arrived' in the public mind. The blow-out took place on the evening of Friday, 22 April 1977, when the casing pipe on Well 14 on the Bravo rig needed inspection and the 'Christmas Tree' (the name applied to the huge fire hydrant which is normally clamped to the top of the oil well when it is producing) had been removed. At that stage a blow-out preventer should have been clamped on over the well in place of the 'Christmas Tree'. In this case, before the blow-out preventer was in place the mud had started to rise; there was then only a gigantic column of mud to hold the oil in place and it was being pushed back up the well by the pressure of the oil below. Within a few minutes oil mixed with mud was appearing on the platform.

The disaster developed in the space of five minutes: from the time when the 'Christmas Tree' was removed to the moment when the oil came gushing out of the wellhead on to the platform. It was a 'blow-out' and the 112 men on the Ekofisk Bravo platform took to the sea in their safety dinghies. The accident that the oilmen most fear had occurred.

Forty-eight hours later oil continued to gush out into the North Sea at the rate of about 3,000 tons a day. Incredibly the oil did not catch fire. Ekofisk Bravo is the largest producer in the Norwegian sector of the North Sea accounting for nearly half the production of the Ekofisk field, about 60,000 tons a day. Once the blow-out had occurred, all the wells operating from Bravo were shut down so as to minimize the chances of the disaster spreading. At the time there were various guesses by oilmen as to the cause of the blow-out: a mistaken estimate by engineers as to the oil pressure; a loss of controlling mud into the reservoir below; the failure of a plug at the bottom of the well. The cause would be discovered subsequently. The immediate concern was to bring the blow-out under control and disperse the huge and growing oil slick that might turn into an ecological disaster.

Ironically, Phillips Petroleum who operate Ekofisk Field were the most experienced North Sea operators: the field had been in operation longest, and just before the blow-out at an offshore repair and maintenance conference in Brighton, Phillips' men had argued the need for all equipment on platforms to have 'fail safe' devices so as to shut wells down automatically in case of disasters.

Once the blow-out had occurred the greatest danger was of fire; were the oil to take fire, the platform and oil slick at sea might have burned for months before being brought under control.

A ten-mile-long oil slick appeared off Ekofisk within twelve hours of the blow-out and all the big oil operators combined to fight what had become the biggest disaster in ten years of North Sea development. The oil companies' disaster fighting ships moved in on the scene, one of the first to arrive being BP's Forties *Kiwi*, a converted tanker and the only specialist North Sea fireship. After some reporters had flown over the disaster and described the mud-coloured slick for the press, the Norwegian government placed a total embargo on air traffic in a ten-mile radius from the Ekofisk field. Then two of 'Red' Adair's catastrophe control men—'Boots' Hansen and Dick Hattenberg—arrived to take charge of the blow-out. When Hansen was asked at Stavanger whether it would take thirty-five days to control the blow-out he replied in suitable 'Red' tradition: 'Thirty-five days? I only work thirty-five days a year.'

Only a few weeks before the disaster occurred, Red Adair in a radio interview had warned that a major blow-out could hit the North Sea at any time and had said 'you don't have anything—everything's sitting out there wide open'. He appeared to have been right. In terms of fighting a disaster all British oil operators are members of the UK Offshore Operators Association (UKOOA) which co-ordinates plans for such emergencies. There are stockpiled round the British coastline about £350,000 worth of chemical dispersants and equipment ready for instant moves into disaster areas.

The two men from Adair's team found that the blow-out had not damaged the structure of the platform; while they attempted to get control the Norwegian government ordered the shutdown of the whole field, which at 350,000 barrels a day is providing the equivalent of a sixth of Britain's needs. The oil is piped 200 miles to a terminal on Teesside.

It was decided not to use chemicals to disperse the slick because of the threat to marine life; instead it was to be controlled by a series of booms while a fleet of skimmers came out from Stavanger to suck up the oil. Boats with chemicals stood by in case the skimmer

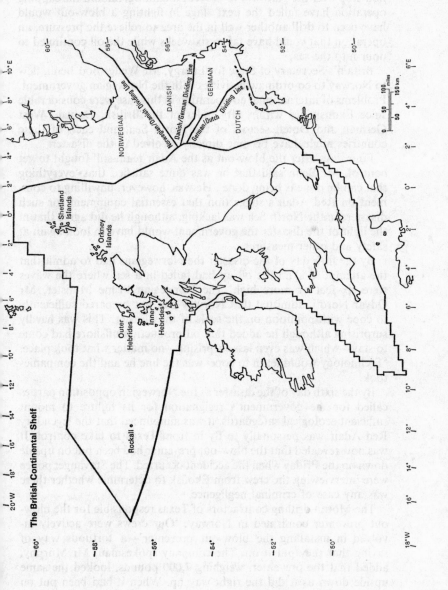

The British Continental Shelf

approach proved impracticable. A fire-fighting boat poured water non-stop over the platform to prevent it igniting. Should the capping operation have failed the next stage in fighting a blow-out would have been to drill another well in the area to relieve the pressure, an operation that could have taken six weeks while the oil continued to pour into the sea.

Britain's Secretary of State for Energy, Mr Wedgwood Benn, flew to Norway to co-ordinate activities with the Norwegian government. Problems of international co-operation in this case were considerable since Ekofisk lies within fifty miles of the British, Danish, West German and Dutch sectors of the North Sea, and each of these countries might have become directly involved in the disaster.

Four days after the blow-out as the Adair team still fought to get control, Mr Benn said that he was quite satisfied that 'everything that can be done is being done'. He was, however, unwilling to comment on Red Adair's suggestion that essential equipment for such disasters in the North Sea was lacking, although he did agree that in the light of the disaster the government would have to look again at safety and other measures.

By the fifth day of the disaster the Norwegians had to admit that the attempt to skim the oil up had failed in a sea where the waves were six feet or more high. The Norwegian Prime Minister, Mr Odvar Nordli, admitted that Norway had not prepared sufficiently to cope with pollution on the scale of the disaster. This was hardly surprising although he added that oil production offshore had come to stay—which was even less surprising—no matter what took place. 'Technology would learn to cope' was the line he and the companies took.

By the sixth day of the disaster as the Norwegian opposition parties called for the government's resignation for its failure to mount sufficient ecological safeguards, it was announced that the legendary Red Adair was personally to fly in from Texas to take control. It was now revealed that the blow-out preventer had been put on upside down on the Friday when the accident occurred. The Stavanger police were interviewing the crew from Ekofisk to determine whether there was any case of criminal negligence.

The Moran drilling contractors of Texas responsible for the blow-out preventer confirmed in Norway: 'Our crews were actively involved in installing the blow-out preventer'—a tortuous way of saying that they put it on. The company spokesman, Mr Murphy, added that the preventer, weighing 7,000 pounds, looked the same upside down as it did the right way up. When it had been put on upside down someone noticed this fact. The spokesman said: 'The important thing is that our people did realize it was upside down and they tried to turn it the right side up.' It was then too late.

Finally, with superb timing as everyone was becoming slightly hysterical, Mr Red Adair arrived to take control. He described the blow-out that had everyone in uproar as 'just another blow-out'. Having told journalists that his lieutenant (Boots) 'is probably going through hell; he will be feeling sick, he will be half blinded and his face will be all swelled up', Adair went on to say that despite the upside down equipment and a series of failures to cap the well he would not describe it as a failure yet: 'It is not that difficult and we have handled bigger and tougher wells than this. We have a whole bunch of tricks and we will fix it just like any other blow-out.' He also told his hearers: 'You learn from the mistakes. You will learn a lot from this one.'

With that parting sally, while special equipment was being flown to Ekofisk from Aberdeen, the refreshing Mr Adair himself departed to deal with the blow-out. Less than a day after his arrival on the scene Adair had capped the blow-out to maintain his legendary reputation. Cynics might be pardoned for thinking—but not saying—that his team did all the work and then deliberately waited for the boss to come as the final act in their performance.

Once the drama of the blow-out itself was over, some sober assessments took place. The Norwegian and British governments regarded the event as a disaster and Mr Benn had immediate talks with the oil companies and UKOOA to look at North Sea safety and pollution control arrangements. The Norwegian government began a public inquiry. And by then the oil slick covered 900 square miles of the North Sea.

As the inquest got under way the Norwegian Petroleum Directorate claimed that 99 per cent of blow-outs were the result either of human or mechanical error; and the anti-pollution lobbies speculated gloomily about the damage to the North Sea and the failure of the attempted skimming operations to have any impact at all. Four Vikoma skimmers (developed by BP) that were sent to the slick between them managed to skim up only 60 tons altogether, though supposedly capable of retrieving 300 tons of oil each a day.

Containing the slick between booms proved even less successful an approach to the problem; no booms have as yet been developed capable of operating successfully in North Sea conditions. But while the experts argued, the governments and oil companies had to look urgently at how to be more effective in any future emergency.

Critics of the oil companies make a fair point when they assert that most of the research and development to date has been devoted to rigs and platforms to get the oil out, rather than to adequate means of controlling disasters.

A week after the disaster the main hope was that the huge oil slick would stay out at sea; and that rather forlorn attitude towards the oil reflected accurately the lack of means to do much about it and highlighted the future likelihood of other disasters doing even greater damage than, in the end, resulted from the Ekofisk blow-out.

In the House of Commons Mr Benn said that the oil operators had to accept responsibility for pollution. Fair to a point yet the government cannot escape responsibility: it wants the oil and its stake in BNOC and 51 per cent participation puts it effectively in the position of an overall operator.

As it happened—and of enormous luck for everyone—the oil slick was broken up and dispersed at sea by the waves and wind. Such luck cannot be relied upon for the future. Little pollution resulted and, as far as could be estimated, minimal damage was done to marine life. This is unlikely to be the case in the future.

In October of 1977—six months later—an official Norwegian Commission of Inquiry into the blow-out found the main reason for the disaster to be human error, and suggested that the blow-out could have been avoided if the oilmen had taken heed of the various warning signs that showed when they were overhauling the well. The report also referred to inadequate organizational and administrative systems and criticized virtually everyone in charge of the rig on the grounds that while they had long practical experience they appeared to have little theoretical training. The blow-out which lasted eight days was estimated to have spilled out 22,500 tons of oil and 60 million cubic feet of natural gas. No one came out well from the report.

The Ekofisk disaster did have the advantage of alerting everyone to what could go wrong.

As a result the British government set up a team of officials to form an emergency 'fire brigade' to co-ordinate action should a similar occurrence take place in the British sector of the North Sea.

It was less than three weeks before the Ekofisk blow-out that Red Adair had warned of what might happen in the North Sea.

Whatever precautions are taken, there'll be a disaster in the North Sea, sooner or later. There are no proper facilities for coping with it. The thing is time, to get trained personnel there. By then the well may have caught fire—then it gets larger and larger, like a chain reaction, from this well, to the next well, to the next well. The more wells you have, on any platform, the more difficult it gets, because the heat will go to the next tree. You get flames, leaks, and it just goes on and on. The hardware to deal with a disaster? At the moment, for a real blow-out, you don't have anything. Just a few little vessels, a thing that will squirt water. BP's Forties *Kiwi* is totally inadequate. I've been to England a number of times, and talked to them on the North Sea about the equipment they would need. . . . Everything's sitting out there, wide open, with nothing to protect it.

Ekofisk would seem to have justified these prognostications. Adair has been called in to other disasters in the North Sea; in 1968 he tackled a gas blow-out on the Hewett A platform although that was a simple job rapidly under control. Since then, he has advised on a number of North Sea emergencies; and has suggested the creation of a special semi-submersible vessel for permanent service in the North Sea that could reach any rig within twenty-four hours under most weather conditions.

Adair is one of the legendary figures in the oil world. He has personally put out over a thousand fires and is reputed to earn a minimum of $250,000 a year in fees for his virtually unique services. He earns them.

Disasters are a part of the oil business and one reason why it is so costly. In the North Sea the first one the public knew about occurred in December 1965 when BP's Sea Gem collapsed and sank with the loss of thirteen lives, only six days after it had reported a gas find in the southern North Sea—what was subsequently the West Sole field.

Another shock came in February 1968 with the loss of Burmah's semi-submersible Ocean Prince. Again in January 1974, Transocean 3 of the Transocean Drilling Company Ltd capsized in British North Sea waters. There have been a number of other disasters, of greater or lesser importance, some involving only the loss of expensive equipment worth millions of pounds, others involving loss of life as in November 1977, when twelve men aboard a Norwegian helicopter that crashed into the North Sea were killed.

Other disasters have been of a different nature as, for example, in 1977, when Hamilton Brothers reported that water encroachment into the wells of the Argyll field was threatening its level of production. Such disasters make plain the dangerous nature of the oil business, especially when conducted in the incredibly difficult conditions of the North Sea environment. The search for oil takes a steady toll of human life.

In the twenty years between 1955 and 1974 there was a total of sixty-eight major rig disasters round the world with the loss of 100 lives and at a cost of $198 million. A number of these were in the North Sea. Disasters feed the fears of those concerned with the ecological and environmental effects of the oil boom. Thus householders of Aberdour and Dalgety Bay on the north shore of the Forth estuary are opposing plans by Shell and Esso to build a terminal for liquid petroleum gas tankers there; the residents' action group has demanded a planning inquiry commission, and cites in its report thirteen serious accidents at petrochemical plants throughout the world causing damage estimated at £140 million. In October 1977 another much slower blow-out took place on the Danish Maersk Explorer oil and gas platform.

The cost to human life forms a permanent feature of the oil industry's operations. Between 1965 and 1974 there were forty-three fatal accidents to workers on installations or attendant vessels in the British sector of the North Sea. There were twenty-one diving fatalities between 1971 and 1975. In January 1975 the Scottish Council of the BMA set up a twelve-man working committee to study the medicine difficulties of oil-related injuries.

According to the Department of Energy, total North Sea fatalities in the ten years 1965–75 came to sixty-five, of which fifteen were divers. There were in addition 225 serious accidents. In 1975, by which year there were 6,300 men working out on the rigs in the North Sea, there were twelve fatalities of which five were divers and fifty serious accidents. In 1976 there were twenty fatal accidents including seven divers. Diving is by far the most dangerous occupation in Britain, not just the North Sea.

As the development of the North Sea continues, so new safety techniques will be adopted and new and more stringent safety regulations be applied by the oil companies or insisted upon by governments. This at least is the theory. The trouble in practice is that now, and for years to come, it will be a case of breaking new ground: new risks will constantly be taken, more accidents will occur and lives be lost. That is part of the price to be paid for such huge developments as those now taking place.

The above are the more spectacular kinds of accident. All the time there are oil spillages from tankers all over the world's sea routes: some are accidents, others the result of deliberate if illegal flushing of contaminated ballast water into the sea, usually from small tankers. At least up to the end of 1977 the record for the British sector of the North Sea was a reasonably good one and most spillages from platforms or tankers were quickly cleaned up.

According to information fed through computers by the Department of Energy in 1976, a blow-out can be expected for every 455 wells drilled. So far there have been four blow-outs, three of them gas. With many more tankers expected to enter British waters to take off North Sea oil, the chances of far greater shoreline pollution have risen correspondingly; this is particularly likely to happen off either

Shetland or Orkney where two of the huge new terminals—Sullom Voe and Flotta—have been sited.

The oil companies should be frank about the possibilities of spillages or other accidents so that all proper precautions can be taken. The statistics of tankers are sufficiently daunting: the world tanker fleet numbers approximately 3,600 vessels of more than 6,000 deadweight tonnage each with a total tonnage of 190·5 million dwt. Between them these transport about 1·5 billion tons of oil annually; the chances of accidents are correspondingly large.

The greatest threat from oil pollution is to marine life and the North Sea is one of the richest fishing grounds in the world. 10,000 birds were known to have been killed as a result of the Torrey Canyon incident; blow-outs with their consequent oil slicks in the North Sea will do comparable damage to birds and fish. Most people think of pollution in terms of oil coming ashore; it also affects fish in sperm or sea birds. As yet we are only on the edges of either controlling or understanding the extent to which oil spills can cause lasting ecological damage.

Following Ekofisk came new pressures from environmentalists and anti-pollution groups for more stringent controls; and though at the time Red Adair's allegations that plans and equipment for fighting disasters in the North Sea were dismissed as scaremongering, the event had proved him to have been right. UKOOA claimed that it had known of the dangers and had not been complacent; it has developed an organization for co-ordinating all the fire-fighting facilities provided by the oil companies working in the North Sea. UKOOA had rejected the idea of operating a fleet of vessels built on behalf of the companies; it also had looked at the design for a specialist vessel (a semi-submersible) submitted by Adair himself, and rejected it on the grounds of expense.

Considering the vast sums being spent in the North Sea and being earned there, it might with justice be claimed that no expense should be spared to provide the most efficient means of fighting catastrophes. At the time of Ekofisk BP were considering a £20 million fire-fighting vessel, and the Occidental Group with Piper and Claymore fields were also looking into the possibility of a specialist vessel to deal with fires.

Two months after the disaster there was delivered at Peterhead an £18 million semi-submersible dynamic-positioning vessel from Norway, capable of a wide range of tasks from seabed welding at depths of 600 feet to firefighting. The vessel—another of the new creations brought forth by the exigencies of North Sea oil—is sufficiently flexible to earn a living for itself in a variety of other ways until the inevitable emergency comes and it goes into action to fight a fire. According to its owners, there is no other barge in the world that can handle oil-field disasters as comprehensively as the 'Uncle John', as it is called.

By October 1977 BNOC had chartered a firefighting ship for permanent duty at its Thistle Field. The vessel can pump 20,000 gallons of water a minute on to the platform in the event of a blow-out. The Department of Energy was clearly relieved to see one more of the many gaps in the North Sea catastrophe defences plugged, and was busy exerting pressures upon other operators to provide comparable firefighting vessels for other North Sea fields.

So far the companies have managed to persuade the government that they can do the job; whether this is the case will not be known until the next disaster takes place and the effectiveness of post-Ekofisk measures can be seen. At the end of 1977 there were seven North Sea firefighting ships and not all of these had been built for the job; some had been converted from other uses.

The government would like to see a new generation of purpose-built firefighting and maintenance ships. Phillips has had such a vessel made in Japan to guard Ekofisk at a cost of £25 million, which is likely to be the standard figure for such craft.

The fact is that the headlong rush to get oil out of the North Sea outstripped any ability or plans to deal with emergencies. As emergencies begin to feature regularly in the North Sea story, so large sums of money will have to be spent to ensure that there are adequate means available to deal with them.

There is no British anti-pollution lobby comparable in influence or strength to those that exist in Scandinavian countries such as Norway or Sweden. One is needed. At present the estimated annual oil pollution of the world's oceans comes to a total of 4,897,000 tons from all sources. Considering the nature of North Sea operations, an increasing percentage of the total is likely to come from this small area over the next few years.

Although the oil companies claim to take all necessary precautions and the government lays down standards for the platforms, issuing rigs with certificates of seaworthiness, it is doubtful whether all the factors that ought to be taken into account are yet known. Moreover, the oil business is a rough, tough one where its members expect to take risks and frequently do.

In the summer of 1977 a senior authority on hazards, Dr David Slater of Cremer and Warner, who made an independent study of the proposed Shell-Esso petrochemical development at Mossmorran and Braefoot Bay, Fife, cast doubts on British standards: 'Since Flixborough, people have been taking a stricter view, but we feel standards are not strict enough and should be tightened up. It can be shown time and time again, from such disasters as Flixborough, that the root cause is failure to identify the full range of hazards inherent in the operation and to safeguard against them.' Dr Slater was talking about hazards on land where conditions are infinitely easier than at sea; if his judgement is correct, it is doubtful that better precautions have yet been devised for North Sea conditions.

As one oilman said after Ekofisk: 'The cost of a blow-out like this can be enormous. The company has to pay the experts to stop the oil flow, and foot the bill for lost production and lost revenues. On top of that there is now unlimited liability for damage caused by oil slicks in some countries.' In view of this judgement, the somewhat grudging company approach to spending money on safety precautions seems hard to understand.

The answer, as always, comes back to the economics of oil—and these should never be overlooked. More controls and supervision, such as further imposition of government safety standards, can slow down the exploitation effort. In an industry where huge worldwide shortages may develop in the next few years thus causing the price to escalate correspondingly, no one wants any slow-down to take place—no matter what extra risks this attitude entails. That is the nub of the oil company approach: profit. That, at any rate, is one side of the picture.

On the other hand, the oil companies claim that they are taking all necessary precautions. They are very pollution-conscious and produce a fair amount of literature to show how they cope with pollution problems. Much of this, however, is a public relations exercise; as one environmentalist suggested, BP are only playing at environmental control at Sullom Voe. And when one sees the huge scars in the land as the thousand-acre terminal site is gouged out of the hillside, this may seem a just criticism, but it is a matter of balance: the companies want the huge oil profits, but so too do Shetland or Orkney or the British government or the various support companies want their share of the oil wealth. Many of those who stand to gain from the oil boom are in the happy position of being able to criticize the multinationals and lay at their door all the blame for any of the boom frenzy that has inevitably arisen. The oil companies make most convenient whipping-boys.

Compensation for pollution damage now runs into millions of pounds. In 1974 twenty of the oil companies operating in the North Sea agreed to provide compensation up to $16 million per incident to make good any damage caused by pollution from British offshore exploration and production. Most of the companies are contributors to the pollution compensation fund which is known as OPOL

(Offshore Pollution Liability Agreement) to pay for both damage and remedial measures.

Liability following Ekofisk was in fact limited to only $25 million. In December 1976 Britain entered into a new international agreement concerning higher levels of compensation. Under this agreement, an operator will be liable for pollution damage to the extent of $35 million immediately and up to $45 million over five years.

Another result of the Ekofisk accident was to increase North Sea insurance rates, as well as bringing more duplicate insurance on to the commercial market. By the mid 1970s insurance for North Sea platforms had become a formidable item of expense for the oil companies. Equally, it was a huge potential source of income for the insurance brokers, with a single platform valued at perhaps $1,000 million.

It will only require one or two catastrophic claims for platforms or other major items of equipment (in the 'Jumbo' class of insurance) for insurance rates to go up very substantially—and they are already high. When, in addition, the possibility of huge pollution claims has to be faced, it can be seen what a vast new market North Sea oil has opened up for the insurance companies.

In statistical terms the potential for disaster in the North Sea now appears high: oil platforms have vast amounts of complicated equipment and machinery on them and high fire risks; the Department of Energy regard the chances of another blow-out as certain. It is merely a question of time—and the next blow-out could catch fire, resulting in a far more dangerous and damaging pollution risk than was the case with Ekofisk.

Argument about Ekofisk will continue for a long time; the oilmen disagree with the Norwegian inquiry findings and say, for example, that the men were adequately trained. The fact is that human error caused the blow-out and, almost certainly, will do so again somewhere else, no matter how many checks and safeguards are built into platform procedures.

The Department of Energy has only fourteen inspectors to cover the North Sea—a tiny number considering the vast developments they have to oversee. UKOOA circulates its members with information about incidents, but too often incident reports are scanty and do not set forth enough information. Detailed reports ought to be filed automatically following any serious accident. That stage has not yet been reached.

There are difficulties in increasing the number of North Sea inspectors. First, there are not enough available petroleum engineers for a job that is both boring and, in North Sea terms, ill-paid; and secondly, an ever cautious as well as parsimonious government is reluctant to expand inspection if, as a result, the government itself becomes liable for a greater portion of the blame if something goes wrong.

In an emergency, the head of the Department of Energy's petroleum engineering division takes over a control centre at Inverlair House, Aberdeen, where he will direct any British battle against an Ekofisk-type disaster. This national Blow-out Emergency Team (reduced, inevitably, to BET) will advise operators and liaise with ministers in London.

It is never possible to assess preparedness for a disaster until the incident takes place; despite claims to the contrary, however, neither government nor companies seem as assured about their ability to cope with a disaster as no doubt the public would like them to be. As the authors of *The North Sea* put it: '. . . there must be a constant awareness of the need to approach the use and management of any resource in the *whole* environmental context.' There is little evidence that such an approach has been taken: oil is too valuable, we need it too much and are too greedy about getting it to take the longer-term precautions that we should.

Environmental arguments take many forms. There have been a number of important cases such as that centering upon the tiny Scottish village of Drumbuie; it was argued that platform building in the loch would lead to scenic disruption and unacceptable social costs, while it was doubted whether the use of the site could yield an economic rent equivalent to the losses the area would sustain. In the event the platforms were built on the other side of the loch.

None of the environmental questions are easy; and while environmental lobbies can always make out powerful, appealing cases to save particular areas, everyone is also anxious for the benefits of the oil boom and its multiplier effects upon local growth and jobs.

Meanwhile a great deal of research is being done. BP and Vickers are producing futuristic machines designed to deal with any kind of oil slick. Shell has run 5,000 possible blow-out scenarios through a computer; according to this study only 5 per cent of any oil spilled into the sea is liable to reach shore and this will take between one and three weeks to arrive, thus giving time for local coastal defence teams to prepare pollution control measures. The study also showed that even the damage from the very worst incident would not exceed $30 million while in 90 per cent of the 5,000 possible cases damage costs would range between $500,000 and $16 million. This, however, is surely enough.

It is a question of presentation. Following the Ekofisk disaster the Shell Sliktrak team (as the project was called) fed in the wind and weather data concerning the Ekofisk oil slick and came up with the

2*

answer that only 1 per cent of the oil would reach land—probably Denmark. In fact none did: far more rapid evaporation of the light oil from Ekofisk took place than even the experts had expected, and this more than compensated for the failure of the various clean-up methods to make even a minimal impression.

Many questions need to be answered and some no one has yet dared to ask. The hazardous North Sea weather conditions, far worse than have been faced anywhere else in the world offshore programme, are only just beginning to be understood and assessed. And what happens when a platform collapses? The question has, no doubt, been thought of; it is unlikely that anyone has come up with any answer other than a fervent hope that it won't happen at all.

Professor G. M. Dunnett of the Zoology Department at the University of Aberdeen, who has looked carefully at environmental and pollution problems, says simply that if a major spill occurs the apparatus available to control it does not work. There is as yet no gear that can either contain or recover spilt oil if any sort of sea is running, although there are many ongoing efforts to develop suitable equipment. Most existing equipment is designed to work in sheltered terminal conditions rather than in the open sea.

Moreover, a consideration of undoubted importance to government, oil companies and local (coastal) authorities, is that the cost of having ships, people and detergent available to cope with major emergencies is astronomical. As a result an equation of probabilities for action has been worked out and the hope is that the equation will prove correct.

Perhaps the biggest problem of all is that of time: the fact is that the companies and the government want the oil and want it in a hurry. The question is whether in any particular case that affects the environment—and most do—enough time can be obtained to ensure that all environmental aspects of the development are fully considered before irrevocable action is taken.

2

History

The British were as unprepared to deal with their oil as generally they have been unready for their wars. Thus when the oil was found it was by American companies in approximately two cases out of every three, while only after a considerable battle was British industry in many cases persuaded to take part in the lucrative offshore supply business at all. But if British business was slow off the mark successive British governments were at first even more sceptical of the oil opportunities.

Why this should have been so is difficult to say. There are, for example, more gas and tar seepages throughout the British Isles than in most other countries; even though these represent only small pockets of gas and oil they ought to have kept the possibility of further discoveries, including offshore ones, in the oil world's mind if in no one else's. In 1955 Britain bestirred herself and declared sovereignty over the barren Atlantic island of Rockall. At the time it was assumed to be for fishing rights in the area; oil conscious hindsight might now suggest a different reason.

In 1962 Aero Service carried out a large-scale aerial magnetometer survey covering 144,000 square miles of the North Sea—that is, somewhat more than half of the North Sea sedimentary basin (much of it is several miles thick) of 221,000 square miles. Indeed, by the beginning of the 1960s those who had a share in the North Sea—Britain, Norway, Denmark, West Germany and Holland—were taking a rapidly increasing interest in its possibilities: not just for gas or oil but for other minerals and fish as growing world pressures upon all resources made this small sea off the coast of the world's most highly developed conglomerate of countries especially valuable.

When the North Sea search got underway it was to have three phases: first, the development of the southern area—which meant gas; then the development of the middle area where Auk, Fulmar and the giant Forties field were to be found; and thirdly, in deeper water and more difficult conditions still, the northern area east of Shetland which contains the incredibly rich series of oil fields—Brent, Dunlin, Piper, Ninian, Cormorant.

BP was the first company to take any real interest in North Sea offshore prospects: the company started with the advantage of having done most of the land exploration in Britain. By the end of the 1960s American companies had become deeply involved and were moving into high gear as far as Britain's offshore oil was concerned. In the early stages of the North Sea venture the risks were no doubt very great; the companies, however, tend to over-emphasize the risks involved— it is part of the image they like to project. In fact, once the first discoveries had established the pattern the later risk element was much less. As the joint authors of one of the first books on the North Sea point out in *North Sea Oil—The Great Gamble* by Cooper and Gaskell: 'It is the experience of petroleum engineers that early estimates of ultimate capacity are generally low.' This has certainly proved to be the case in the North Sea.

It is curious that after it had become clear how much gas and oil there was to be exploited offshore, there persisted suspicion and reluctance upon the part of British industry to become involved in the huge support business that was to grow up. Partly this stemmed from the history of oil; almost all aspects of the business have been dominated by the Americans. Thus in the 1920s in Trinidad, then the only British oil field in the world, all the equipment used there came from the USA; oilmen did not want British equipment since they had become used to American products and sought them automatically. This was and remained a huge advantage to American oil related industries and something that British industry has to fight to overcome.

The history of oil and petroleum products goes back a long way in Britain, especially in Scotland. Petroleum and bituminous deposits were first recorded in Lancashire near Wigan by Thomas Shirley in 1667; they were again mentioned in 1739 in the same area by Dr Clayton. Dr Plot was responsible for discovering naphtha at Pitchford in Shropshire and the petroleum of Pitchford came to be sold as 'Betton's British Oil' for the relief of strains and rheumatism. By the beginning of the nineteenth century descriptions existed of petroleum deposits or seepages at Worsley, Wigan, West Leigh in Lancashire; Longton in North Staffordshire; Coalbrookdale and Wellington in Shropshire; and in 1811 petroleum 'exudes' from limestone near Bristol were described.

Then in 1847 James Young, the founder of the Scottish Shale Oil Industry, began working a petroleum deposit in the Riddings Colliery at Alfreton in Derbyshire. In 1850 he registered his famous patent 13292 for obtaining 'paraffine oil or an oil containing paraffine, and paraffine from bituminous coals'. Exploitation of shale in the Lothians began in the 1850s and Young's refinery on the outskirts of

Bathgate produced lamp oil, paraffin wax, lubricants and sulphate of ammonia. Shortly thereafter Young's process for obtaining paraffin and paraffin oils from coal and shale was being used in a number of refineries in the USA under licence from Young's company and the oil industry may be said to have been launched. Subsequently there was to be enormous litigation over Young's patent.

In the latter half of the 1970s we have become accustomed to endless production graphs showing the output of the various North Sea fields. British production of oil shale in 1894 came to the respectable figure of 1,986,383 tons from the following 'fields':

Area	Tonnage
Edinburgh	709,141
Lanark (east)	86,881
Linlithgow	1,168,488
Stirling (east)	2,497
Lanark (west)	4,250
Renfrew	11,152
Flintshire	1,372
Stafford (north)	2,602
Total	1,986,383

The fact that all but 4,000 tons of this production came from Scotland may be a comfort to the SNP which now claims that most of the oil is in Scottish waters. The figure of nearly two million tons—considering needs and the then state of the industry—compares well enough with Britain's oil consumption of 1975–78 which was at about seventy-five millions tons a year.

The Kimmeridge shale in Dorset has been worked since the sixteenth century as a source of alum and the Weymouth works were established in the 1850s. Today there are small oil deposits offshore in the Dorset area. Mineral oils have been used as illuminating agents since 1859 and the first act to regulate matters concerning petroleum was passed by Parliament in 1862: 'An Act for the safe-keeping of petroleum', and since then there have been innumerable acts covering most aspects of the industry. The shale oil industry in Scotland came to an end in the early 1960s.

Onshore production currently accounts for 100,000 tons of oil a year. The first serious search for oil in Britain took place during the First World War; another was mounted in 1936 and in 1937 the Eskdale gas field in Yorkshire, capable of producing 2·5 million cubic feet of gas a day, was discovered. Geologists doubt that any major oil fields will be found on land although about 900 wells have been sunk, mainly by BP. The first major oil field found in

Britain was at Eakring in Nottinghamshire in 1939: this and others in the region yield about 120 tons of oil a day which gives an idea of the tiny scale involved. Five wells at Gainsborough in Lincolnshire produce sixty-five tons of oil a day, and one well at Kimmeridge in Dorset produces thirty tons a day.

The extraordinary reliance that the industrial economies now place upon oil is a recent occurrence. As the MacKays show in their book *Political Economy of North Sea Oil*: 'In 1950 coal was still king, accounting for 90 per cent of primary energy requirements. Oil's share of the market increased only slowly until 1957; but from that date its advance has been rapid despite substantial discrimination in favour of coal, the prime indigenous source of fuel.' Through the 1960s Britain taxed heavy-fuel oil both to raise revenue and to protect coal, and by 1967 the tax amounted to 40 per cent of the pre-tax price of fuel oil giving coal a far greater level of protection than virtually anything else.

Despite such protection oil consumption increased rapidly as cheap oil captured more and more of the market. By 1966 Britain was a two-fuel economy: 60 per cent coal and 40 per cent oil. It was then envisaged that by 1975 it would be a four-fuel economy divided between coal (down to 34 per cent), oil (41 per cent), gas (14 per cent) and nuclear power at 10 per cent. In fact oil had by then captured half the market.

The great North Sea search was to follow the discovery of natural gas in Holland. On 14 August 1959, a drilling rig in a field near Slochteren in the northern province of Groningen struck natural gas —what turned out to be the second largest field in the world containing some sixty million million cubic feet of gas. The geology of Groningen indicated the likelihood of more gas to the north and west—that is, under the North Sea. The early search, therefore, was for gas rather than oil. By 1964 BP was exploring with its barge Sea Gem and by the second half of the 1960s some sixty-six companies comprising twenty-four groups were operating in the North Sea.

Almost all 'oil talk' is about the North Sea. Oil and gas are found in sedimentary basins of rock structure and apart from the North Sea there are a number of these structures north of Wales in the Irish Sea, west of Shetlands and in the Channel towards the Atlantic. The Groningen gas discovery led to the search that established the North Sea as one of the world's best prospective oil and gas areas. Since then the search has extended to the seas west of Shetland and Orkneys and to the Irish and Celtic seas.

Britain has been fortunate in geographical terms: she qualified for approximately half of the 221,000 square miles of the North Sea once the international carve-up got underway: Holland, West

HISTORY 35

Germany and Denmark only qualify for relatively small areas, while
Norway's much larger share is complicated by the problem of the
Trench down her coastline. At least sufficient agreement was reached
between the countries bordering the North Sea in terms of the
Geneva Convention of 1958 which Britain ratified in 1964 to allow
exploration and drilling to begin thereafter.

Under the Continental Shelf (Jurisdiction) Orders of 1964, 1965
and 1968, the United Kingdom sector of the North Sea was divided
into Scottish and English areas along the latitude 55° 50′ north.
Scottish and English law applies respectively to these two areas. The
Scottish area is 62,500 square miles and the English area 32,800
square miles so that the British sector divides in the ratio two to one,
and as it happens that part which so far has proved most prolific in
oil finds is the Scottish area. The Trench which borders the Norwegian coast and goes down to depths of 2,400 feet has in fact been
ignored for purposes of delimiting the British-Norwegian waters.

Although a small oil find was discovered in Danish waters in 1967
natural gas was the objective in the early years and it was largely
due to the drive of an American geologist, Edwin Van den Bark of
Phillips Petroleum, that the search was maintained at a time when
hardly anyone else thought it worthwhile. His efforts led to the
discovery first of the small Cod field in Norwegian waters and then,
in 1969, of the huge Ekofisk field. Meanwhile the major gas finds of
the southern North Sea were brought to light in the mid 1960s:
BP discovered West Sole in 1965 and then in 1966 Shell found the
huge Leman field, to be followed by Indefatigable and Hewett and
then the Viking field in 1969.

With the discovery of Ekofisk, however, attention moved north
from the gas area and the search for more oil intensified. In 1970
Phillips again found the first British oil field, Josephine, although it
is at present considered too small to be developed. Later in 1970 BP
discovered the Forties field. By 1971 the first oil was being produced
from Norway's Ekofisk field.

The size of stakes in the North Sea is enormous. Norway's giant
Statfjord field, of which 11 per cent is in the British sector, will cost
£4,400 million to develop; Shell-Esso's Brent field will cost £2,900
million. These vast sums were committed after the initial doubts had
been overcome—and there were a good many of these.

The sheer size of the Groningen gas find in Holland led to fundamental re-appraisals of North Sea possibilities, although as early as
1955 BP's Tom Gaskell had suggested drilling on the Dogger Bank.
Once the companies realized the possible extent of North Sea finds
the search became intense and ten years after the first wells had been
drilled—by the beginning of 1974—some 450 exploration wells had

already produced a dozen commercial gas fields and nearly twice as many commercial oil finds. More were to come.

When the Yom Kippur War occurred in October 1973 producing in its wake the partial Arab oil embargo and then the fivefold rise in oil prices, it added a new dimension of urgency to the North Sea oil search: for both financial and security reasons Britain wanted her own oil as fast as it could be developed.

While the crisis emphasized the importance of the new oil finds it also revealed that the British government was unable to control the activities of the companies (BP and Shell had refused Heath's demand that they should land all their oil in Britain), to tax them adequately or to direct the flow of the oil itself. It was, therefore, no accident that the 1974 Wilson government at once got down to devising an oil policy although some plans relating to a North Sea tax regime had been worked out by the Tories before they went to the polls.

North Sea oil has largely obscured in the public mind the extent and importance of the earlier gas finds. Groningen in Holland covers an area twenty miles square and it was only discovered after a programme lasting thirteen years in which two hundred wells were drilled After its discovery Sir Philip Southwell of Brown and Root says he drew two lines on the map from Holland to Eskdale in Yorkshire and from Holland to the Nottingham oil fields: in the resultant North Sea triangle, he said, there would be gas. He was right.

There was a broad belt of gas across the southern North Sea including Leman which is now the world's largest offshore field in production. The first gas finds in the southern sector of the British North Sea were found in 1965; by 1967 natural gas was being used in British homes and it now supplies 97 per cent of British gas needs. Curiously the experts—who can often enough turn out to be wrong—thought that the British sector was less promising for gas than offshore Holland or West Germany.

Much of the credit for the first British finds belongs to BP's chief geologist, Falcon, who retired in 1965. In December of that year BP announced a first gas well that was capable of producing ten million cubic feet a day. Important as the gas finds were, however, they soon came to be overshadowed by oil. Although small finds of oil antedated Ekofisk, it was that discovery by Phillips which revived interest in oil prospects. It is a feature of the industry that finds may lie dormant for some time after discovery before companies decide they are 'commercial'. Thus, for example, the Montrose field was found in 1969 by Amoco and the Gas Corporation, yet not declared commercial until 1973. BP discovered the Forties field in 1970 but only announced it in December 1971. And though the giant Brent field was discovered during June–July 1971 it was not announced for thirteen months while further appraisal wells were drilled. In 1972 Frigg, Beryl, Cormorant and Thistle were discovered, followed the next year by Dunlin, Hutton and Alwyn, and then Shell-Esso increased their estimate of Brent's resources by an additional 1,500 million barrels.

All the oil fields have been found in the northern North Sea and can be divided into three groups: the southern group comprising Argyll, Auk and Ekofisk; the Aberdeen–Orkney group comprising Forties, Piper, Beryl and Frigg; and the east Shetland group consisting of Brent, Ninian and Thistle.

A turning point came in 1973. According to Professor Gaskin of Aberdeen, the oil price hike by OPEC gave an enormous boost to North Sea oil exploration 'since it turned an interesting but, in world terms rather marginal, area into a highly attractive prospect, both economically and politically'. The marked change of attitude towards the possibility of further OPEC price rises that was soon enough to be adopted by the British government as well as the companies is evidence enough that high prices will suit our economy from now on.

Controversy surrounds the question of American involvement in the North Sea. According to the veteran American oilman, Bob Dyk of Hamilton Brothers, the British government could not have got the oil development off the ground at the speed it clearly desired without the Americans. The companies that provided most of the platforms and modules for the gas fields in the south were mainly American, and they then moved north to mop up much of the oil supply business too. In the early days both drilling and pipelaying activities were dominated by American companies.

Slowly the public became aware of the impact upon employment and industry that the oil finds were likely to have. The biggest benefits ought to have gone to the shipyards for the giant rigs and platforms, yet in 1965 there was no particular enthusiasm in the industry to undertake such work: firstly, because at the time the yards were full; and secondly, because of the uncertainty of the work. Even so, North Sea oil breathed new life into east coast towns such as Lowestoft and Great Yarmouth which became service centres and shore headquarters for the oil/gas companies, while a number of fishing harbours suddenly found themselves newly important as huge equipment depots. The companies organized their bases—BP at Cleethorpes, for example—and it became practice for a base to be designed to cater for a number of companies. The most important of the oil base towns that have prospered since the gas and oil finds are Great Yarmouth, Lowestoft, Sunderland, Middlesbrough, West

Hartlepool, Aberdeen, Immingham and Peterhead. Certain companies such as Brown and Root, George Wimpey, John Laing and International Drilling have become particularly associated with the offshore industry or certain aspects of it.

Everyone has now seen on television or in the press pictures of drilling rigs or the spectacular great platforms being built, towed out to sea and then 'sunk' into place, but a great deal of experimentation has gone on in the short time since Sea Gem tragically collapsed off the Norfolk coast: it was a work barge that had been converted at Le Havre into a self-elevating platform for drilling. Sea Gem was followed by a whole generation of new and weird-looking structures: North Star was the first four-legged British-built drilling platform constructed at John Brown's for the Phillips Group; Harland and Wolff built BP's Sea Quest, a giant semi-submersible weighing 15,000 tons at a cost of £3·5 million.

The statistics of this monster make interesting reading: it has a supporting leg in each corner 35 feet in diameter, is 160 feet long and stands on submersible pontoons 100 feet by 60 feet and 25 feet deep. Built in the form of a triangle—100 yards by 100 yards by 100 yards— it can operate in depths of water up to 135 feet—the structure is 320 feet high and can operate in less than 135 feet of water if it can rest on the seabed or more if it floats. It carries the equipment needed to sink a 20,000 feet well. Sea Quest was designed to cut down vertical wave motions to less than one-fifth. It requires a crew of forty and in deep water is held in place by nine anchors, each weighing 30,000 pounds.

This is an early generation North Sea invention; many and different types with even more impressive statistics have followed. There is a huge variety of platforms now existing in the North Sea; it seems that almost every oil field has different requirements and so new platform techniques are tried out. The first structure to be installed in the North Sea was the Shell-Esso platform for the Auk field which went into place in July 1974 and stands in 280 feet of water. Two months later the first two Forties platforms went into place, and with deck levels 552 feet above the seabed they were the biggest up to that time. Complications attendant upon platform building as new in-information was constantly fed through to the designers were enormous, and BP's first platform, for example, incorporated one thousand major design changes, while its second platform took half the time to build and cost considerably less.

British performance in the early days in relation to some of the mammoth orders that were going was poor: thus pipes for the Forties field were manufactured in Japan and laid by the Italians and Americans. By 1975, however, a clearer picture was emerging: steel and concrete platforms were being built at half a dozen sites in Scotland, while the pattern of pipelines from the fields to shore was becoming clear as were their termini.

At the beginning many people had cold feet about what might be involved; there followed an over-provision of sites for platforms. Then came the fourth licensing round that produced an average of one strike in four wells drilled, so that huge pressure built up to get the oil out. A cyclical situation developed: first, enormous outlays on platforms; then inflation and a downturn in platform orders so that for two years no orders were placed; moreover, the success of the fourth round had produced cash flow problems and costs escalated once more. Since a company producing a platform could have no certainty about a second order, it wanted all its costs back in one go and was not able to amortize them over four or five platforms. By the mid 1970s the insurance premium for a jack-up platform could be in the region of 9·5 per cent; frequently the equipment owned by a major oil company is not insured. Great technical skill is required for operations in the North Sea; one platform for the Frigg field fell off a barge. There have been mistakes in pipelaying leading to buckles. Brown and Root had to replace three barges.

The question of involving British industry in the North Sea has been a complex one. At first nearly all the services and technology came from Norway, Holland, Japan and Texas. When BP found the West Sole gas field they asked Brown and Root (an American subsidiary in Britain) how quickly the company could lay the pipelines from the field; Brown and Root answered: when BP could supply the piping—which they did by diverting supplies meant for Iran. In fact British industry only picked up about 5 per cent of the work connected with the southern gas fields; much of it went to Holland because of the Shell connexion.

Between January 1972 and August 1974 the first development orders were placed for a total of sixteen gas and oil fields, all of which were intended to be in production by the end of 1978. By then the size of the oil industrial market was becoming clear. Yet it was only in 1972—seven years after the first gas discoveries—that the government commissioned a report on the industrial prospects of the North Sea and by then in fact many of the opportunities had passed, at least as far as British business was concerned. Subsequently, when Offshore Supplies Office (OSO) had been created—late—great credit was due to its drive and the fact that it managed to capture as large a slice of North Sea business for British firms as it undoubtedly did. Why the British industrial sector was apparently so loath to become involved in North Sea activities is far from clear.

During the 1970s the impact—actual and potential—of North Sea oil onshore began to be apparent. In the early days, for example, crew boats supplied the rigs but soon helicopters took over a large part of the business so that Aberdeen became the busiest civilian heliport in the world. The helicopter business was more or less divided between Bristow Helicopters and BEA (British Airways).

As the business possibilities became increasingly apparent so, too, did wider political implications. These were far-reaching for Britain and Norway in particular and more generally for the EEC, for in the wake of the 1973 oil 'crisis' any development that could make Europe less dependent upon OPEC supplies seemed highly desirable. At first the government simply wanted Britain's oil; after the fivefold price rises, however, the government looked increasingly to the oil as a source of revenue.

It must remain a mystery of British politics why it took both major parties—though certainly not the SNP—so long to realize that Britain stood to be a major gainer from North Sea oil. The oil was Britain's own: there was a huge potential tax revenue for government; an end to annual balance of payments crises; and a series of new offshore related industries. In fact at both the political and business levels the country dragged its feet during the opening of the North Sea and many opportunities were lost.

Britain divided her North Sea territory into blocks of 100 square miles each. The first licences, covering 83,000 square kilometres of the North Sea, were awarded in 1964. While exploration licences were granted on the payment of £20 and were valid for three years at £1,000 a year, a production licence gave exclusive right to 'search and bore for and get petroleum'. These licences were granted for an initial period of six years on payment of £6,250 per block; £10,000 to be paid in the seventh year; and thereafter an annual payment of £5,250 up to a total of £72,500.

Licences may only be granted to British resident citizens and companies incorporated in Britain which are resident for tax purposes. Favourable consideration was given to those companies which had contributed to the British economy. Sixty-one companies applied for licences under the first round covering about 400 of the 960 blocks on offer; fifty-one of the applicants received licences and within three months of the operation the first well had been 'spudded in' on Boxing Day 1964.

It was government policy to encourage and if necessary compel a company to work adjacent blocks rather than just hold on to them; further, it was determined to ensure that different companies holding contiguous blocks should co-operate. Some fields extend into more than one block so that they are shared by several companies or groups and it is normal practice for these to work together, decide

which company will act as operator and apportion the percentage
rights in each block.

The general guidelines governing the award of licences under the
first round were as follows:

> First, the need to encourage the most rapid and thorough explora-
> tion and economical exploitation of petroleum resources on the
> Continental Shelf. Second, the requirement that the applicant for
> a licence shall be incorporated in the United Kingdom and the
> profits of the operation shall be taxable here. Thirdly, in cases
> where the applicant is a foreign-owned concern, how far British
> oil companies receive equitable treatment in that country.
> Fourthly, we shall look at the programme of work of the applicant
> and also at the ability and resources to implement it. Fifthly, we
> shall look at the contribution the applicant has already made and
> is making towards the development of resources of our Con-
> tinental Shelf and the development of our fuel economy generally.
> *(See appendix I for conditions governing rounds 1–4)*

There was great competition for licences in the Dogger Bank area
where an average of eight applications for each block were made.

An additional object under the second round of licence awards
was to open up the Irish Sea. Two extra criteria were added to the
guidelines in this round which took place under the new Labour
Government in 1965: to consider the contribution applicants had
made to the UK balance of payments and to creating employment;
and to facilitate participation by public enterprise in the development and exploitation of the resources of the Continental Shelf—
which at that time meant the National Coal Board and the Gas
Board. The major gas finds in the southern North Sea came closely
upon the second round of licence awards. When the various criteria
were considered it was likely that the applicant with the most
intensive work programme had the best chance of being awarded a
licence.

The clear emphasis upon rapid development was encouraged
further by the requirement that each licensee should surrender one
half of his area after six years, so there was an obvious incentive to
determine what the whole contained within that period. On the other
hand the annual block rentals were low.

By the end of 1972 four rounds had taken place. There had been a
significant departure in round 4 when some of the blocks were
auctioned. This round took place in 1971–72 and of the blocks offered
fifteen were put up to auction: these raised £37 million. Block 211/21
was the greatest attraction; the lowest bid for it was £256,000, the
highest (by Shell-Esso) was for £21 million. Two wells drilled in it

failed. As one commentator put it: 'The fact that the highest bid was made by such a formidable combination of accumulated experience as Shell and Esso tends to suggest bad luck rather than bad judgement.' Further, this particular bid failure helps to strengthen the general oil companies' case that the business carries high risks. Later Shell-Esso found the Cormorant Field next door to the famous golden block.

A good deal of controversy surrounded the question of an auction for licences, and the 1972–73 Committee of Public Accounts returned to this point again and again when they interrogated those responsible for the awards. Lord Kearton, chairman of BNOC, argues that there is no merit in a system of auctions. The system has long been used in the USA. Professor Robinson of the Economics Department at the University of Surrey, who has spent considerable time studying North Sea questions, argued in 1977 for the use of auctions in future awards so as to encourage a return to greater influence by market forces and less government regulation. It is certainly no easy question to resolve.

In the four rounds between 1964 and 1972 licences were awarded for blocks to partnerships and groups representing approximately eighty companies from a number of nations. Of these rounds the fourth was the most important resulting in 24,000 square miles of area being licensed. The first three rounds were awarded entirely according to administrative discretion; the fourth round was partly competitive—fifteen blocks—and partly according to administrative discretion.

In retrospect it can be seen that the ministerial use of discretionary power ensured that the two British majors, BP and Shell (which though 60 per cent Dutch-owned is regarded for these purposes as a British major) had between them come up with 35 per cent of the valuable North Sea finds by 1973—BP 20 per cent and Shell 15 per cent—yet the majority of the finds were in the hands of the Americans. Although British participation had increased from 30 per cent in the first round to 43 per cent by the fourth, the factor of ministerial discretion had so favoured British interests—rightly, most nationalists would argue—that their involvement in the most favoured areas was high and in consequence their share of proven reserves was higher than their percentage participation.

The government decision in the 1960s to go for speedy development meant bringing in foreign companies, since Shell and BP alone did not have sufficient resources to develop all the licensed areas as quickly as required. The MacKays in their book *Political Economy of North Sea Oil* argue: 'Foreign interests never accounted for less than 62·5 per cent of the areas licensed and in this American interests predominated . . . at November 1974 American-based companies controlled 38 per cent of the estimated production for established North Sea oil fields. . . .' The same authors suggest that the policy framework established for the North Sea has been more successful than is commonly realized and has ensured a high rate of exploration and exploitation. And, for example, they say: 'There is little doubt that the major objective was met. Exploration has been more rapid and more extensive in the UK sector of the North Sea than in any other national sector, although a major contributory factor has been the high success rate achieved in UK waters.'

The fifth round of licences was not offered until the end of 1976 and by that time the government approach to the North Sea had changed fundamentally: the new tax regime had been introduced; participation was being negotiated; BNOC had come into existence. Such events may have been decried by the oil companies; the bidding for further licences was none the less as intense as ever, for even with far greater government involvement the North Sea had become recognized as a superb oil investment. None the less the changed situation—not only the growing government role but the fact that many of the blocks on offer were deemed to be less attractive than formerly—meant tough company negotiations with the Department of Energy especially as in this round BNOC automatically had the right to a 51 per cent stake in each licence award.

Despite oil company grumbles the British regime (apart from that of the USA) is the most generous of all oil-producing countries in the world: 51 per cent BNOC participation means that the state corporation bears 51 per cent of exploration costs. Elsewhere the companies do it all and government only steps in after oil has been found.

In the end fifty-three applications were made for the far smaller fifth round on behalf of 133 companies and covered fifty of the seventy-one blocks or part-blocks on offer. BNOC took a majority stake in all blocks. The round was notably hard on the small independents such as Cluff Oil, Premier or Ball and Collins who did not get a look-in. On the other hand the majors—BP, Esso and Shell—and the important second rank companies such as Thomson and Tricentrol did well. Amoco which at the time was still battling with the Department of Energy over participation failed in its fifth round application. Thus the Department made plain that companies which showed unwilling to co-operate over participation might find difficulty in obtaining fresh exploration acreage. As a result of its 51 per cent participation in all the awards BNOC seemed likely to face a minimum exploration budget of £100 million. BNOC was also due to act as an operator for the first time in four blocks.

By September 1977 following completion of the fifth round there was a total of 262 companies with licences in the North Sea as operators, as members of consortia or simply as explorers. By then between 10 per cent and 20 per cent of the total British area had been licensed, including about 20 per cent of the inherently likely areas.

The days of the small independents working alone have passed. Only a major can expect to act alone; others, even quite large companies, must join consortia if they expect to be granted licences. Licence awards are subject to completing a seven-year exploratory programme which includes partnership with BNOC. No company can do any work without the consent of the Ministry. Detailed programmes have to be submitted to the Department of Energy: these include geological data, drilling, timing and many other technical aspects of the work. The Minister has to be satisfied that the work will be carried out safely; in fact, step by step ministerial approval for North Sea developments is now required. A sixth round is scheduled for 1978.

The growth of government awareness about oil possibilities makes a fascinating study. In May 1964 the government ratified the Geneva Convention following the enactment that April of the Continental Shelf Act. The Ministry of Power could then grant licences to search for and extract oil and gas in designated parts of the Continental Shelf. Cooper and Gaskell claim, with reasonable justice, that: 'It was only the push of the much-maligned international oil companies that made the British Government get moving in what was a reasonable international affair that could not be law until twenty-two of the governments who had drawn up the convention obtained the consent of their individual nations.' The British ratification was the twenty-second.

The same authors, too fulsomely, go on to say: 'However, once the importance of the North Sea had been realized, Britain acted swiftly and efficiently and produced an excellent set of rules for the exploiting of her Continental Shelf territory. This action has been rewarded by the successful discovery of valuable accumulations of gas.' They were oilmen writing in the early days; the government action of the 1960s has had many subsequent critics.

Defenders of the early allocations of licences argue that the Ministry went to endless trouble to be fair to everyone: this argument is designed to appeal to the well-known although erroneous belief that the British like fair play. It would have been more to the point had the government been tougher in safeguarding British interests—that, after all, is supposedly what it exists to do. The justification offered for the early so-called 'give away' approach has been that government wanted the fastest possible exploration and exploitation. This raises the question: why the need for such speed? If the answer is that the government approach is to use the oil wealth as a quick means of solving immediate problems, then the long-term outlook associated with Britain's new oil wealth must be a gloomy one.

Once North Sea possibilities began to emerge, government pressed ahead with its maximum exploitation policy which, it argued, was essential to deal with Britain's recurring balance of payments problem. This produced the 'give away' approach; later, when the rules were changed, the oil companies threw at the government the same accusation they had used against the Arabs: that it had broken its contracts. Of course it had done so—and, moreover, it had to do so and would have been lacking in its trust on behalf of the British people had it not done so. The question now is whether it has gone far enough. It took a long time for government to secure for the British people a reasonable share in their North Sea wealth. As Anthony Sampson argued in *The Seven Sisters*:

> But the British government were very casual and too anxious to get the boundaries settled to argue with Norway. Thus the British were allocated only thirty-five per cent of the North Sea, when they might according to most legal authorities, have obtained a much larger area by taking the issue to the International Court at The Hague.

This accusation points up what may well turn out to be the most consistent and in the end most disastrous aspect of the oil story: the government (like everyone else involved) was in too great a hurry because it wanted quick revenues to solve immediate problems.

It is one of the ironies of the story that the British government which had always been ready to back up the oil companies against the oil states of the Middle East found in the case of Britain's own oil that it lacked the expertise to deal with the companies. Moreover, it appeared afraid to tackle its own oilmen. As Sampson also says:

> The first huge areas of the sea, of a hundred square miles each, were leased to the companies as generously as though Britain were a gullible sheikdom, with concessions running for forty-six years. And the British government would gain almost nothing in taxes....

Wolfe, the Scottish Nationalist, in his book *Scotland Lives*, makes much the same point: 'The way in which the Conservative Government has been virtually giving the oil rights away with hardly a squeak of complaint from the Labour Opposition is completely irresponsible.'

The greater early success in British exploration as opposed to that

in other waters reflects her feverish need to remedy a constantly
ailing economy. During the early 1970s the man who emerged as the
scourge of the oil companies and campaigned for a time virtually
alone for a change of government policy was Lord Balogh, who once
remarked that 'the Arabs have experts who have forgotten more
than the Foreign Office ever knew'.

In contrast government was then arguing that it ought not to be
too harsh upon the companies as this might encourage OPEC to take
a tougher line against companies in the Middle East—one of the
more dubious defences of the early policy which reflected an odd
conception of the government's role, as though to protect the oil
companies' interests abroad was more important than to tax them at
home.

By 1974 constant upward revision of North Sea oil estimates
encouraged a braver government approach to the companies. Moreover, with the Labour Party which now took office, Balogh's campaign for government controls and a stake in the North Sea had at
last paid off and a policy emerged. In July 1974 a White Paper proposed a state corporation and a special oil tax regime as well as state
participation as yet undefined. Later, when Wilson, for reasons
unconnected with oil, decided to demote Wedgwood Benn to the
Department of Energy—in terms of political tactics a mistake since
the Department proved an ideal base for Benn—the public (not least
because of Benn's excellent flair for publicity) at last began to see
that the British Government had an oil policy and was determined
to take a proper share of the oil resources into public control.

Only in 1972 did the government take a serious look at the offshore
industry and its possibilities for British business. By then British oil
production was expected to range between 2·7 million and 3·5 million
barrels a day by 1985. The government-commissioned IMEG report
suggested that offshore activities would be worth £300 million
annually between 1973 and 1985; at the time the British share stood
at only £75 to £90 million or 25 per cent. IMEG argued that the
British share ought to reach 70 per cent of the business by the late
1970s and, remarkably, this came close to being the case, at least for
some sectors of the business.

The introduction to this report makes sombre reading for British
industry. The authors show how Britain failed in the 1950s to become
serious contenders in the refinery building business which remained
almost exclusively in the hands of the Americans; and how, after
pioneering work in developing liquid natural gas (LNG) carriers, the
British then lost the market. The report said:

The possibilities exist to do much better this time, in the context of the offshore industry, but it will be necessary, we believe, to take firm action to ensure that the possibilities are realized in practice. ... In overcoming the severe technological and operational difficulties of the North Sea environment, non-British enterprise is becoming progressively more entrenched. The time for British firms to establish is now or not at all.

The saddest aspect of this report is the fact, which it recorded only too clearly, that British industry could not automatically grab the lion's share of a huge new development on its doorstep.

Arguing for a strong British participation in offshore engineering and contracting, IMEG said that at the time (1972), 'these functions are mainly in the hands of US and US-experienced engineers who tend naturally to favour proven equipment from known and trusted suppliers.' The main IMEG recommendation was for the government to establish a Petroleum Supply Industries Board—a recommenda- tion which resulted in OSO. The report also suggested that in granting future licences government should take account of the opportunities offered to British industry by the oil companies.

One of the key figures in the early days of North Sea oil was Angus Beckett, the civil servant in charge of oil policy from 1964 to 1972 who established the offshore licensing and control system. Aspects of this were fiercely attacked by the Commons Public Accounts Committee in 1973 after Beckett had left the Civil Service. The basis of the criticism was that the government had given far too much away to the oil companies. Beckett subsequently became chairman of William Press, the company responsible for a large proportion of Britain's conversion to natural gas and now in the business of manufacturing modules for North Sea platforms.

Beckett is highly sensitive to the criticisms levelled against him but defends his record stoutly. He argues that it would not have been possible to achieve a sufficiently fast level of development in the North Sea without major American participation. The Americans had to be allowed in at the initial stages if the objective of rapid and thorough exploration and exploitation was to be met: they had the finance, the technology and the expertise while five of the seven 'majors' were American. Beckett points out that if British companies achieved a 30 per cent or more presence in the North Sea (which they have done), this is above their average presence in other oil provinces round the world.

In defence of the objective of rapid exploitation Beckett advances sound enough arguments: the balance of payments and security of supply, while arguing that the government's energy policy at the time was one of abundant supplies at reasonable prices and freedom

of choice for the ultimate consumer. In relation to the huge involvement of American companies, Beckett says there were no pressures
exerted upon the government by them to be allowed to participate
because there was never any question of cutting them out. And to
help justify this government attitude he points out that British oil
interests included BP and Shell activities in the USA: had Britain
restricted American involvement in the North Sea the USA would
have retaliated. Freedom of operation for British oil companies in
other parts of the world was a major consideration which included
not offending OPEC.

In the first round, the main British or part-British companies
involved were BP, Shell, Burmah, Trinidad Leaseholds and one or
two smaller companies. By the fourth round the policy was to encourage a percentage participation in consortia of companies that
were not strictly oil at all, such as ICI, P & O, RTZ and the banks.

At the time of the gas discoveries in the southern North Sea, few
companies wanted to invest in new capital-intensive facilities to
build platforms or modules, although this was not true of certain
American subsidiaries such as Brown and Root. Even by 1966,
according to Beckett, when it was clear there was a real gas bonanza,
British industry still showed a deep-seated wariness at committing
investment: not a single jacket for North Sea gas was built in Britain,
and although the pipes for the West Sole field came from Britain this
was only because BP had 16-inch pipe ready for shipment to Iran
and switched it to the gas field. No mills existed that could make
larger pipe.

Industry was reluctant to become involved because the North Sea
operation demanded huge capital outlays and it appeared far from
certain these would bring adequate returns. Nonetheless, five exploration rigs were built in British yards, the clients being more
influenced by the possibility of obtaining further licence awards as a
result, rather than by the efficiency of British industry.

This background helps explain early government reluctance to
impose too many restrictions on the oil companies in case by doing
so it frightened other industry away. In fact government hardly
imposed any restrictions at all.

Some of the new openings were grasped at once, especially in the
service industries—catering and transport, for example—as well as
certain technological fields such as seismic interpretation. The fact
is, however, the pioneer potential of the North Sea was spotted first
by the Americans. Beckett makes the point that with such reluctance
apparent, it would have been unwise for the government to have
pressed arduous terms upon the companies. There was little difference
between the two major parties during the period covered by the first

four rounds. The Tories were in power for round 1; the Labour Party for rounds 2 and 3; the Tories again for round 4. Labour wanted greater involvement by the nationalized industries but this represented the only real difference of approach.

In 1964 the Gas Board was making a profit: it had pioneered LNG and approached Shell and BP in the early 1960s to look at the North Sea for gas but they had turned it down. The Gas Board then turned to Amoco. The National Coal Board had also become involved with US Continental Oil as a partner.

Summing up the policy largely associated with him, Beckett says that under rounds 1 to 4 the primary aim was rapid North Sea development so as to provide a breathing space in which to evolve a long-term energy strategy. He maintains that government powers should be used to ensure that oil and gas resources are deployed in the best interests of the nation, a sentiment with which no one would argue. But while he says it is right for the government to control the rate of extraction this should only be after the companies have recouped their development costs as soon as possible—which means going for a maximum economic rate of extraction. Such a policy, however, commits the future: once embarked upon a maximum economic rate of extraction it is difficult later to cut back.

Beckett also argues strongly that the aims of government and of the companies need not be incompatible, provided the companies are not sold a false bill of goods—a phrase he applied to retrospective participation. The argument can be reversed: the roles are not incompatible provided government is not taken in by the companies. Beckett condemns what he describes as interference when government demanded 51 per cent participation in 1974. This, he says, was to break the contract with the companies. Such an argument does not stand up. No British government is or can be bound by its predecessors, and to advance such an argument is effectively to oppose any change of policy at all. It is the nature of government which possesses supreme national power to break 'contracts' in order to establish new critieria of behaviour in society. Whether or not this power is used wisely is another matter.

Beckett came in for more than his share of criticism for the apparent generosity of the licence awards under the four rounds he controlled. The Committee of Public Accounts inquiry under Harold Lever was published in 1973. This exhaustive inquiry revealed that the Exchequer would receive a far smaller share of oil revenues than other oil-producing countries, and that taxes were being pre-empted by the demands of overseas administrations. The inquiry brought out the easy terms for licences under the first four rounds as well as the extent of evasive action by the oil companies designed to avoid the paying of taxes. It in fact revealed the lack of any policy towards the North Sea at all.

The Committee advised that there should be legislation to increase taxes on North Sea oil and that the method of licensing should be reviewed. The Heath government was prepared to accept the main recommendations of the inquiry and change the tax system so as to ensure that profits from the North Sea could not be offset against losses from elsewhere. The Inquiry highlighted glaring omissions in the existing approach to the North Sea. Thus it said: 'We were indeed surprised that a thorough examination had not taken place much earlier . . .' in reference to the 1972 IMEG report on opportunities for business. It recommended:

> The government should take action substantially to improve the effective tax yield from operations on the continental shelf; and should consider among other methods the possibility of imposing a system of quantity taxation.
>
> Before any further licences are issued all aspects of the regime for licensing, especially as regards oil, should be reviewed in the light of this Report . . . in order to secure for the Exchequer and the economy a better share of the take from continental shelf operations.

Once the Report was published it was only a matter of time before tougher government controls were enforced.

In their detailed examination of witnesses the Committee constantly reverted to the question of licensing conditions and asked why in the fourth round there had been a mixture of discretionary awards and auctions; and why, since the fifteen blocks offered for auction raised the large sum of £37 million, this method had not been persisted in.

The Committee was making a valid point: that, apparently, the system of awards had been too generous; the defence advanced was that such easy terms had ensured what the government most wanted —rapid and thorough exploration and exploitation. The kernel of the criticism was that once £37 million had been bid for fifteen blocks it seemed unnecessary to return to discretionary awards. Comparisons with other oil-producing countries were drawn. In fact it was time for a change, for a more stringent approach, and as usual the method of government was for an inquiry to provide the justifications for the changes that in any case were going to be imposed.

Another key figure in the oil question was Lord Balogh, who had been the first and most important critic of the earlier 'give away' approach to North Sea oil and had the distinction of taking a tough line that, reasonably in the British context, might be called 'socialist' long before most other members of the Labour Party thought about oil at all. He claimed scathingly that the story of ministerial ignorance and incompetence was frightening. He said the Party was little help to him in his fight to get government control of North Sea oil and that he got no backing in the House of Commons. Most people thought he had a bee in his bonnet.

It was Balogh's insistence that produced the Lever Inquiry. In February 1972 he had a major article published in the *Sunday Times* in which he made this important historical point:

Around 1912 Asquith's Government, fully as laissez-faire as Mr. Heath's, secured the majority shareholding in what is now BP to keep the Navy's fuel oil supplies in British hands. This was the most profitable investment any British Government has ever made.

He went on to argue that up to 1972 the size of the finds was played down by the companies:

It is obviously in the oil industry's financial interest to minimize the size of gas discoveries, so as to secure better conditions for oil exploration and a higher price from the Gas Council, the only customer.

And then came the bite: the Arabs obtain 75 per cent for their oil and

Even the Netherlands . . . secured 76·5 per cent participation in profit from its onshore gas fields. Apart from a few leases in which the nationalized industries participate, the British public's total gain is only 50·4 per cent from tax and royalties.

Of the tax loophole Balogh continued:

Moreover, these taxes can be offset against investments elsewhere. The record of tax payments of the oil companies to Britain is not encouraging. The idea seems to be that the British public should help the companies to make up for the losses suffered elsewhere.

Balogh compared the prices paid for a therm of North Sea gas— between 2 and 3·6 old pence—to 1·75 pence paid by the Russians to Iran for gas at the frontier from a field 1,000 miles away; and said that though the oil companies claimed they were paid too little, in fact they continued both to extract the gas and sell it at a profit to themselves. He finished this remarkable article by saying:

It is imperative that an impartial committee reinforced by a fearless accountant should investigate and inform Parliament and the public on the true state of affairs, and prevent a further increase in the cost of gas to the Board which will inevitably lead to yet another twist in the inflationary spiral. Nothing less will do.

The committee of inquiry followed. Not surprisingly Balogh came to be disliked in the oil world. At the time Frank McFadzean, then Chairman-designate of Shell, replied to Balogh's *Sunday Times* article. He made the usual point about the risks the companies took, asserted they were not playing down the extent of the resources and warned that a policy of exclusion could, for example, lead the Americans to retaliate in Alaska. He said: 'Britain should be the last country to risk starting a new round of protectionism in the world.' Not, in fact, quite an answer to what Balogh was arguing. Although he demolished Balogh's argument about gas prices in terms of the comparison with the Russian-Iranian deal, McFadzean ended nastily and, as it happened, inaccurately: 'It is right and proper that there should be informed public discussion on North Sea oil and gas. Lord Balogh's article makes no contribution to the subject.' In fact Lord Balogh's article made such a crucial contribution to the subject as to infuriate the oil companies who have not forgiven him the role he then played.

Replying to McFadzean's letter Balogh made the further point—one that subsequent events bore out—that once Ekofisk and Forties had been discovered there was very little real risk in further North Sea activity: the astonishingly high rate of drilling success, one well in four, bears this out.

Subsequently Lord Balogh has argued that the country lost £4,500 million of revenue which was offset against company oil losses elsewhere in the world before the new tax regime was applied. When Labour came back to power in 1974 Lord Balogh was made Minister of State at the Department of Energy under Varley with special responsibility for the North Sea.

Beckett and Balogh represent opposite poles in the story of Britain's oil: 'give away' and control. It is possible to sum up the argument by saying the oil could not have been rapidly exploited except by the generous award system under Beckett; but then it required the Balogh approach to ensure an adequate government take. Not unnaturally most oilmen think Beckett did an excellent job.

In his book *North Sea Oil and Gas* the geographer, Chapman, says that while it may be unfair to criticize the method of awards under rounds 1 to 3,

. . . it has been officially admitted that fewer blocks could have been offered in 1971 without reducing the momentum of exploration. The point is supported by events in the Norwegian sector, where drilling activity has been maintained at a fairly high level despite the very limited area extent of the 1968 and 1974 licence rounds.

His point is that once the awards have been made and development under those award conditions takes place, the government is stuck with the results whatever these do to its policy. Lord Kearton described the fourth round as a disaster.

It is easy to criticize with hindsight. One civil servant said that Beckett's four rounds (with criticisms) represented the only way to get North Sea oil effectively flowing while equally, once it was flowing, Balogh's approach in turn became the only possible government attitude. He also argued that if Balogh had been in charge at the outset and had then attempted to impose the taxes and controls he later espoused, the companies would not have opened up the North Sea.

On the Beckett-Balogh differences Tom King, Tory shadow spokesman on energy, points out: first, that no oil was produced in Beckett's time; second (a political point) that he was made a Labour scapegoat; third, that hindsight after the bonanza has boomed is easy; and fourth, that Barber, the Tory Chancellor, said in his 1973 budget that government intended to introduce a new North Sea oil tax regime. A form of oil tax already existed in a Treasury paper when the 1974 election put the Tories out of office. Following the 1973–74 oil price rises a major British oil tax had become essential. King in fact makes a fair case for the lines taken in their time by both Beckett and Balogh.

Gordon Wilson, the Scottish National Party MP, has said: 'The first mis-calculation was to proceed by intermittent large licensing rounds rather than by smaller and more regular rounds.' Most of the *post facto* criticisms have a sound basis, yet when the operation started few could have known either the extent of North Sea oil deposits or the difficulties to be encountered: weather delays, problems of logistics when vital equipment was not produced on time; political delays that led companies to hold back on further investment until they saw what was going to happen; and when all these factors of delay are added together, they in turn lead to huge interest bills for the companies on loans running into hundreds of millions of pounds.

Once the arguments have been exhausted one can look at the end result. The first British oil flowed from the continental shelf in 1975. By the end of 1976 seven fields were producing at an annual rate of twenty million tons or a quarter of British demand. By the end of 1977 the pound was strengthening and the current account was no longer in the red. Moreover, the shockwaves of participation, licence terms, the new taxation regime and BNOC had been absorbed by the companies. As *The Banker* put it: 'The dreaded "participation" turns out to be merely an option to buy oil for BNOC, and an assurance that most of the refining is done in UK.'

By the end of 1977 there had been more than fifty oil discoveries and fourteen fields had then been proved commercial and were under development. It was probable, though by no means certain, that the biggest fields had been found. There were certainly more to come.

3

Exploration and Resources

Policies and approaches to the North Sea have been a curious mixture of planning and chance. The Crown since 1934 has possessed absolute rights in oil and gas found either onshore or in British territorial waters, and the 1958 Geneva Convention extended rights of the littoral states to include both exploration and exploitation of the natural resources of their seabed areas.

After the big gas finds of the mid 1960s there was thought to be little likelihood of oil finds, although the major companies continued to explore. Some companies had given up and others were about to do so when Phillips made its Ekofisk find at the end of the decade. Thereafter the search for oil was on at speed, and as Tugendhat and Hamilton say in their book, *Oil: The Biggest Business*:

> By the end of 1973, after the loss of three rigs, the expenditure of some £500m on exploration and about twice as much on development of both oil and gas, the drilling of some 460 exploration wells and more false starts than the industry cares to remember, the North Sea had been proved as a major new oil and gas province of world importance.

The offshore oil business has a comparatively short history. The first offshore rig was only used off Louisiana in 1949. Today there are about 300 rigs in use and another 100 under construction. The oil business is riddled with predictions that have turned out wrong and this may well be the case even more for offshore activity than that on land. The North Sea oil province is one of the many discoveries that has upset the constant predictions of a coming shortage.

A study by the Workshop on Alternative Energy Strategies (WAES), *Energy: Global Prospects 1985–2000*, published in 1977, makes the statement: 'In Europe, reserves in the North Sea—the one major oil region—are limited, and no further major discoveries are expected.' Such pronouncements, even when they come from the experts, carry less rather than more conviction when it is recalled that Groningen was only found on land after thirteen years of intensive search in the area.

The ratio of finds to wells drilled in the North Sea has been phenomenally high. Even if all the big fields have now been discovered, and if a find ratio of only 1 in 20—the world average—were to be accepted as normal, a great deal more oil remains to be found.

A Cassandra-like attitude to the future has become a part of the oil image: constant warnings of a coming energy gap—the WAES report suggests one as early as 1981 if Saudi Arabia, Kuwait and Abu Dhabi should decide to peg the level of their output—are offset by continuing new discoveries. Since we live in the oil age we shall go on using it up as long as it continues to be discovered until there really are no more finds to be made. Then—and only then—will we seriously move into other fuels.

Even though immediate developments appear to belie the warnings of coming crises, a growing shortage of fuels as we now use them will take place before the end of the century. The time factor is therefore crucial: it takes ten years or more to develop an offshore oil field, to build a large generating station or to open up a new coal mine. Thus we need to be sure at least ten years in advance when oil is really going into decline so as to plan the next generation of fuel.

Despite current British euphoria, world pressures upon dwindling oil supplies will become so great from 1985 onwards that urgent new measures for the development of alternative energy need to be taken now. Against this background President Carter has tried to impose a sensible energy policy in the USA; but the Americans take no notice. Too many people have warned too often of a coming crisis which so far has never materialized. Against a growing world shortage Britain would be foolish to allow herself to become complacent. Shell's Peter Baxendell has said: 'The North Sea and Alaska have given us a temporary respite, and perhaps we will be fortunate in locating equivalent reserves fairly rapidly elsewhere.' Perhaps, but it should be regarded as a respite and no more.

Petroleum possibilities extend far beyond oil fields. The huge known deposits of oil sands, heavy oil and oil shale round the world are far larger than reserves of conventional oil. It is perhaps unsurprising that the CIEC—North-South Conference (Dialogue)—that met off and on for many months in Paris following the 1973 'crisis' to discuss the so-called search for a New International Economic Order looked at energy in 'a world context' for the first time. That laconic communiqué in fact meant that the advanced industrialized countries told the oil-rich OPEC states that they had a duty to supply the former with oil. The fact is that all the potential new sources of energy—oil sands, hydro-electric power, nuclear

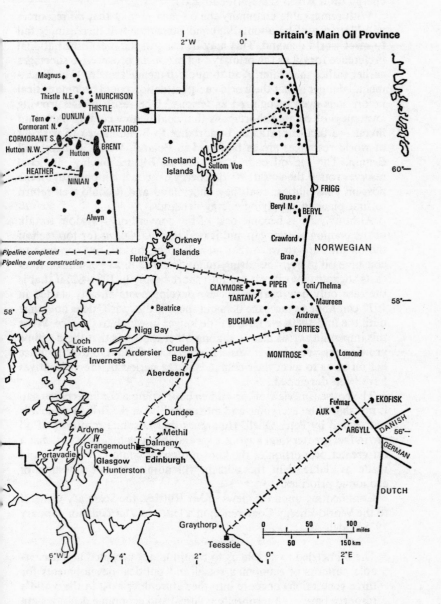

Britain's Main Oil Province

power, solar or wave energy—will provide only small amounts of energy on a world scale prior to 2000.

With remarkable unanimity the oil men predict that oil resources will 'flatten out' by about 1990 and thereafter will increasingly fail to meet world demand. This may be true; in the meantime national preference for oil as the primary fuel produces prospective shortages earlier rather than later. And to quote Baxendell again: 'The fundamental danger is that the world energy situation could become critical before it is even recognized as serious.' One result of the growing awareness of coming shortage is that coal is now coming back into favour—a fact of particular importance to Britain since 15 per cent of world resources are to be found in Poland, West Germany and Britain. The big oil companies such as BP are buying into coal reserves round the world. World energy experts are looking at all the post-oil possibilities; coal they understand and it could well return to first place in supplying energy demands.

Although it has become part of the conventional wisdom to talk of the coming energy gap and it is almost *de rigueur* for top men in the oil industry to warn that oil will soon run out, we continue to consume oil in ever increasing quantities. The most pessimistic forecasts suggest that oil will run into short supply in 1981–82; if that is the case only new coal or nuclear developments already started in 1977 can hope to meet the demand then. If the 'crisis' does not come until the mid 1980s we have a little longer in which to prepare. What this impending crisis means, among other things, is that there will be growing pressures by her western allies upon Britain to over-produce her oil so as to meet their demands in the period before alternatives have been developed.

The consensus view of the oilmen concerning a coming energy gap is not shared by everyone, and most notably on the British scene it is not shared by Peter Odell. He argues that absolute resources of oil are in fact greater than anyone says and, more controversially, that a far greater proportion of the known reserves could be extracted and made available than the oilmen will admit. It is a question of economic priorities.

Commenting upon the views of Mr Ruttley, the Secretary-General to the World Energy Conference, in a letter to *The Times* of January 1978, Odell says:

> The oil needed to enable us to continue our accepted and acceptable patterns of economic, social and political developments for three generations or more into the future does exist in the world's resource base . . . appropriate political and economic decisions are required to ensure that this oil can be made available for use by

the succeeding generations. In other words, the future availability of oil is not a physical resource question: it is one of a politico-economic character with important technological components.

Despite constant oil industry statements that little more is likely to be found, the search does not let up and according to the Norwegians, for example, seismological exploration indicates good prospects north of latitude 62° in Norwegian waters. It will be a question of cost and technology.

The world resource argument will have a growing impact upon the exploitation and use of North Sea oil, or any oil found on the European continental shelf. As far as Britain's own resources are concerned they represent no more than 3 per cent of the world total of known reserves; with new finds they could be boosted to 4 per cent.

Although the technical business of oil exploration is highly advanced it still remains a hit-and-miss affair when the actual wells are drilled. The first phase in exploration is to locate geological formations that may hold petroleum deposits and this can be done in a number of ways, though seismic surveying is the most common. Between 1964 and 1973 a total of 468 wells were sunk in the North Sea—266 in the British sector, 80 in the Norwegian, 20 in the Danish, 90 in the West German and 12 in the Dutch. Once oil is found and proved in commercial quantities, the extraction begins and highly technical and expensive gear is moved into place on a platform ready for production drilling. Exploration leading to a find costs $50 million on world average. Currently surveys are costing the oil companies about £15 million a year.

As a general principle the government would like all the oil off Britain to be found as soon as possible; thereafter, depending upon policy decisions, some can be left in the ground to await later development. The build-up to self-sufficiency has had two phases. The first was entirely concerned with gas, the big finds such as West Sole and Leman being discovered in the mid 1960s, Amethyst in 1972, Lomond and the huge Frigg field in 1973. The size and importance of Britain's gas finds have been constantly overshadowed by oil.

The British Gas Corporation in its own assessments of the situation is encouragingly optimistic. Thus in their publication, *Plans for British Gas*, they say:

> Nevertheless, proven crude oil reserves for the world are equivalent to about 30 years' current production. The natural gas reserves/production ratio is even greater. In world terms offshore exploration for oil and gas is still in its infancy, and with the stimulus of higher prices there must be strong hopes of major discoveries available for supply into the next century.

They go on even more hopefully for Britain:

We also believe that the era of significant discoveries of hydro-carbons around the shores of Britain has not yet come to an end.

During June 1977 the Department of Energy announced that it was to take a tougher line on the flaring of gas associated with North Sea oil production in the interests of greater total conservation; thus Shell-Esso were ordered to suspend production of oil from their Brent 'B' platform until they had installed gas re-injection facilities. The delay while the installation takes place is reckoned at a cost to the companies of 1·5 million tons of oil valued at £90 million. The company wanted to shut down only briefly and then install the equipment in the summer of 1978, but the Department argued that this would mean a loss of one million tons of oil equivalent in gas during the winter.

It is difficult to argue on behalf of the companies that they only have the good of the country at heart, when they are quite prepared to waste gas on such a scale because it is so much more profitable to get the oil out.

The oil build-up has been faster than expected and by mid 1977 Britain was producing approximately half her needs. A variety of predictions have been made about the total output to be expected in the 1980s. One is that by 1980 Britain will produce three million barrels a day or 150 million tons a year—well in excess of national requirements; an even more optimistic estimate suggests a production of 180 million tons a year by 1982. According to yet other analysts an oil production of 158 million tons in 1980 could be matched by gas production equivalent to 48 million tons of oil.

1976 was the busiest summer of activity ever in the North Sea and by the end of that year Argyll, Auk, Montrose, Beryl and the giant Forties field had all started production. The year's build-up was especially important since, by then, the oil companies had learnt the worst about government intentions—participation, BNOC and the new tax—and having absorbed those shocks to their systems, again felt able to invest in North Sea possibilities. They had been holding back during the previous two years.

This new surge of oil investment indicated that the tax and control system was in no sense more than the companies could reasonably absorb. At the end of the year a confident Mr Wedgwood Benn said that Britain was right on target to become self-sufficient in oil by 1980.

Balance of payments benefits in 1976 had reached £1,000 million. 1977 became the year when oil production made further dramatic contributions to the balance of payments as well as beginning to yield a substantial government revenue. The emphasis was always upon maximizing production as fast as possible so as to take care of financial problems. By April 1977 the government announced that trade would be in balance for the year and that by 1980 the £4,000 million oil import bill would be eliminated. Government also announced that oil reserve estimates had been increased from 2,290 million tons to 2,500 million.

By mid 1977 most North Sea oil fields were producing above their original estimates and the six fields then in production provided half the country's current needs. The government was becoming increasingly confident that by mid 1978 Britain would be fully self-sufficient in oil—eighteen months ahead of schedule. This rapid build-up emboldened the government to take a tough line with Shell-Esso over Brent gas flaring.

By the end of the year output from the Forties field had reached 500,000 barrels a day, Claymore had come on stream, Thistle was about to, overall gas production was up and while for the first nine months of 1976 North Sea crude accounted for 9 per cent of the country's needs, for the same period in 1977 it accounted for 40 per cent. Future discoveries could still be very substantial; much of the North Sea—even if not the most inherently likely areas—remains to be drilled and activity is increasing in the Celtic Sea and west of Shetland. There were sixteen oil strikes in 1976 and the level of finds shows little sign of declining.

It is the view of the industry, however, that there is unlikely to be another major find of the magnitude of Brent or Forties and that improved seismic techniques make huge misses less likely. But many more finds of smaller fields are probable. The Mesa Petroleum Company's discovery of oil in the Moray Firth only fifteen miles off the Scottish coast produced hopes of a major new oil province.

A number of discoveries were named during 1976 and 1977 such as the Burmah Oil Development find eight miles north of the Thistle field. Other companies announced the abandonment of wells as dry. In August 1977 Texaco discovered oil in block 15/23, 125 miles east of Aberdeen, and in October Phillips made a discovery 110 miles northeast of the Shetlands in block 210/15. In January 1978 BP announced the abandonment of a well on the northern limits of the British sector of the North Sea as dry. Statoil of Norway discovered fresh natural gas and gas condensate south of Ekofisk. Three fields in that area—Ekofisk, West Ekofisk and Cod—were in production at the beginning of 1978; in the next few years a further six—Tor, Edda, Eldfisk, Albuskjell, Valhall and Hod—are expected to come on stream. There are more possibilities of further discoveries including some of medium size. Many small accumulations of oil, however, will have to wait for improved technology before extraction is commercially viable.

So far the exciting discoveries have been in the North Sea; increasingly, however, the search is being extended west of Shetland, into the Irish and Celtic seas and the Western Approaches. In 1977 there were some discoveries in the sea west of Shetlands, though not on any spectacular scale. The significance of the finds lay more in the fact that they would stimulate further searches. There had been fourteen unsuccessful attempts to find oil before the first strike; as usual there followed predictions that the area had nothing to offer. The oil in the sea west of Shetland—so far—has been heavy grade as opposed to the more valuable light sulphur oil of the North Sea.

Following BP, which made the first strike in the area, both Texaco and Mobil moved rigs into the seas west of Shetland and Esso resumed operations there. Where one 'major' finds oil, the others are usually close upon its heels. Southwest of the BP discovery Phillips began drilling in 720 feet of water in August 1978. By October both Esso and Elf had found more heavy oil, boosting hopes that the area could become another substantial oil province. Commercial quantities of this heavier oil could play an especially important role for Britain, since such heavy crude is required for much of Britain's refinery mix to ensure the right grade of feedstock. At present such heavy oil is still imported from the Middle East.

By the end of 1977 the companies were in a dilemma since they had to hand back to the Department of Energy part of their blocks that had been awarded in 1972. In February 1978 after deep drilling, a further failure was announced by Elf. The area has shown promise but not much else. Later, when the search becomes more frantic, this area is liable to produce substantial quantities of oil.

The problems of the Western Approaches are complicated because of the rival British and French claims. By July 1977, however, nearly 40,000 square miles of sea in the area—after a protracted dispute between the two countries—were divided almost equally between Britain and France. Both countries could then embark upon their exploration programmes. The area is thought to have large reserves. The Department of Energy will almost certainly award a number of licences in the 1978 round along the median line between the two countries to make sure, as one civil servant put it, that the French don't get too great a start over us.

Now Britain faces further arbitration in the Western Approaches to determine how much of the area she can claim and how much goes to Ireland. The question of islands is of particular importance to Britain. The Channel Islands were ignored for the purpose of establishing the median line between Britain and France. Similarly

Britain's attempt to have the Scillies considered as a projection of the mainland were also ignored by the Finnish arbitrator, who ruled instead for a point halfway between the Scillies and Land's End for determining the median line between Britain and France. These island decisions could set a vital precedent should a future wrangle between England, Scotland and the Shetlands follow any SNP-inspired Scottish breakaway from Britain.

Oilmen say it is too early to make predictions about the Celtic Sea or the Atlantic Approaches. Exploration of the Celtic Sea began in 1973 and it has huge sedimentary areas likely to contain oil and gas. By 1977 Amoco was drilling the ninth well in the British sector and by the end of the year the oil companies had come to the conclusion that the sea was not going to yield another bonanza. So far the nine wells drilled have all been dry.

There has been a good deal of wishful thinking, partly oil- and, still more, government-inspired. Thus in 1975 when he was at the Department of Energy Mr John Smith talked of twenty-eight wells being drilled by 1978; and a year later Dr Dickson Mabon talked of 1977 being make-or-break year for the Celtic Sea. It was neither. Across the median line in Irish waters gas has been found in the Kinsale field, and during 1978 some sixteen wells are likely to be drilled. No doubt there are some rewarding finds to come; high hopes of a massive new development should not be pinned upon the area.

North Sea oil is especially valuable because of its high quality, low sulphur content and proximity to EEC markets—a combination of circumstances that add a dollar a barrel to it. The returns on the oil have been sufficiently rapid and large, despite what oilmen often describe as prohibitive taxes. Indeed, bankers called 1977 'pay-off' year, as some fields commenced repaying loans after one and a half years instead of seven as provided for in their loan agreements, so fast were the funds coming in.

A major oil argument concerns recoverable reserves. According to purely economic criteria, recoverable reserves are far less than what is technically recoverable. And as government attempts to gain more revenue for itself through Petroleum Revenue Tax (PRT), so too this will reduce further the actual amount that it is profitable for the companies to extract. Herein lies the essence of an argument between government and companies that will last for years.

As Odell and Rosing point out in their highly controversial monograph, *Optimal Development of the North Sea's Oil Fields*,

... the declaration of a field's recoverable reserves by the company or, on behalf of the company, by a firm of consultants is very firmly related to the level of investment that the company is prepared to put into the field.

The authors appear surprised at this; in fact such an approach is bound to be the one followed as long as British oil operations are conducted within the parameters of the western capitalist system. As one top oilman addressing a lay audience said brusquely in answer to a question about the life of North Sea oil: 'You can have the oil out of the North Sea as long as you are ready to pay for it.' The answer was interesting not least for its clear assumption of a 'them and us' situation.

But there is a flaw in the Odell thesis that oil companies will only skim the most profitable oil from a field: companies regard every drop of oil in a miserly fashion; it is their life blood, and despite any suggestions to the contrary they do not disdain it. Their licences are for forty-six years; and companies do not relinquish oil fields. The most relevant question to ask, perhaps, is when a particular field should be developed.

In one sense both government and companies tend to play down the extent of oil resources. The companies claim that they do not want to give a false perspective: if more oil materializes estimates can always be upgraded, which is better than promising more than ultimately can be produced. Governments—apart from an occupationally compulsive leaning towards secrecy anyway—like to have something in hand in a political sense, and oil certainly falls into this category.

The variation between fields is enormous and there is no typical North Sea field; nor is it possible to know the pattern of new fields yet to be found. Fields do have common requirements such as a landfall terminal and available refining capacity, and the position of these facilities will govern certain aspects of production. It is virtually impossible to map a reservoir with accuracy and in consequence oilmen and experts come up with many answers about the total ultimate reserves in the now known North Sea reservoirs—let alone making more general predictions about what is still to be found.

The unexpected is a normal rule in the oil business: in some cases this can be spectacular—faster production than expected or greatly increased reserves; and sometimes it can be bad news—water flowing into a reservoir as it did into the Argyll field in 1977. Certain fields such as Brae are especially difficult to appraise and in that case, for example, it is far from clear whether the field is going to turn out to be one of the largest in the North Sea or only marginal.

Figures vary enormously and in the case of the Buchan field, the oil analysts Wood Mackenzie believe that the amount of oil in place lies between 580 million and 730 million barrels, of which between 65 million and 300 million could be extracted; another analyst concludes that there is 650 million barrels in place and that about 130 million could be recovered. Buchan happens to be an especially difficult structure to estimate, but it illustrates the complicated nature of the oil business and the fact that no absolute rules of recovery can be applied across the board.

In the case of Hamilton's small Argyll field, production fell from a peak of 38,000 barrels a day in mid 1976 to 20,000 by September 1977. It was the first field on stream; even so, such figures give an indication of how quickly the fall away from peak production can take place. That September, however, a new find was made a few miles south of the main field, one that will probably add a few months to the field's total life. As a result Argyll should last well into 1979.

Brae is a highly complicated field over whose eventual development and production its own consortium members are at odds. While the operator, Pan Ocean, did not want to make pronouncements, Mr Harold Hoopman, the president of Marathon Oil which acquired Pan Ocean, said in New York in July 1977 that reserves were 'well in excess of 500 million barrels'. Brae covers a huge area, but is a long straggling structure divided into three main reservoirs with many areas where the oil-bearing rocks have a very low permeability. It is ranked as a field that may bear three platforms—almost in the Forties or Brent class—but it is far from clear how it should be developed. Of nine wells drilled, the first produced oil at a rate of 22,000 barrels a day; the second at 4,000; the third at 13,000; the fourth and fifth wells were dry; the sixth produced at 600; the seventh at 1,385; the eighth at a high of 33,000; and the ninth again was dry. The tenth and eleventh wells were being drilled at the end of 1977.

Oilmen go from one extreme to another: the most optimistic Brae estimates have suggested 1,000 million barrels of reserves; the most pessimistic only 200 million. Wood Mackenzie, perhaps the top oil analysts, cover themselves by saying recoverable reserves range between a low of 180 million barrels and a high of 560 million.

The small fields present particular problems of technology, economics and politics. For the companies it is not an economic proposition to build platforms for a field that will only have a lifespan of five or so years and at its height yield about 50,000 barrels a day. Instead they would prefer to use floating rigs (on Argyll, for example, a converted mobile rig tied to subsea wells on the seabed was used); but the disadvantage of these is that it becomes harder to sustain the pressure of the oil reservoir artificially when it goes into decline.

On the other hand the government became noticeably tougher in its attitude towards production during the latter half of 1977, when estimated output was on target and the Department of Energy could afford to be more conservation-conscious. Government wants to ensure that the maximum amount of oil is extracted from the small fields; it will not let itself be hurried into agreeing extraction methods that do not meet its requirements.

The most famous field is BP's Forties: because of its size (1,800 million barrels of reserves), because it was early to come on stream (1975) and peaked in 1977 producing at the rate of 20 million tons, or a quarter of total British needs. It was only one of more than fourteen fields declared commercial and either producing or under development by the end of 1977. These fields vary enormously in size and the development techniques being used on them: some such as Forties or Brent rate four platforms; others such as Argyll have no platform.

The most prolific area of all lies to the east of Shetland and includes the vast Brent field, Statfjord which is mainly in Norwegian waters, Cormorant, Dunlin, Heather, Ninian and Thistle. The capital costs of developing these fields have been very great. Brent will cost £2,900 million (no doubt more with inflation) to develop and should peak in the early 1980s at about 550,000 barrels a day, plus 100,000 barrels a day of gas liquids. It also has large reserves of associated natural gas and at a further capital investment of £500 million for a 280-mile pipeline will supply gas to the British Gas Corporation; gas deliveries will be in the region of 500 million cubic feet a day of dry gas in the early 1980s.

One of the smallest Shell fields is Auk, with a peak production of only 40,000 barrels a day. It came on stream in February 1976 and was too small to warrant a pipeline, so the oil is loaded on to tankers from an Exposed Location Single Buoy Mooring (ELSBM) and then shipped to the Teesport refinery.

The name roll of North Sea oil fields sounds exciting and to the oilman is undoubtedly romantic as well: Argyll, Auk, Beryl, Brent, Claymore, Cormorant, Dunlin, Heather, Montrose, Ninian, Piper, Statfjord, Thistle—all of them are either already producing or under development. Others such as Brae, Buchan, Fulmar, Magnus or Tartan (with more to come) are still being examined and await the the go-ahead for exploitation. (See Appendix II for a breakdown of fields.)

As of January 1978 with Thistle coming on stream nine of the first fourteen fields were in production. Heather and Ninian will come into production in the second half of 1978, Buchan, Cormorant, Dunlin and Statfjord in 1979 and Murchison and Tartan in 1980. Buchan, Murchison and Tartan are in fact part of the second phase of North Sea development and will be joined by about a dozen smaller fields currently awaiting development. The search goes on. At the same time onshore oil activities, however limited in scope, continue. In December 1977 the Department of Energy awarded onshore licences to prospect for oil and gas to the British Gas Corporation, Shell and others and a new gas find was made in Dorset.

There has been much argument and speculation about the extent of Britain's oil reserves, with the companies on the ultra-cautious side, the government somewhat less cautious and a few specialists such as Professor Odell taking a very different view as to the extent of the oil reserves. In fact the argument is less about how much oil is under the sea—most people come reasonably close to each other in estimating the amount according to known data—than about how much of the oil can and should be extracted. It is a question of economics versus a form of socialist nationalism.

According to the Norwegian Parliamentary Report No. 25 published in 1974, there are between 4,000 and 5,000 million tons of oil in the British sector of the North Sea and about the same amount of gas. The Report stated that the North Sea would produce between 150 million and 200 million tons of oil in 1980 and that 50 million tons of that would be from the Norwegian sector.

Writing in 1975 the Mackays said there were then known recoverable reserves of commercial oil amounting to 1,800 million tons. Also in 1975 Stanley Gray, Exploration and Production Co-ordinator of Shell, gave as a reasonable figure of reserves south of parallel 62°, 35,000 million barrels of oil and between 130 and 160 million million cubic feet of gas.

In 1977 a BP executive suggested that if Britain were to take its full consumption of oil from the North Sea at the rate of two million barrels a day, then known resources would last between fifteen and twenty years. Alternately, between 1979 and 1990 the North Sea could supply a third of Europe's needs. There is, in fact, a fairly general consensus among the major oil companies as to the extent of reserves and they all keep on the conservative side in their figures.

In its annual *Brown Book* the Department of Energy gives recoverable reserves at 2,500 million tons, and estimates that depending upon further finds the figure could be extended to between 3,000 and 4,500 million tons—the upper limit including areas that have been designated for exploration but not yet licensed.

George Williams of UKOOA estimates 3,000 to 3,500 million tons of oil in the North Sea; 1,000 million to 1,500 million tons of oil equivalent in gas; and a natural liquid gas equivalent to 10 per cent of the 3,000 million tons of oil. This figure of 3,000 million tons of oil is the approximate equivalent of the 6,000 million tons of presently recoverable coal in the country. As of 1977 about half this 3,000 million tons had actually been found; the balance is expected to be discovered as the search proceeds and much of that will come from about eighty fields.

Shell's Peter Baxendell said in March 1977 that he reckoned 3,000 million tons to be the right estimate for the whole British sector:

> This figure is at the lower end of the spectrum of available forecasts but I believe justifiably so. However, that three billion ton figure represents a total worth as crude in present day terms of around $300,000 million.

He added that his figure represented between thirty and thirty-five years of self-sufficiency for Britain at current consumption rates, although it would not work out like that in practice.

By the end of 1977 the total reserves of the fifteen British fields then under production or development were estimated at 9,000 million barrels; and the reserves of the two dozen or more other discoveries awaiting development amounted to a further 6,000 million barrels apart from anything more to be discovered. This total, though small in comparison with Saudi Arabia's known—and conservatively estimated—reserves of 107,000 million barrels still puts Britain into the top ten oil reserve countries.

The pace of new discoveries is now liable to be more gradual; smaller fields are more costly to develop anyway so that bringing the second generation on stream will be a generally slower business. Yet though the pace could slow down there could well be further surprises and one or two new big fields may yet be found.

The size of reserves is known fairly accurately to the operating company within a short time of the discovery of a field and this becomes generally known quite soon thereafter. During the 1980s Britain will be a middle level oil producer on a par with countries such as Venezuela, Nigeria, Kuwait or Iraq.

Estimates are constantly revised upwards. Such revisions depend upon several factors such as appreciation in the ground—Brent was valued upwards long after discovery; the recovery rate for a particular field—it may well turn out better than originally expected; and future discoveries. What oilmen believe is viable can easily be shown to be wrong five years later, with advances in technology or new finds in the area.

Currently the recovery rate from most fields works out at about

40 per cent, so that 60 per cent of the oil remains in the ground. According to most oil experts, greater technological recovery rates are unlikely and those that do occur ought to be treated as bonuses. But though the companies are sceptical of any great improvements in recovery rates, it is not unreasonable to suppose that the pressures now existing for oil technology over the next decade or so will add between 10 and 15 per cent to the recovery rate. This will involve secondary and tertiary recovery methods. According to Algy Cluff, the determined boss of a small independent, Cluff Oil, there is a lot more oil to be found. He is not alone in that belief.

As Cluff also says, the more oil we find the more relaxed we (the British) can become. Certainly the longer Britain can be self-sufficient in oil the better for balance of payments, the economy as a whole and long-term energy requirements in a world in which economic pressures will grow ever more strong.

The 1978 round of licence awards will aim at finding enough extra oil to prolong the twenty-year two-million-barrel-a-day plateau that was envisaged as things stood at the end of 1977. If self-sufficiency is to be maintained throughout the 1990s, then successful discovery and operation of more oil in deeper waters will be needed in the period 1985 to 1990. Deep-water oil—at deeper levels than anything found so far—will be the next test of oil technology.

Closely related to the question of reserves and self-sufficiency is that of the lifespan of a field. All oil fields have a notional life but in fact last much longer than the generally accepted figure of fifteen years. Oilmen do not know what the life of a field will prove to be. They are notably canny about this subject anyway; but, for example, some oil fields in Oklahoma are still producing 100 years after discovery. With a remarkable display of unanimity, oilmen become vague when asked about the life expectations of a field. There could be as many as forty or fifty years during which Britain produces up to 120 million tons of oil a year. As old oil hands will tell you, oil does not dry up but goes on indefinitely and, indeed, oil estimates will rise until the last field is discovered. Then when the final decline does set in, tertiary recovery methods will come into their own.

Thus it is now expected that Britain's oil will last well into the twenty-first century although in declining quantities. Most of this oil will come from the fields east of Shetland. There is a great deal of further heavy investment to be made. Such calculations, however, depend upon demand: both Britain's own level of consumption and any decisions she makes about producing more oil for export purposes and so depleting the resources faster. According to the OECD, British energy consumption will reach 250 million tons oil equivalent (mtoe) by 1985, while her oil should just top the 100 million ton level in 1980 and could reach a level of 145 million tons in 1985; in 1980 this would be equal to 40 per cent of the country's needs and in 1985 to between 45 and 55 per cent.

These facts are not especially in dispute although experts will argue about the high and low estimate margins, some favouring one and some the other. Once we move into the realms of policy, however, controversy rears its head—often in the person of Professor Odell. He argues there is far more oil in the North Sea than the companies or government for that matter are admitting, and that Britain therefore could be fully self-sufficient until 2000.

More controversial is his contention that the companies cream off fields to achieve maximum profitability, leaving oil in the ground which could be recovered if decisions were taken on other bases than those solely of maximizing profits. Tony Benn has made the Odell question more irritating still for the oil companies by appointing him as a part-time consultant to the Department of Energy. Odell argues there is a 90 per cent probability that the North Sea as a whole (British and Norwegian) contains 78 billion barrels of oil and a 50 per cent chance that the figure can be increased to 109 billion barrels; these figures contrast with Shell and BP estimates of 50–55 billion barrels.

Such arguments are, in part, pointless because they cannot determine how much of the oil will actually be extracted whatever systems —secondary and tertiary—are used until the attempt is made. Thus of the Department of Energy's estimate of 3,200 million tons of recoverable oil which could last Britain for thirty-five years, at least 700 million tons of it is at present sheer guesswork while a further 550 million tons is classified as 'possible'.

Recovery rates are governed by two quite different types of criteria: technological and economic. Up to 1920 or thereabouts the oil recovery rate stood at approximately 25 per cent. Then came techniques of gas injection and secondary recovery pushed the rate up to a figure between 35 and 40 per cent where it stands today. With further tertiary methods of recovery this percentage could be pushed considerably higher—at a price.

The question Odell poses is an economic one. Companies only extract and want to extract oil at an economic rate which provides them with a reasonable profit; in view of the risks involved and the size of the investment that has to be made, they regard a reasonable profit as high if it is related to other activities. Odell's recovery rates might well be achieved if recovery was the sole object of the operation and costs or profit were regarded as unimportant. The question he does not answer is who would pay the bill if such an approach were to be adopted. The companies certainly would not; nor would any government that one could foresee coming to power in Britain at the present time.

The company attitude is clear enough: once a field has been discovered it pays to work it as fast as possible since virtually all the costs have been incurred in the development phase before the oil flows and the company has received any returns. Thus there are always huge debts to service at the beginning of a field's life. But with regard to oil self-sufficiency, the lifespan of a field has to be set against profitability.

The authors of *Scottish Oil Shakedown* (a Church of Scotland publication) make the point:

> The most recently discovered fields . . . have ensured for the United Kingdom self-sufficiency in oil by 1980/81, with the probability of material surplus potential thereafter, *provided the operating companies continue to see development as a commercial proposition.**

This is a central proviso that must dominate all oil calculations, standing in the way of the Odell thesis that there is far more oil than anyone either admits or is willing to extract. The oil is there; the problem is whether it can be extracted profitably.

So far it would appear that extraction policy has been set by the companies rather than government, and as late as 1977 the government said there would be no restrictions on production of fields then cleared for development through into the 1980s. There is no policy to control the rate of extraction. Government aims have been: self-sufficiency by 1980; a turnround in the problem of balance of payments; a major addition to government revenue. These three objectives are being achieved. The only evidence of any policy to control the rate of extraction came in 1977 when Mr Benn ordered Shell-Esso to take action to stop gas flaring on the Brent field.

Government control over the rate of extraction can be exercised in a number of ways: by delaying or spacing further offshore licence awards. To do this, however, also means that government does not find out what ultimate reserves are, something it would prefer to know as soon as possible. Secondly, government can hold back permission to develop any field found after 1975. Thirdly, government can order production cuts. However, an assurance was given in 1974 that there would be no cuts before 1982 and none of more than 20 per cent. Finally, government can withhold permission to increase oil production until proper facilities for using (as opposed to burning) gas have been installed in a field (which was the case with Brent in 1977). Taking these conditions together the depletion control

* Author's italics.

policy has few teeth that can be applied effectively before 1982; nor is there any sign that government has in mind a serious depletion control policy in any case. As a BP paper puts it:

> . . . whichever of the specified price situations prevails, the production of North Sea oil is worth a great deal: 'real' rates of return *to the nation* are between 40 and 50 per cent, after counting as a cost the profits and finance charges incurred by foreign companies engaged in developing the fields licensed to them (and assuming a similar foreign engagement in future discoveries).

This is very well put in statesmanlike style from a company point of view. The government will get the maximum benefit from allowing increased prices when fields have flattened out in terms of rates of production.

Any depletion policy must depend upon the export policy which the government adopts after 1980, when self-sufficiency has been reached. That in turn will depend upon the pressures Britain's allies exert upon her to produce above her own needs so as to meet some of theirs as well.

Odell argues that the appreciation factor will turn out to be one of two: that is, discoveries will amount to twice the original announcements. It might be argued that Odell's main function is to needle the companies into explaining and defending their assertions and policies. Certain events have supported Odell's claims even though the companies say his calculations are based upon inadequate information. Brent was upgraded by a vast amount after the original estimate, and in 1976 BP announced that Forties would produce 25 per cent more than originally forecast.

Odell, the director of the Economic Geography Institute at Erasmus University in the Netherlands, has acted as a constant goad and critic of oil company policy ever since leaving Shell. His calculations about the North Sea, which have been based upon studies of oil patterns elsewhere in the world, suggest that the British sector of the North Sea could produce between 300 million and 500 million tons by 1990—a figure far above any oil company forecast.

Further, he argues that with intensive effort Europe could be 80 per cent self-sufficient in energy resources from the mid 1980s. One answer to Odell from an oilman is simply: 'If you think the oil industry is cautious, try getting finance for a high-risk offshore oil development. The bankers don't want to know what we hope to produce if things go well, they want our most cautious estimate based on the information we have. There is no room for optimism, only for such facts as we possess.' As ever the argument comes round to money.

It is the accepted wisdom of the oilmen that the world supply will peak some time in the 1990s; in part this assessment is based upon current methods of extraction allied to current economic returns. More oil could be extracted at far greater cost. As *The Banker* put it in an issue that dealt with oil in May 1977: company estimates of technically recoverable oil reserves are actually estimates of what can *profitably* be taken out of the ground. Odell may be right to say the North Sea has 80 billion barrels of recoverable oil; equally Shell may be right in commercial terms to argue there are only about 25 billion barrels that it would be profitable to extract.

Odell performs a useful function by overstating the possibilities; it seems unlikely that much oil will be extracted by secondary and tertiary methods. This, for example, is the view of Lord Kearton. Sir Philip Southwell concedes that the Odell thesis is correct, but says it is easy for him to make such a point while the companies have to be conservative and cautious since they are responsible to government and shareholders.

In a monograph published in 1977 Professor Odell attacked the way in which fields had been developed. He suggested that had six instead of four platforms been installed on Forties, the field's production would then have been maximized. His basic argument is that more jobs and revenue could have been provided from the North Sea if development had been tackled in a different way. He makes the point—almost, it would seem, with surprise—that company estimates of a field's recoverable reserves are firmly related to the level of investment; what else would he expect? He argues that because of the purely commercial attitude of the companies this requires '. . . a continuing and intensive government involvement and participation in the decision taking process right from the earliest days of analysis of a field's potential'. He casts doubt on the ability of BNOC to achieve this part of its role on the grounds that it has been set up in such a way that its 'objectives must become identical with those of its private company partners'. Odell's underlying contention is that company and national interests conflict. This seems a reasonable argument to put forward.

But as one cryptic observer of the oil scene commented of the company–Odell conflict:

> If Odell turns out to be right he will say 'I told you so' although everyone will be so pleased at the fact of more oil and its economic consequences that it won't matter. And if Odell turns out to be wrong, who will remember him anyway?

4

The Companies

The names of the oil giants—BP, Shell, Esso—have long been familiar to the British public; since the opening up of the North Sea, however, some lesser known names have also made headlines: Occidental, Tricentrol or Phillips; while a host of new 'independents' have appeared for the first time: Cluff Oil, Thomson, LASMO, Exploration Holdings.

Oil power is mesmeric and Britain's sudden recent emergence as an oil-producing country has meant that oilmen appear in new roles—saving the ailing economy, predicting about the future (the famous 'energy gap' and what we should do about it), or more generally telling us how to solve our national problems.

The oil companies are in the business to make money—preferably, and often, lots of money—for themselves and their shareholders. Once this is understood, so too is their natural hostility to Wedgwood Benn, BNOC or any other government-imposed control that curtails their profitability. It is important to restate this obvious fact about the oil companies: otherwise, one may be misled by their constant claims that what they do is synonymous with the national good.

The companies do not exist to carry out policies in the interests of the country. Because of their enormous present power and the fact that oil more than any other single commodity is the most valuable one to the economy, the companies may sometimes be represented—or represent themselves—as carrying out a unique economic function for Britain. This is not the case. They are capitalist, conservative, money-making businesses; they have their share of patriotism or nationalism and often a good deal more than their share of gall or arrogance—it is a function of success—but they have no more right to lay special claims to playing a unique national role than boilermakers, shipbuilders, coalminers or any other group. At the moment, however, they can claim to be in the ascendant.

The companies generate intense loyalties to themselves and, at the professional level, look after their employees exceptionally well. They have a superb public relations system and go to great lengths to present themselves to the public as 'responsible'. But to quote a Scottish banker looking at what might develop should an SNP-inspired break-up of the United Kingdom take place, the oil companies 'swim in the sea in which they find themselves'—a fact that the 'majors' amply demonstrated to Mr Heath when in 1973 he tried in vain to alter their policies to solve Britain's crisis needs.

Indeed, the companies claim that they are ready to work with anyone: they adapt to the political circumstances in which they find themselves whether in the Middle East, South Africa and Rhodesia, Europe 'in crisis' or a British break-up row affecting their position in the North Sea. Such sponge-like resilience is their method of survival; it has stood them in good stead even if it attracts the hostility of politicians, not least because it enables the companies to elude many of the controls that politicians of the left would, in theory at any rate, like to impose upon them.

Although they protest at government interference in their activities, the potential for the companies in the North Sea is better than anywhere else in the world, being both more secure and more profitable than activities elsewhere. The public has been constantly fed with details of the vast sums needed to open up the North Sea, the huge costs of rigs and platforms; it is time they were given a few details concerning the equally vast profits to be made in the North Sea and the enormous returns already coming back in 1977 and 1978.

There are great difficulties to overcome—the famous 'frontiers of technology'; these are being overcome and no one should play down the technological achievements involved. But companies make their profits downstream in the refining and petrochemical business, and in retailing, so it follows they have a vital interest to maintain a steady flow of crude oil to ensure maximum use of their downstream investments. The North Sea will enable the companies to do this for the next twenty or thirty years.

There may be some truth in the claim that the oil companies would leave the North Sea if squeezed too hard, but this is about 99 per cent unlikely since the sea represents not only a stable area politically but also, unlike the Middle East, one where they have sure access to crude supplies.

Listening to an oilman telling a Scottish audience in booming Aberdeen that farmers and fishermen come first in the Grampian region, then the bankers and insurance men, while trailing well behind these stalwarts are the oilmen who have brought such new life to the area, it is difficult not to smile at such mock humility, especially as the same speaker went on to tell his hearers that they could have the oil 'as long as they paid for it'. Oil is not just big business; it is hard business. A rig in position, for example, has an operating cost of £100,000 a day including the support vessels. It therefore requires a loyal crew and, should labour troubles arise, the crew will be replaced at once. At the same time it is a paradox of an industry dominated by great multinational corporations that it relies so heavily upon the expertise of others, so that a huge proportion of the work done in the North Sea is carried out by contractors rather than by the personnel of the oil companies.

On the other hand, the nerve centres of the great companies are highly geared to take economic-political decisions. Thus Esso's economic centre works upon future trends: volume predictions about what is needed; 'guesstimates' of government policies for a feel of the forward business climate; and Shell produces some of the most advanced statistical data anywhere in the world.

The business attitudes of the companies are clear enough: if an exploitation area becomes unattractive they move elsewhere. When tackled about profits, for example, the companies do not presume to know a fair allocation of profits as between themselves and the people; rather, they make what they can and then move on. In money terms the more years it takes to repay the original investment needed to get a field going, the less attractive the field becomes. Thus, always, it is a question of quick returns.

The curious relationship between the companies and government—one of tension and suspicion yet also of mutual dependence—is not perhaps the best sort of relationship as far as the public at large are concerned, since it rarely means a cutback in price except on the occasions of the highly artificial and usually shortlived price wars over petrol. As the Mackays say in dry yet telling language:

> The interdependence of oligopolistic producers has given rise to a classic textbook situation where each individual firm (and each host country) believes that price cuts will be followed by its competitors, so that all face a fall in revenue. Competition therefore has often taken a non-price form, and this, together with the marketing power and efficiency of the small group of majors, is the first important factor underpinning a market price which is significantly above the long-run price of oil production.

In other words, they charge the public too much.

Extraordinary efforts are made by the major oil companies to demonstrate that what they are doing is in the national interest; and, negatively, that there cannot be a conflict of interest between them and the 'nation'—presumably as it is embodied in Parliament. Yet such efforts are often unintentionally belied; for example, when the majors ask for talks between themselves and government over tax or other issues as though they are mini- or not so mini-states, instead of only companies. Other businesses neither expect nor get such consideration; the oil companies often do.

During 1977, however, the companies were smarting as a result of relatively successful government efforts to exercise at least some control over their activities in the North Sea: the new PRT regime, BNOC, participation had all been put into operation, with commensurate diminishing of company power.

There is an element of self-righteousness about the companies too; for example they claimed that the Labour government had broken the fourth round of licence agreements by launching its 51 per cent participation policy. Of course it did; but then how else was such a policy to be started?

For all their power, the companies are acutely sensitive to criticism; they are or often appear to be on the defensive and seem to expect criticism automatically. A cynic might argue that the fact they expect it means they deserve it. Criticism of their industry and especially of the majors is inevitable; not that they are more deserving of criticism than other industries, but because they are so much more powerful and wealthy. Power and size attract criticism and at least a part of the industry's sensitivity is an over-reaction to this fact. In economic terms and sometimes in political terms as well, the majors are more powerful than many states; it must follow—whatever policies they pursue and however good or bad their records—that they will be targets for attack. Sometimes they lay themselves open to such charges; the way their top men are treated like cabinet ministers and guarded like heads of state leaves little doubt as to how they regard themselves. The majors could show a little more sense of humour. For the foreseeable future they will be targets; they may as well enjoy it.

Two oil bodies that have emerged as a result of North Sea activities are UKOOA and Brindex, both representing the interests of the oil companies. UKOOA (United Kingdom Offshore Operators Association) was formed in 1964 shortly after the first round of licence awards when it was known as the UK North Sea Operators' Committee. Its object was to provide the industry with a forum for discussion of technical and administrative matters and to provide, where practical, a means of communication with government. In 1973 UKOOA Ltd was fully registered and took on a permanent staff. Membership of the Association is restricted to oil companies operating on their own behalf or acting as operators for others, and in 1977 it included a total of thirty-seven companies then operating on the UK continental shelf.

UKOOA has a large number of committees whose subjects include clean seas and emergency services, communications, employment practices, exploration, full and fair opportunity (for UK business to obtain North Sea orders), oceanographic, offshore fire and emergency control, offshore protection and safety. There are others. The government has welcomed UKOOA as a useful organization representing the whole industry with whom to consult, and UKOOA has become progressively involved in all offshore matters. It has been accepted by both companies and government in its role as spokesman for the industry.

Brindex—the Association of British Independent Oil Exploration Companies—has a membership of some twenty-eight on the whole small-ish companies which include Attock, Cluff, LASMO, Oil Exploration (Holdings), P & O Petroleum, Thomson Oil, Tricentrol. It acts as a voice for the small independents who struggle valiantly to get their share of the North Sea between the giants.

As of August 1976 Brindex members' share of proven North Sea oil reserves stood at 4·4 per cent and of gas at 1 per cent. In the fifth round of licence awards in 1977, five blocks were offered to consortia in which Brindex members were involved, while ten members of Brindex applying for licences were successful. According to the association:

> The U.K. oil industry is dominated by major multinational companies with world-wide preoccupations and the creation of BNOC has by no means diminished the need for the smaller companies in the private sector.

Brindex says its members are developing British expertise in the industry which provides Britain with its greatest opportunity for economic recovery, and argues:

> Competition in the private sector of the industry is the best way of ensuring innovation and growth in oil exploration, and smaller companies have a large part to play in ensuring maximum economic recovery of oil.

The association claims that it provides the investing public with North Sea opportunities and advances the advantages of the 'independents' as they are known in the industry. Brindex wants British (as opposed to multinational) industry to be more involved in oil. It argues that the independents make efficient use of risk capital; that they supply a career structure in oil; that their work alongside that of the majors will ensure the discovery of maximum volumes of oil and gas from the North Sea basin.

Brindex has a hard task to increase the share of the independents in the oil scramble, though they may pick up some significant smaller finds that are beneath the interest of the majors. Government has shown little enough interest in encouraging the independents; it has been too concerned to get the big oil finds flowing fast.

BP, which is Britain's largest industrial concern and eighth largest industrial company in the non-Communist world, staged a spectacular public relations exercise in January 1978 when a limited edition first-day cover of British energy stamps was mailed direct from the Forties field: posted on a platform and flown by helicopter to Aberdeen. The point of the exercise was to emphasize BP's contribution to Britain's energy—and with Forties, West Sole gas, her other fields and her onshore oil her contribution is indeed a large one.

It is interesting to reflect that the fortunes of Britain's oil giant did not look anything like as rosy in the 1960s as they do today. Despite the discovery of the West Sole gas field in 1965, the company in the latter 1960s faced growing pressures upon its traditional oil sources in the Middle East, while Sir Eric Drake as late as April 1970 could make his throwaway remark about not rating highly the chances of commercial oil finds in the North Sea. Since then the giant Forties field—currently perhaps the most profitable field anywhere—has come on tap as has the huge Alaskan discovery, so that in 1977 BP could benefit from the biggest share sale ever when the government made available more than £500 million worth of its BP stake to the public.

It was practice in 1976 and 1977 when the economic outlook for Britain was especially gloomy to look to BP and the Forties field as the one source of inspiration in an otherwise miserable picture. Late in 1976 BP's chairman, Sir David Steel, announced that extensive drilling had shown the field could be upgraded from producing 400,000 barrels a day to 500,000 barrels by the end of 1977: this was equivalent to announcing not only the discovery of a medium sized oil field capable of a daily production of 100,000 barrels, but also that it could be brought on stream in a year at virtually no extra cost.

It is little wonder that BP shares are doing well. The rate of 500,000 barrels a day—peak production for Forties—should be maintained for about five years until the end of 1982. BP will make £800 million profit from Forties in 1978 and for several more years while it is at peak; this may seem huge and tempt those on the political left to suggest that taxes are not high enough, but it should not be forgotten that government holds 51 per cent of the shares.

BP continues its North Sea search and has many stakes other than the Forties field. It discovered a small yet potentially good commercial gas field off the coast of Lincolnshire in 1977; it has major holdings with Conoco and Statoil in the Norwegian sector of the North Sea; it has made new finds north of the Frigg gas field. Of potentially even greater interest was its discovery of oil west of the

Shetlands during the summer of 1977. More drilling has to be carried out before the commercial possibilities can be assessed, yet the find is of great significance. In mid 1977 BP had nine rigs in action and had still not drilled some of her awards under the fourth round; nor had she started to drill her fifth round block awards.

The government stake in BP often makes for confusion in the public mind. For years it was 51 per cent until BP took over Distillers; then when shareholders took up their allotments of new shares, the government deliberately did not do so with the result that its holding was reduced to 46·8 per cent. Government, however, had two of its nominees on the BP board though the company has always been treated as part of the private sector. The fact that the government holding was allowed to drop below 51 per cent was of particular importance at the time since BP was then becoming involved in major operations in the USA where anything smacking of state control would—so it was believed—have had adverse effects upon the company's chances. When Burmah collapsed the Bank of England took over BP's 23 per cent holding in that company, effectively adding this to the government stake which then rose to a high of 68 per cent.

Subsequently, not least because of BP's vast Alaska operation, government decided not to make BP the state oil corporation and BNOC was created. Thereafter there was no good reason for the government to hold 68 per cent of the company shares and in the light of its IMF loans and the need to raise more money and show tighter policies, the Chancellor, Denis Healey, allowed 17 per cent of the government's stock to be offered to the public in 1977, government this time retaining enough of the shares to restore its holding in BP to the old figure of 51 per cent.

The recoverable reserves of the vast field at Prudhoe Bay on the inhospitable North Slope of Alaska are probably more than 9,600 million barrels of oil and 26 trillion cubic feet of gas. BP, with a junior partner, Sohio, has 54 per cent of this field. The figure of 9,600 million barrels means this source of oil is more than five times as large as the Forties field. The saga of BP's Alaska venture and the technological difficulties in building the pipeline have been every bit as dramatic as the North Sea. The importance of Alaska in the British context is twofold: first, that it makes BP immeasurably more wealthy and influential as an oil company than otherwise it might be; and second, it provides the much used argument (though whether really valid is another matter) that BP could not act as a state oil corporation because of its position in the free-enterprise US oil business. Whatever the profits BP makes from Alaska the British Exchequer will take its 51 per cent.

In Britain BP is involved in all aspects of the oil business: refineries; the petrochemical business; marketing. After eleven months of intense negotiations in which the company deployed a battery of lawyers and specialists, a participation agreement was concluded with BNOC in June of 1977 giving the state oil corporation a 51 per cent interest in BP's offshore interests including Forties and Ninian. BNOC is government and government has 51 per cent of BP anyway.

At the beginning of 1977 BP announced that it was to double its investment in Britain over the following five years to £2,700 million, of which three-quarters would be in Scotland: £1,200 million was for specialized manufacturing plant and other downstream activities; £900 million for chemical manufactures. These were huge sums by any standards. At the time that BP's chairman made these announcements, Dr Jack Birks, director of BP Trading, told the press that the outlay of £850 million on the Forties field would be recovered some time in 1978; thereafter, with capital costs written off, the field would have a further twenty-three years of life ahead of it.

The power and wealth of multinationals like BP can be appreciated when their financial returns are examined. The declaration of quarterly returns for such a company is always an event in the City. Thus third quarter results for 1976 came to £51·9 million profit and shares rose 11 pence to 737 pence. The fourth quarter return for that year—when the government tax on Forties was increasing—came to £56 million and shares then stood at 886 pence. Net income for the year was £185·9 million. The group income from sales for the year was around £12,000 million. Thus the profits for the year were larger than a good many national budgets; the group sales figure far in excess of the GNP of half the members of the UN.

By the time the first quarter results for 1977 came in—with sharply boosted Forties production—they stood at £90·5 million. The shares gained 8 pence and went to 930 pence. Second quarter results at £75·7 million net profits pushed the half year results to £166·2 million. Third quarter earnings were down to £44·1 million, but even so this meant that the first three-quarters of the year had yielded £210 million as opposed to a total 1976 figure of only £185·9 million. For many years to come BP will act as a barometer of British economic fortunes, results coming as one of the highlights or gloom spots of the year.

In his mini-budget of December 1976 when the British financial position was exceptionally bad, the Chancellor announced that the government would divest itself of a proportion of its BP shares so as to give the government room to manoeuvre, as well as help it meet the IMF loan conditions. The sale then and later was vigorously opposed by Mr Wedgwood Benn. BP welcomed the sale since it

wanted the shares more widely dispersed thus heading off the possibility of direct nationalization: with the Alaska development 40 per
cent of the company's assets are in the USA.

As market speculation and excitement mounted over the forthcoming sale, it seemed likely that American investors would be
offered the chance to buy about a quarter of the shares, while the
remaining three-quarters were earmarked for British investors.
Valued at approximately £600 million by May 1977, the share sale
represented the largest of its kind ever. Since both BP and the government had an equal interest in the sale the build-up which preceded
the event was most skilfully orchestrated. A week before the shares
went on sale, BP applied for permission to raise its dividend by more
than the maximum allowed. The Treasury rejected the application;
but the move enabled BP to spell out its future dividend policy and, of
course, produced more publicity. It was part of an exercise to ensure
the sale went well; BP had just finished dealing with the embarrassing
disclosure about its political payments in various countries.

When finally the shares were put on the market in mid June, 1977,
the price was fixed at 845 pence a share for the 66,800,000 giving the
value for this 17 per cent government stake at £564 million; the offer
was for 300 pence down payment on 24 June with the balance of
545 pence not due till 6 December. The operation went like clock-
work; the issue was three and a half times oversubscribed.

The sale was carefully co-ordinated between London and New
York, where the 25 per cent on offer to the American market was
sold. Advertising for the issue alone cost £225,000 while the total bill
for the entire operation came to about £10 million. The sale reflected
the excitement of oil, its certainty on a market that had long been in
trouble and the strength of BP. Thus a British newspaper could break
into superlatives: 'The biggest sale on earth is over. Applications for
British Petroleum shares have swamped the banks dealing with them.'
When it came to the point, about 225,000 British investors applied
for shares and one way to meet these applications was for the
government to cut down the amount of shares offered on the
American market from 25 to 20 per cent. The small man was given
preference—one way at least in which investors have been made to
feel they had a stake in North Sea oil.

In the event this well stage-managed sale satisfied everyone: the
government got the money it wanted, retained its 51 per cent in BP
and satisfied the IMF; BP saw a lessening of government control, a
widening of its general spread including a most satisfying American
rush for its shares, and a popular blazoning of the company; and the
small investor had a good look in and felt that at last he had got
something out of oil. It must have been a long time since American

investors showed such interest in buying a British share in such quantities.

The oil companies—discreet in all their dealings anyway—have developed a canniness in relation to public pronouncements and government that does credit to their sense of self-preservation. On the issue of profits, for example, BP's Dr Birks claims that a rate of return of 20 per cent is reasonable, although he says it could be modified if there were compensating tax advantages to be gained. This 20 per cent figure, the oil companies hasten to point out, is generally put forward as being reasonable by City analysts. Between 50 and 60 per cent of BP profits, for example, are reinvested in oil ventures somewhere round the world.

To the question: Is a 70 per cent government tax at the margin reasonable?, comes the retort that it reflects the pattern of international oil business (except in the USA where there is not the same excess tax) and is comparable with other places. To the question: Are BP interests synonymous with those of the nation?, comes an unhesitating and uncompromising 'yes'. This 'yes' is then substantiated by several facts: that government (which in BP's case holds 51 per cent of the shares) has seen fit not to interfere further; there is the growing impact that BP oil is making upon the country's balance of payments position as well as the rising government tax take; and North Sea oil represents security of supply for Britain.

An intriguing question for the layman is the extent to which oil extraction can be increased by improved technology from the average 40 per cent level now achieved. This is an especially contentious field because it does not simply involve technology; it is also a question of economics and brings us back to arguments identified in the oilman's mind with the name of Odell. Most oilmen are at one in claiming that future technology may make a marginal difference to the oil take, although no great hopes should be pinned upon a substantially enhanced rate of extraction.

Much research is going on, yet there is little evidence that the balance will change: that is, that technology will enable a much greater amount of oil to be recovered than is economically feasible at the present. In January 1978, for example, BP were injecting chemicals into the Forties field to see how these could improve the take. The key to increased production lies in the marginal fields and the extent to which these can be exploited. That will depend, so the companies argue, upon tax concessions. In other words the oilmen say: tax us less and we will develop marginal fields that otherwise we would not bother about. The government can always reduce the margin of tax in order to obtain more oil from 'secure supplies'.

Company sensitivity to government interference is always close to the surface. On the question of controls in relation to depletion policy, for example, BP's Dr Birks reacted instantly:

> Any retroactive action that creates alarm in the industry reduces the rate of investment; this is true whether the action is in the form of tax, government oil take, or control of output.

Now such statements bear examination. It has become a feature of debates about North Sea oil for the companies to talk of 'confidence' and how government interference reduces this and so leads to cutbacks in investment with all the consequences that flow from such cutbacks. If the primary objective of the companies is to make money, then such a statement can be turned on its head. It is, of course, natural that oilmen will represent their actions in a certain light: 'we are providing a service, but it can be undermined if a foolish government undermines confidence'.

This argument can be seen in a totally different light from outside the industry. The companies are experts at manipulation: when they see the prospect of government action that might limit their profits or further control their activities, they do their best to forestall it. The tactic they frequently employ is that of trying to frighten government with the mystique of 'confidence': no oil will flow, or less oil, so that the government take will fall (with all its consequences) if there is interference. Sometimes such an approach succeeds and government backs off. In fact the companies deliberately hold back investment if, by doing so, they think they can win a particular battle, especially if they believe the government to be desperate to get the oil flowing ever faster, as has been the case through the 1970s. Having held back their investment they talk of the mysterious force 'confidence' as though it alone is to blame. This needs to be taken with a grain of salt. BP is a British institution and one that the government fosters as a good shareholder and also sometimes treats with a circumspection that comes close to awe. BP does very well out of such an attitude.

Shell is as pervasive a multinational as is BP—but it is not wholly British. With Esso it controls the largest gas field in the North Sea—Leman—and the largest oil field in the British sector, Brent, as well as a number of other fields including Auk, Cormorant, Dunlin and Tern. Shell's first delivery of oil to the British market came in February 1976 from the small Auk field. Since 1964, according to William Bell, Shell-Expro has been in the forefront:

> . . . drilling more exploration wells than any other operator and leading the search for oil as it was pressed north into deeper and more difficult waters. More specifically, Shell-Expro pioneered the

exploration of the most prolific North Sea oil province, the so-called Brent Province, located some 160 kilometres northwest of Scotland.

Speaking of the huge Brent development Bell claims:

Thus, the initial deliveries of Brent oil late in 1976 mark a notable double first—exploration and then first production from this northernmost area of the North Sea. It is difficult to exaggerate the scale and complexity of the project or to pay adequate tribute to the accomplishment of all those involved.

By 1976 Shell were investing at the average rate of £1 million a day in their Brent developments. The combined Shell-Esso expenditure on North Sea development between 1975 and 1980 is expected to come to more than £3,000 million. There was no particular reason why there had to be a Shell-Esso partnership though it has clearly worked well for both companies. They had already worked on joint ventures in Holland and regarded the North Sea as an extension of their European operations. Esso had tax problems and was uncertain of what would develop in the North Sea—as were most of the other companies.

Shell regards its North Sea operations as of major importance—apart from the size of the fields—both because of security of supply and proximity to the major markets. Shell are no longer just an oil company; they regard themselves as an energy company. One senior Shell man produced what is perhaps the most startling *post facto* justification for the enormously high company profits in the pre-North Sea era: 'If we had not done so' he said 'then we would not have had the capital resources available to develop the North Sea when it came along.'

Watching Shell returns is another major City preoccupation. Shell is the world's second largest oil group: 60 per cent Dutch—Royal Dutch Petroleum; and 40 per cent British—Shell Transport and Trading. In 1976 its earnings came to £1,300·4 million. The size of Shell's North Sea stake in the following fields—Indefatigable and Leman (gas), Auk, Brent, South Cormorant and Dunlin—were estimated to be worth a net income to the group of £300 million in the 1980s, while the development of some of its other interests—North Cormorant, Fulmar, Tern, Albuskjell and Statfjord—would add about another £150 million a year to its total North Sea take a few years later.

Another curious retrospective argument put forward to justify the taking of vast profits *in the past* is that these subsequently have been balanced by the huge rise in inflation. Shell, like the other companies,

4

argues that the North Sea fields without the price rises of 1973 and 1974 would have been non-starters. This seems hard to believe considering the extent to which they had all committed themselves to capital investments before 1973.

On the question of tax, Shell's Mr Pollard says with diplomatic judiciousness that a 70 per cent tax rate is the sort of thing—now—that is to be expected on a world-wide basis. Shell reckon that 70–30 is 'par for the course'. But when it is a question of marginal fields, there has to be a different range between the technical costs and the total value of the oil to be extracted. Should a conflict arise between Shell and government about what is to be taken out, two possibilities present themselves: first, that Shell relinquishes its licence of a field and, for example, BNOC takes over the development; or, the government provides sufficient incentive to persuade the company to develop such a field—that is, tax cuts.

Like all the companies Shell would like a minimum of government interference; if this is not possible it adopts a chameleon-like approach depending upon the particular local situation. Only by adapting do Shell and the other majors continue to be so successful.

Esso, the British subsidiary of the giant Exxon, is very deeply involved in the North Sea indeed—both on its own and in its partnership with Shell. As the company points out, the North Sea represents the biggest challenge to the oil world yet: the capital cost of work on a field in the North Sea is 'six times that of an equivalent one in Nigeria and twenty-five times the cost of developing one in Saudi Arabia'. Dr Pearce, the Chairman and Chief Executive of Esso, says that on the whole the companies regard the tax regime as reasonable. A 20 per cent profit, he says, is the lowest consonant with ongoing development. Although he is now top man in Esso, Dr Pearce started as a geologist and will remark in his amiable way that producing oil is a 'hairy business', and no one knows how production will shape up until it actually does; nor, he says, did anyone in the early North Sea days expect the huge escalation of costs which took place. Although it may be possible to develop faster, the North Sea is still very much on the edges of technology so that mistakes can be immensely costly.

Esso is at pains to point out that reports of high oil profits given by some of the analysts embody a fallacy: they take a particular window of averages although the overall picture is different. There is, however, a fallacy also in this company defence of high North Sea profits. North Sea oil is Britain's own resource in a quite different way to her interests through her companies in, for example, Middle Eastern or Nigerian oil. She therefore, through government, has a special, indeed absolute, right to control that oil in isolation from other company commitments elsewhere round the world. In that respect she is only interested in the 'window' onto the North Sea.

On the question of profits, while admitting that those for North Sea oil are currently above the world average, Dr Pearce claims that by about 1980 they will be no more than average, while later they will fall below the average. Perhaps; but this will depend upon prices. Like BP, Esso maintain there is no conflict of interest between their aims and those of the country. As Pearce says: 'The company has to take a long-term view on questions of national interest.' His implication is clear: governments are short-term in their approaches. It was a nice reversal of the roles normally assigned to government and companies by politicians.

On technology Pearce is more generous than some to Odell: he says the Professor is theoretically right about the extent of North Sea resources *provided* there is no question of costs involved—which is more than some oilmen would concede. A great deal of research is being done by the companies upon ways of increasing the oil take, but such technological advances will not be cheap to implement.

The general approach to the North Sea by the companies is to obtain a take of 40 per cent—rather than 35 per cent—and to get it as quickly as possible. With the huge initial capital expenditure involved in the North Sea, companies want as much back as early as they can obtain it. Moreover, oil company employees have a vested interest in as much as possible being taken as soon as possible, since this will affect their jobs.

Should government decide upon cutbacks in production as part of its depletion policy then, Pearce argues, if it is no more than a question of 10 or 15 per cent such a cutback could be borne by the companies—provided 'the misery is spread equally between the producers'—a telling way of putting the problem. If it is a question of a large cutback of up to 50 per cent, then it would be better to leave the oil in the ground: that is, not develop a field until ready to take it all out.

Another important factor to be considered is the lifespan of the giant platforms costing many millions of pounds. They ought, once in place, to be used to a maximum; if they are expected to stand on the North Sea for an extra ten or fifteen years as a result of depletion policy, taking only half or two-thirds from the wells a platform services, this will mean an increasingly expensive bill for maintenance work to keep the platform operational at the tail-end of its life. As yet no one knows how long the platforms will last.

The best depletion control policy would be that of spreading out the licences regularly. The best way to maximize the production from the small fields would be to modify tax and the government take to about 50 per cent and, because of the cost of platforms, look instead to subsea completion systems.

And here another question arises: that of employment. Platforms provide more jobs than would other systems, although the bulk of jobs are unskilled or semi-skilled. Subsea systems will provide more skilled and higher paid jobs, and though these may appear to be fewer in number the high technology involved would generate many ancillary activities. In real terms, though superficially it may not appear so, a platform has a small technological spin-off; the real technological spin-offs will come from other systems.

The difficulty about high technology systems is that they deprive the politicians of the opportunity to claim—as they can with a platform order—that they have provided a thousand jobs. As the oilmen believe, it is better to go for the higher technology and, moreover, produce on time.

When oilmen are tackled as to whether or not Britain should produce a surplus of oil for export, they hide behind the convenient claim that such a decision concerns the national economy and not oil companies; yet it is clear that their preference and pressures work towards maximizing rather than cutting back production, which means there must be a substantial amount of exports.

Apart from the majors, many medium-sized and small or 'independent' companies are just as busy in the North Sea. One of the most interesting of the consortia formed is that headed by Occidental who say:

> In 1966 Occidental Petroleum made its first move into the international oil scene—in Libya. Thus it was still considered something of a newcomer by the major oil companies when it organized its North Sea consortium in 1971. This consortium consists of Occidental Petroleum, 36·5 per cent; Getty Oil International (England) Limited, 23·5 per cent; Allied Chemical (North Sea) Limited, 20 per cent; and Thomson North Sea Limited, 20 per cent.

The group, which has both the Piper and Claymore fields, has been one of the more successful ones.

Tricentrol claims that it decided to 'plunge' into the North Sea in 1964 and the Chairman then told the board:

> The company may be a small one, but it is 100 per cent British and we should not let this unique opportunity to explore in the U.K. waters pass us by.

They didn't; but to raise the kind of development finances they would need, Tricentrol had to form a commercial division and, for example, purchased Luton Commercial Motors as a source of income. With the profits from the Commercial Division, Tricentrol was able to participate in the important fourth round of licence awards and one of these covered block 211/18 where the Thistle field was found. As the company report states:

> This field, in which Tricentrol has a 9·65 per cent stake, is rated the sixth largest commercial field of those yet discovered in the North Sea on the U.K. Continental Shelf.

Constant changes alter the pattern of oil ownership in the North Sea. Thus the American company, Ashland Oil of Kentucky, bought one fourth of Santa Fe International Corporation's 21·7 per cent in the Thistle field for £47·8 million. Other similar 'buying in' deals have altered consortia membership in a number of fields. This is often necessary when companies—especially the smaller ones—need to raise capital to meet their share of a field's development.

Typical of the American approach to oil is the story of Hamilton Brothers. Thus Hamilton Brothers Exploration Company was formed in 1971; the parent company is Hamilton Brothers Petroleum Corporation. First off in terms of production with the small Argyll field, Hamilton produced 8,280,000 barrels of oil in 1976 using a floating production facility—the first of its kind in the world. It takes a shorter time to produce the oil and costs less than a conventional fixed platform. In its 1976 annual report the company said:

> North Sea exploration and development has been slowed the past two years by legislative support of Governmental participation and increased taxation. It appears that the oil industry can now evaluate the current government policies and their effects on industry operations. Therefore, activity is again increasing.

Deeply imbued with the American free enterprise approach to oil exploitation, the company has not taken kindly to either Wedgwood Benn or general government determination to take its share of the oil wealth. As Bob Dyk, Hamilton's veteran oilman and boss of the British operation, says: 'if they would just leave us alone, we could get on with it.' This clearly refers to government in all its forms.

One of the most interesting new North Sea companies to emerge is LASMO. A merger of two exploration and development consortia —London and Scottish Marine Oil (LASMO) and Scottish Canadian Oil and Transportation (SCOT) took place in 1976. The two consortia were mainly owned by about forty institutions. After the merger LASMO decided to raise the development capital it needed for its North Sea involvement—a 9 per cent interest in the large Ninian field—by a direct appeal to the stock market.

LASMO resulted from a 1964 meeting between Jack Pierce, who runs the Canadian Ranger Oil group, and Michael Belmont, a stockbroker in the firm of Cazenove. By 1970 they had brought together their own consortium of insurance companies and investment trusts to form SCOT. Ranger and LASMO, which eventually absorbed SCOT, teamed up with BP to seek acreage in the fourth round. Their stake in Ninian is the result.

When LASMO went public in July 1977, offering 8·5 million shares at 155 pence each, the company was valued at £75 million, putting it into the top league of British oil companies after BP and Burmah. LASMO raised approximately £75 million on the stock market and from institutional backers to cover its share of the development of Ninian. Later it raised a further £30 million by a new share offer. It is, so far, the only company to have raised the money it needed for its North Sea operations by the issue of shares.

Many small independents have appeared on the North Sea oil scene as have companies whose names are not normally associated with oil. Oil Exploration (Holdings) Limited, for example, has interests in the Hewett Gas Field (4·60784 per cent); and also in a number of proven but so far undeveloped fields: Andrew Oil, Ann Gas, Josephine Oil, West Josephine Oil, Thelma Oil—mainly at 8·52 per cent. It acquired Bates Oil Corporation—a small American company—so as to strengthen its position, possibly starting a trend of British companies buying American rather than the other way about. All the small companies are in partnerships of one kind or another. The more ambitious ones want to become operators themselves. Major British names such as ICI or P & O are also involved in the North Sea.

One independent that has shown great determination to compete with the giants is Cluff Oil. It has an interest in the Buchan field now controlled by BP. Algy Cluff, whose company it is, complains that the interests of the small independents have not been given sufficient attention by the government. The independents have put up 4 per cent of exploration development money and made 4 per cent of the discoveries—as good a record as the majors. The importance of encouraging small operators, Cluff argues, is to build up experience for the future. The independents hope to be used by the big operators once the latter are sure of their expertise. The fifth round of licensing was hard on the small companies who got very little from it. Seventy-five per cent of the small companies are—and have to be—in consortia.

Cluff will tell you ruefully that his company did not get a licence in the fifth round because he insisted that if he did, he wanted to be the operator. Cluff feels that small British companies who want North

Sea acreage are obliged to be passive members of consortia operated by American companies. He repeatedly asks why small British independents should not be allowed to act in the role of operators. The answer is twofold: the claims and influence of the big companies are too strong; and the government—whatever it might say—does not want to take any risks backing the independents, if to do so is to risk delay because such companies lack finance and expertise.

Cluff, who is certainly enthusiastic about North Sea possibilities, argues that the oil finds offered the opportunity of a lifetime; so Cluff Oil came into being. He raised between £11 and £12 million for exploration and £1·5 million in equity; then sold 30 per cent to partners. Cluff Oil will get royalties from the Buchan field. It is, he says, essential for a small independent to continue getting blocks so as to reassure shareholders that the company remains in business.

Having taken a severe view of both government attitudes and the City, Cluff claims it to be a myth that exploration capital cannot be raised; however, it is a question of going to places outside the City such as Birmingham and Manchester. From the point of view of a small independent such as Cluff Oil with a share in one field (Buchan), it makes sense to put the maximum of the company's profits into another field.

Cluff has made his own proposals to BNOC whereby independents can have an operating licence during the exploration stage, and then hand over the role of operator to BNOC if oil is found, so that the state corporation can then assume that role. Thereafter there would be a 49–51 per cent relationship. It is neat.

One of Cluff's basic points is that the bigger companies are not interested in the smaller fields—certainly not at the present time—but that the small companies both are and should be; it is an obvious role for them. Thus it would make sense for BNOC to develop partnerships with the small independents so as to develop such fields. In the USA there are 6,500 independents; in Britain a mere six. This, Cluff suggests, says little for British entrepreneurial talents. He may have a difficult time fighting for a place in the North Sea, but refuses to let the giants get away with everything. Cluff would like to give the British investor a chance to put his money into the North Sea.

Perhaps his most telling point is that over the next fifty years every bit of the Continental Shelf will be explored for resources—not just oil—and the companies with the expertise in such exploration will be in high demand. He wants Cluff Oil to be one of them.

The oil companies, big and small, base their plans upon the assumption that oil prices will continue to rise, and that as long as it lasts, oil will remain the premium energy resource. Despite their complaints of high government tax the companies make huge profits.

While complaining of state interference the companies—at least the majors—also suggest that their interests and those of the nation are synonymous. Their interests are not necessarily antithetical to those of the nation but the companies are not responsible for a whole range of activities that are the province of government (security, employment, social conditions) which are nevertheless affected by oil company operations. Thus conflicts of interest do arise and (apart from any ideological considerations about capitalism versus state control) it is disingenuous to suggest there are no conflicts.

The companies in fact have developed a highly sophisticated and often successful system of complaint: they protest at what they say they believe government is going to do, even though they may really believe something quite different. The future rate of depletion of North Sea resources could well be the centre of a major government versus company storm in the 1980s once full self-sufficiency has been achieved.

As Professor Colin Robinson of Surrey University says: 'There is no problem in demonstrating that oil-company determined depletion rates will be non-optimal.' The question to ask, however, is whether or not government can force the optimum depletion so as to get maximum value for the country out of North Sea oil.

The oil companies are expert at setting up bogeymen to knock down: Wedgwood Benn is their pet bogeyman. He does not attempt to appease the companies. The companies press their luck all the time, and so far they can hardly believe what they are getting away with in the North Sea, especially as it has been under a so-called left-wing government.

5

North Sea Technology

The oil and gas boom has created a new technology. The structures being used are constantly changing as new techniques for dealing with weather conditions are applied. In the early 1970s there were about twenty-four drilling rigs operating in the North Sea and the semi-submersible was coming into favour because of its greater operating stability. By October 1974 of 161 offshore drilling rigs then on order, seventy-five were semi-submersible, fifty were jack-up units and thirty-six were drill ships. As a result of earlier North Sea experience the second generation of semi-submersible rigs were being built with improved clearance from the surface of the sea, so as to survive operations in even the fiercest weather. These structures have a displacement of 20,000 or more tons.

Of twenty-nine rigs operating in the British sector of the North Sea in 1974, nineteen were American, four were American/European, three were Norwegian, one was French, one belonged to Royal Dutch Shell and one to BP. Such figures help show the extent to which activity is in non-British hands. Once oil or gas is discovered, the facilities required come under three main headings: fixed production platforms and their equipment; pipelines or tanker loading facilities; onshore terminals.

The advance in the North Sea moves steadily farther north and into ever deeper waters so that drilling is now taking place in 1,000 feet or more of water. The North Sea, indeed, is far more important on a world scale than even its immediate returns would suggest, since successful technological advances achieved in it can be applied later to the Arctic Ocean, the Bering Sea or other difficult oil-bearing waters.

A new jargon—of jack-ups, semi-submersibles and condeeps (gravity structure)—has been developed, and the technological revolution that these terms cover is one with potentially huge spin-offs for industry at large. And as particular problems have to be faced in connexion with the development of an awkward field, so the engineers devise new techniques and more complicated equipment comes into use.

4*

Much North Sea technology is new, yet in the end the only way to prove the presence of oil is to drill. This means drilling a hole of between 17 inches and 30 inches in diameter whose sides are supported by steel casing, sometimes to a depth of many thousand feet. While this orthodox drilling goes on, the engineers are designing new ways to cope with oil that lies beneath one of the roughest seas in the world.

Part of the problem lies in the fact that companies producing a platform, for example, are trying to design something at the same time as they develop new techniques. There has been a rapid increase in the sophistication of the companies involved, especially British ones that have only recently entered these fields. Much of the new technology is also increasingly capital-intensive.

In the twelve or so years since the first gas finds in the mid 1960s, the techniques for dealing with ever deeper waters have undergone some major transformations. At first it was a question of bringing in American technology which had been developed to exploit oil in the Gulf of Mexico; but as the radically different and more difficult North Sea conditions became apparent, so European and British companies grasped some of the opportunities which this huge new offshore business offers. Although American companies are still in the lead they face growing competition from their European counterparts.

As the search moves into deeper waters, so the oil industry is turning to subsea completion systems which will allow production and processing equipment to sit on the seabed with automatic controls operated from the surface. The problems of working in depths from 400 to 1,000 feet are greatly exacerbated by the possibility of maximum wave heights on the surface of 100 feet. In North Sea winter conditions there are waves above 15 feet for 20 per cent of the time, while in severe storms they can reach a height of 65 feet. The oil reservoir of the huge Brent field, for example, is encountered 10,000 feet below the seabed and the paths of some of the deviated wells will travel as much as 17,000 feet before they reach the outlying parts of the field. Each North Sea platform has a number of wells drilled from it, most of which are deviated, some for oil and others to inject water or gas into the field to maintain pressure. A well may be deviated as much as 60 degrees away from the vertical.

The amount of equipment now out in the North Sea is staggering. A typical rig has a crew of seventy-five men and for a ninety-day exploration stint may require 3,000 tons of material, which will include casing, fuel, mud, cement, spare parts, food and clothing. Helicopters have become the main means of transporting personnel. Drilling, once started, will usually only stop at a level where the geologists consider that all possible oil strata have been penetrated. During exploration a rig will require 1,000 tons of material a month and this will normally be provided by two supply ships. The development phase of a field takes between two and five years and wells are drilled on average one a month, each well requiring a total of about 2,600 tons of supplies. Once a field is in production its life—on average—is reckoned at between twenty and twenty-five years.

So far the major fields have been found along the median line between Britain and Norway and this involves further technological complications—at least for Norway—since as yet no way has been devised of laying pipelines across the Norwegian trench which lies along the Norwegian coast and reaches depths of 2,400 feet. The Norwegians are researching methods of laying pipelines in deep and difficult conditions; meanwhile lack of technology to allow large diameter pipelines to be laid across the trench means that oil from Ekofisk, for example, has to be piped to Britain.

Technology, unfortunately, develops out of disasters and the collapse of BP's Sea Gem in December 1965 demonstrated that existing techniques were not good enough, even for the relatively shallow southern North Sea being explored at that time.

The vagaries of North Sea weather provide crucial tests of forecasting and planning. Thus as a starting point, the design of an offshore drilling rig is dictated by the maximum wave height that could be encountered, since the platform must be above that. The oil companies brought to the North Sea experience from less difficult waters of the need for specialized wave forecasting, and knew how to establish a reliable system. Europe and Britain in fact have excellent government weather stations whose information is much used by the companies. There are daily meteorological forecasts for the North Sea. As Shell's Baxendell has said:

> The North Sea environment is unique in its sustained nastiness. It is not just the wind or wave height or the water depth, but a combination of all three factors (and others) that make North Sea operations quite distinct from anywhere else in the world.

There are three weather ships stationed in British waters and maintained by the oil companies and the Department of Energy: one northeast of Shetland—sixteen companies contribute towards its cost; one in the Atlantic west of Orkney; and one in the Celtic Sea.

Corrosion has emerged as a factor of immense importance whose effects are as yet by no means clear. The harsh North Sea conditions have produced a speed and unpredictability of corrosion that no one had either expected or calculated upon. As pipelines and platforms age, so the problems are likely to increase. In the summer of 1977 a

new form of corrosion—or rather corrosion in an unexpected place—
was found on the Ekofisk field. It had occurred inside a pipe at the
point where the pipe bent upwards from the seabed towards the oil
platform. The Norwegians promptly informed their British counterparts of this development and the government ordered a new round
of inspections in Britain's fields. No proper instrument yet exists to
discover corrosion inside a pipe. All steel will corrode and the
problem is to spot the corrosion in time and slow down its rate.
Internal corrosion, however, is far more difficult to discover and
deal with.

The opening up of the North Sea has meant the development of a
new supply system. Onshore bases need to be as near as possible to
the exploration, a fact that has injected new life into seaports such
as Aberdeen, Peterhead, Lerwick, Dundee and Great Yarmouth.
Each rig requires an average of two supply ships in constant atten-
dance as well as helicopter services, and the time factor for them
between base and rig is of vital importance. A service base has a
number of fundamental requirements: all-weather harbour, deep-
water wharves, access roads, storage area. It should be sited at a
centre of population where there is an airport and be able to maintain a constant twenty-four-hour service. Base facilities should also
include: equipment to load boats, fuel supply, fresh water supply, a
heliport, the presence of supply and service companies. It needs
workshop facilities, telex and telecommunications, office accommodation and staff and emergency medical facilities.

Supply logistics for the growing number of sea installations are
the key to all the other operations. Strong winds are the worst hazard
for helicopters, although these can lift in wind speeds of up to fifty-
five knots and will do so in seventy in an emergency. The average
cost of helicopters is £550–£650 an hour and each one flies about
1,250 hours in a year.

Although a drilling platform requires two supply ships all the
time, a stationary platform also requires two supply ships during the
installation phase and then one ship when in production. The British
sector of the North Sea will require about two hundred supply ships
by 1980; the Norwegian sector about forty or fifty.

Supply ships are both the key to logistics and the principal bottle-
neck. They average 1,200 tons, are 200 feet long and cost about
£2 million. They have to carry every conceivable commodity to the
platforms: drill pipes, cement, mud, food, fuel, spare parts. If a rig
is forced to shut down because supplies have run out, this can cost
the operator £20,000 a day. Eight-foot waves are about the maximum with which a supply boat can cope when it is unloading
alongside a platform.

When reverse transport is considered—oil from the fields back to land—there are two alternatives: a pipeline; or some form of tanker loading facility. Both methods are used in the North Sea depending upon the size and location of the field. Pipelines will be used for all the bigger fields; tanker loading facilities for smaller fields where the lifespan and quantity of oil involved is too small to warrant the laying of a pipeline. At some of the fields massive storage tanks for the oil have been sited on the spot: at Ekofisk, for example, a giant concrete storage tank with a one million barrel capacity stands in seventy-five metres of water.

Technology is moving towards a new era of seabed operations. Some companies have already developed automated seabed systems directed by remote control through a riser system of pipes and electrical cables. Elf-Aquitaine is now operating such a system off Gabon. Such systems are at present in the experimental stage. In ten years' time they will be commonplace.

As developments on the seabed and a growing number of installations at the base of platforms require constant inspection, so midget submarines with crews of two or three are becoming a part of the industry. A new class of underwater vehicle which can weld, inspect or wrap pipe automatically is being developed. Different techniques are being evolved from field to field depending upon depths, the size of the reservoir and its expected life. There is no automatic common practice or approach.

The companies would like to move away from the very expensive fixed platform and instead use drilling templates fixed on the seabed: one is to be used—permission has been granted by the Department of Energy—by BP on the Buchan field. There are political-economic problems involved in this approach: a subsea system on the seabed or a semi-submersible rig of the kind used by Hamilton on Argyll can be moved off to other areas and government fears that a company might do this once it has 'creamed' a field, instead of obtaining the maximum amount of oil out of it.

On the other hand, once a fixed platform is *in situ*, it can only extract oil from that field, so it may as well be used to the limit. Apart from these political worries, manoeuvrability of rigs has a number of advantages: they can be moved from one part to another of a difficult field whose structure could not possibly be fully tapped from a fixed platform. Such movable rigs may well be developed to extract oil from the second generation of medium sized fields that should be opened up over the next five or so years.

Heriot Watt University has now become the leader in underwater and petroleum engineering. Research being developed in a number of centres covers such problems as fatigue crack growth in steel, measuring currents and their effects, new diving equipment, marine fouling, wave slam on rigs.

The aspect of North Sea technology which has made the most spectacular impression upon the public mind is that of the huge platforms: they have been filmed and televised at every stage of construction, pictured out in the middle of remote Scottish lochs rearing up like huge prehistoric monsters. They have to await the summer 'weather window' to be towed out into position and settled into place—a precision job that represents a triumph of handling and navigation. Finally they stand as an ever growing army of oil sentinels across the waters of the North Sea, their shapes looming out of the northern mists, gas flares acting as beacons.

There are two kinds of platform: steel and concrete. Steel platforms take longer to make; they have to be towed out and then up-ended and sunk into place. Concrete platforms can include huge storage space in the pontoons upon which they float. The Brent platforms, for example, are of condeep design: the base consists of sixteen cylindrical shells, each 66 feet in diameter and 185 feet high, with three vertical columns 230 feet high to support the deck and modules. The whole weighs 175,000 tons and is able to store one million barrels of oil. The working deck of a platform must be kept above the tops of the highest waves; we have seen that in the North Sea these can be as much as 100 feet. The structures, if they are not semi-submersible, may have to stand in as much as 500 feet of water.

Most of the platforms which have been built in Britain were constructed in remote sites in Scotland. They bring many problems as well as opportunities with them: they can disfigure the landscape, at any rate, temporarily; they can and do disrupt employment patterns and bring in a large number of temporary workers, who put great strains upon housing and other amenities in a small rural area; and there is no certainty that once a platform is completed there will be any more work for the site.

On the other hand these problems can be faced and overcome if the community wants the work—and most do—and is willing to tackle the attendant problems. A number of major companies such as Redpath Dorman Long (RDL), McDermotts, Highland Fabricators (a combination of Brown and Root and Wimpeys), McAlpine and Laing have become involved in platform work. In 1974, the Secretary of State for Energy, Mr Varley, emphasized that as many platforms as possible should be built in Britain: at that time their average cost was £60 million; now it is much higher. The majority have been constructed in places such as Nigg or Kisshorn in Scotland. The competition, however, is keen: from Norway, France and Holland, in each of which several platforms have been built. One spin-off from this activity has been a number of orders from South America, for work offshore Brazil, for example. The Russians have shown interest in British platform expertise for their developments in the Caspian Sea.

The platform industry has swung between concrete and steel and after the huge concrete structures of the mid 1970s, the industry turned back to steel. As 1978 opened, the industry was waiting for orders for about a dozen new platforms for the second generation of fields such as Fulmar and Beatrice, but it was far from clear how many of these orders would go to British yards and how many would be placed in Europe. In the period 1974–75 sixteen platforms were ordered for the British sector of the North Sea, of which six were built abroad. When the switch from the early steel platforms to concrete took place British industry appeared largely unready to cope.

A concrete gravity platform costs about £100 million and is equipped with living accommodation for eighty men. Concrete platforms do not need to be piled to the sea but are held in place by their own weight, once fully ballasted with sea water: this can ensure stability in the worst weather. Further, more can be fitted on to them before they are towed out to sea. Despite these advantages, however, since steel has long been used and found adequate in the Gulf of Mexico while the world steel price is depressed, the industry has turned to steel platforms again.

British industry was not prepared for North Sea oil. All four platforms on the Forties field were designed by Brown and Root, an American company, which subsequently built two of them; the steel came from Japan, France and Scandinavia; and five of the ten deck modules were built in Holland. Since then, the competition for such work has become fierce: the British yards have the advantage that BNOC is now an automatic participator in North Sea fields and will influence the way orders are placed; at the same time the Norwegians, Dutch and French chase the platform orders and British tenders are often behind theirs in costs and—from bitter experience of the companies—sometimes fail to complete on time. Thus, when Texaco placed its order for a platform for the Tartan field in September 1977, only part of this went to a British company, RDL, and the rest of the order to France. Moreover, RDL probably only got their part of the order as a result of political pressure.

After this partial victory for British industry with the Texaco order placed in the Methil yard, Dr Dickson Mabon, who had had talks with Texaco before their decision was finalized, was praised by the local Scottish MP, Mr Gourlay, and the Minister of State for Scotland, Mr Mackenzie, for his efforts. Dr Mabon said:

The Government are determined to get North Sea orders into British yards and factories. But it will only do so on the basis of the full and fair opportunity policy. UK companies must stand on their own feet, produce the goods to time and at a competitive price.

The French group, UIE from Cherbourg, had made a tender that was between £4 million and £5 million lower than that offered by RDL.

The central platform for the Ninian field is, according to Chevron, the biggest thing that has ever been moved on earth: it weighs 600,000 tons. After it had been built by Howard Doris in Loch Kisshorn, the huge concrete base was towed out to deep water near the Isle of Skye where the 6,000 ton steel deck was fixed on to the concrete base. It will be towed out to the Ninian field during the 'weather window' of 1978. New methods of navigation are required to manoeuvre these giants into place.

There are many uncertainties surrounding platform orders: thus late in 1977 only three of Britain's eight platform yards had orders—McDermotts at Ardesier, Highland Fabricators at Nigg and Howard Doris at Kisshorn. The other yards were closed but hopefully awaiting the new generation of orders. The government never used its yard at Portavadie or that at Hunterston.

Once a platform is in place, quite different problems arise. They are, on average, 100 miles out to sea and stock a month's supplies, including all consumables and spares. Precise planning and exact use of limited storage space are necessary, or else vitally needed materials can be lost or mislaid.

The work boats that bring the bulk of the supplies to the platforms are weather dependent, and their limit for craning goods up on to the platforms is an eight-foot sea. In fact twelve-foot seas occur for 15 per cent of the time, eight- to twelve-foot seas for 30 per cent of the time, while the eight-foot sea in which craning is possible occurs for about 40 per cent of the time. A supply vessel may have to stand off a platform for up to two weeks.

The larger vessels—up to 4,000 tons—are loaded as warehouses with casing and chemicals; they can stay out in very rough weather (to Force Ten) while smaller vessels can move into a platform to use a good weather 'window' that may not last for more than a few hours.

Supply vessels are on contract: they are equipped with tanks for powder solids and liquids and carry a great deal of deck cargo. The contents of their tanks can be pumped or blown up on to the platform decks using compressed air. During long spells of bad weather, supplies may have to be 'snatch' lifted off the vessels alongside a platform: this is dangerous work requiring great skill and a mistake can lead to a crane being pulled into the sea—as once happened. It is only done if everyone agrees: the crane driver, the captain and the platform manager. A snatch can be made in a twelve-foot sea.

Men are moved to and from the platforms by helicopter, and these are also used for transporting drugs, certain light and fragile equipment such as electronic gear or special equipment needed in an emergency. Helicopters can handle underslung loads of up to two tons, but require specially trained crews for these. Should such a load be needed, it is usually considered as a black mark against those responsible for the platform—a failure of planning. Helicopters also bring in the mail and newspapers.

Normally platforms are autonomous; in an emergency, however, a platform can be shut down from the land. Communications between land and platforms are by tropospheric scatter radio waves which use the curvature of the earth and ensure contact at all times. There are some direct lines both ways linking key people. Everyone on shore, for example, will carry a book of names and telephone numbers of people to contact in various emergency situations.

Production from a single platform may be worth £1 million a day; an emergency stops that. A blast gasket needing replacement would constitute an emergency; should it be a question of a spare part, local people onshore may be contacted and have to stand by for up to two days with a spare part, when in fact what is required has been obtained elsewhere. In an emergency a company will activate several possibilities of which the most efficient or convenient will be used.

The other form of emergency concerns personal injury. There is a State Registered Nurse of senior grade on each platform, and a 'hot' line to a duty doctor onshore who will be available over twenty-four hours. A rota of doctors in Aberdeen covers all the oil companies. In the event of a serious accident the doctor will discuss details over the line with the SRN and give instructions. A surgical team will be put on standby. This includes a surgeon and an anaesthetist who are in the oil companies' pool; these are normally NHS volunteers on retainer. In the event of a standby alert, police and helicopters will be contacted. Once on the platform the team will do whatever is necessary so as to enable the injured man to be transported back to land by helicopter and so to hospital. On average there are serious 'casivacs', as they are called, once a month, possibly twice. Compassion cases may also constitute emergencies when a man has to be brought home for family or other personal reasons.

The most intriguing question about platforms is what their lifespan will be. Because of uncertainty about this—especially in view of the harsh weather conditions of the North Sea—it is a good reason for arguing, as the companies do, that all platforms be used to a maximum, which means once one is in place full production from all its wells. It is in fact an argument against at least one method of depletion control.

The North Sea has a rapidly growing network of pipelines—about 600 miles in 1976—the longest being 220 miles from the Ekofisk field to Teesside. By the end of 1978 there should be well over 1,000 miles of pipeline on the seabed. Not all the fields are large enough to justify pipelines: four of the first to be developed—Argyll, Auk, Beryl and Montrose—depend upon tanker loading.

Pipelaying in deep water is a challenging business requiring semi-submersible barges. The area north and west of Shetland will present major problems. Where practical a pipeline system is made to serve a number of fields. This will be the case with Brent, Cormorant, Dunlin, Hutton and Thistle which will all be linked into the same system, connected to a common terminal from which a pipeline will carry one million barrels of oil ashore a day by 1980. Seventeen companies are sharing the £250 million costs of these facilities.

The first major field to be developed, the Forties, has its oil piped 106 miles to Cruden Bay and thence 130 miles overland to Grangemouth. At the time, that pipeline represented the most difficult job tackled in the North Sea. The pipeline laying season is from May to September. Five pipelines now come down Scotland from Cruden Bay to the Grangemouth area, which meant the land being disturbed five times; there was little advance planning, this being typical of the speed of oil developments. The Brent complex of fields will pipe their oil to Sullom Voe in Shetland; Piper and Claymore pipe theirs 130 miles to Flotta in Orkney. More systems are to be installed.

The gas fields had pipelines much earlier: the first, for BP's West Sole field, was laid in 1966; Shell-Esso's Leman field had a pipeline to Bacton in 1967, to be followed a year later by another pipeline from the Hewett field. The only way to get gas ashore is by pipeline from which it is fed into the national grid.

Laying pipelines requires specialized equipment and expertise; they are laid from huge barges after being coated and cased in concrete. They must be laid in the seabed to avoid fouling. Currents have to be taken into account: in one case where these were ignored, a section of the pipeline rose to the surface shortly after laying, causing a good deal of embarrassment to the company which had not taken the advice of local fishermen.

North Sea pipelaying has produced its own technological advances. The most spectacular of these is the Viking Piper, described by its owners as the world's first 'third generation' lay barge. The statistics of this formidable vessel give an indication of what it is expected to do: it can generate enough power to support a small town—18,800 hp; its work deck is the size of two football fields; it has a 100-yard stern ramp for the pipe to go down; it carries 300 tons of anchor and 25 miles of cable. The vessel has a semi-submersible hull which is 'transparent' to large waves so that energy passes through it. The Viking will lay pipes in seas up to 15 feet and is built to sustain the proverbial 'once in a hundred years' storm for which the North Sea is reputedly famous. It lays pipes of diameters from 16 to 44 inches to depths of 1,200 feet. The barge is owned by a consortium of companies from Norway, France and Britain and is the largest semi-submersible vessel in offshore construction.

Expenditure on pipelines up to 1980 will come to not less than £1,000 million. British firms were slow to become involved in this aspect of the business and most of the steel from the early offshore pipelines came from abroad: for Forties, Piper and Ninian it came from Japan. With British steel in the doldrums it is difficult to understand why it did not move faster to obtain the lion's share of North Sea orders.

The oil industry must also face the problem of terrorism. Government is canny about naval measures to guard the increasing number of platforms dotted over the North Sea; equally, pipelines present easy targets since it is virtually impossible to guard their entire lengths. At a public inquiry at Dunfermline in 1977 to consider a Shell-Esso pipeline system between Mossmorran and the tanker terminal at Braefoot Bay—a seven-kilometre liquid gas pipeline— Shell's pipeline engineer, Mr Arie Den Hartog, said of terrorism: 'That is outside the scope of the whole design.' Under cross-examination Mr Hartog agreed that a rupture of the pipeline would cause a serious disaster. The possibility of terrorist acts against pipelines or platforms is an aspect of Britain's oil developments that requires careful thought. It is a subject, understandably, upon which companies and government say little.

The landscape of the East Coast is being altered by terminals, the landfalls where the oil and gas is piped ashore or landed from tankers. Flotta in Orkney and Sullom Voe in Shetland are two huge oil terminals that have been built from scratch in sparsely populated rural islands. St Fergus, Easington and Bacton are where the gas comes ashore. These terminals are not to be confused with the supply bases such as Peterhead which service the platforms out at sea. The inquiry concerning Shell-Esso's storage proposals for their gas development at Mossmorran, the deal worked out between the Shetland Island Council and the oil companies for Sullom Voe, or the care taken by the Occidental Group to ensure that its Flotta terminal in Orkney fitted into the rural-ecological landscape, are all part of the same question.

Britain's post-war refining capacity was increased from 2·5 million tons in 1947 to 150,260,000 tons in 1977, so that Britain now has a huge surplus capacity to her needs. Even if British consumption in boom conditions meant that she required 127 million tons of refined products by 1980 (one estimate), she would still have excess capacity of more than 20 million tons. Ideally such capacity should be used to refine exports, but all Europe has surplus refining capacity and since the refining process adds enormous value to crude oil, no one willingly imports refined products when they are capable of doing the refining themselves.

The refining problem is a complicated one. The Department of Energy as a general principle has laid down that 60 per cent of North Sea oil should be refined in Britain. The EEC Commission wants to cut down surplus refining capacity throughout Europe. Yet a new refinery is being built at Nigg in Scotland by the American company, Cromarty Petroleum, and there are pressures upon ICI to double its Teesside refining capacity. BP's Dr Birks says it does not make economic sense to build any more refineries in Britain. The unions oppose any cutbacks in refining which threaten jobs. The companies find that to run refineries at half or two-thirds capacity is—or can be—uneconomic. Early in 1978 government and companies were meeting to work out a British policy in time for the March 1978 meeting of EEC energy ministers.

Diving is a dramatic, individual occupation and developments in the North Sea make it worth looking at in some detail. North Sea diving started in the early 1970s; prior to that date surface orientated air diving had been mainly used during the development of the southern gas fields which are in shallower water than the oil fields. Diving at depths of fifty or more metres involves the use of mixed gas—oxyhelium—for it is not possible to dive at this level on compressed air, certainly in UK waters, owing to government regulations. The traditional routine consists of: diving, decompression, then a spell of normal life. With the greater depths encountered in North Sea work, saturation diving, where men may be underwater in submersibles for up to thirty days, has become the norm, since the older approach of bounce diving with its shorter spells of work is uneconomic. Saturation diving makes tremendous demands upon the men involved and requires a particular temperament from the diver.

The importance of diving operations to the North Sea is difficult to over-estimate. According to the profession, development would come to a standstill in a matter of days if the divers stopped work.

A number of companies involved in North Sea diving also operate submersibles—Vickers, Oceanics, Intersub, P & O and Comex (they are now all using lockout-submersibles whose costs range from £400,000 to £1 million a unit). Of the oil companies BP own one diving company and have interests in others; Brown and Root and McDermotts are large offshore construction companies but also have diving interests. There are three phases in offshore diving work: exploration, construction (which is civil engineering underwater), inspection and continuous maintenance. Two types of diving contract are offered to the companies: rig-exploration diving, which represents the easy end of the business; these contracts may run for between twelve months and three years. And construction contracts: this is the part of the business where big money is earned, and contracts run for two-, six- or nine-month periods. Construction involves larger teams of divers and the work is often highly sophisticated.

The weather is a key factor in all diving operations; total weather changes can occur within the hour in the North Sea. In any case it is almost always cold beneath the surface. In rough weather the problem is to get divers safely through the surface of the sea—either way. At present there are only a small number of vessels which are equipped to allow diving in previously unacceptable weather conditions.

Diving covers an ever-increasing range of jobs including cleaning, welding, cutting, inspection, the use of explosives or changing valves on subsea completion systems. Complications increase, of course, with the range of work. As undersea engineering develops so there will occur accidents of the kind that now take place on the surface. Saturation diving means that a man may be days away from medical care, since in such circumstances he cannot return to atmospheric pressure in perhaps less than five or six days. Should he be badly injured, the medical attention he can receive may depend upon the training of his fellow divers. Knowledge of lungs under pressure is minimal, and it is doubtful if a serious injury at great depth could be treated with absolute confidence.

As yet there is little knowledge of corrosion, tidal effects or other aspects of weather underwater; moreover, inspection techniques are still in their infancy. At present men under water use cameras to relay conditions and damage to engineers on the surface.

The amount of diving required in the North Sea is substantial and growing. On BP's Forties field, for example, divers go down on most days: inspecting, repairing, maintaining. This pattern applies to all the major fields and on a commensurate scale to the smaller ones. Where there are structures—either platforms or pipelines—regular inspection and maintenance will be required. Diving techniques are dictated by depth: down to 20 feet decompression is not involved; deeper, it is. Bells are required for all diving below 100 feet. When oxyhelium is used—it is a very light heat-conducting gas—the diver risks being frozen internally; consequently the gas has to be heated before he breathes it, so that he is insulated on the outside by his diving suit while breathing in heated gas.

Deep diving in the North Sea rendered the old methods uneconomic: that is, after fifteen minutes' work the diver had to undergo hours of decompression. As a result new techniques were developed over the period 1970–73. Now divers are saturated, or under pressure in deep decompression chambers, for up to thirty days. They live in tiny quarters, six or eight together, from which they will go out in their suits to do their work. At the end of twenty-four days they will begin a five- or six-day course of slow decompression. Saturation diving of this kind is leading to enormous advances in techniques.

Already there are some ten subsea systems operating in the North Sea; before long there will be many more. Currently there is political pressure for the fixed platform method of extracting North Sea oil, since this means a greater amount of onshore work; but with advances of technology this situation is liable to change, certainly during the 1980s. Four submersible developments have so far taken place: first, the unmanned submersible; second, the manned submersible; third, the manned diver lockout submersible of which there are about six in operation; and fourth, the atmospheric diving suit which allows a diver to go down at the pressure of the atmosphere, thus representing an entirely new technique. The unmanned submersible market is growing; there are now about fifty of these in use. Six companies are in the process of marketing about a dozen unmanned submersible designs, costing between £500,000 and £600,000 each.

World diving opportunities are growing fast; most diving concerns offshore oil and gas, and such undersea work is becoming increasingly sophisticated. The North Sea, the Gulf of Mexico, the Persian Gulf and the shores of Africa are at present the main areas where diving activity is concentrated, and about 40 per cent of the world's deep diving is in the North Sea.

As diving goes deeper and operations become more sophisticated, so costs soar. Equipment for diving to a depth of 100 feet may cost £15,000; equipment for a dive at 500 feet will cost up to three-quarters of a million pounds apart from the costs of the surface ship. It is the North Sea which has ushered in the era of commercial saturation diving. On a big diving contract the cost of gas alone may run to hundreds of thousands of pounds. Increasingly, the oil companies tend to contract with a company to cover all the work needed for a particular field.

As a profession divers form an elite group: normally they work in pairs. They are in high demand and there is now a growing shortage of experienced men. At first all the divers in the North Sea were highly trained, but the demand for their services grew so fast that the profession expanded more quickly than the newcomers could gain experience. There is an increasing demand for divers at wellheads and as a rule six are to be found on a rig. Diving is an individualistic business, the men are independent and have to use their own judgement all the time. It is hazardous work and the high pay is certainly earned. Safety standards require constant upgrading. The Health and Safety at Work Act covers diving and men have to be trained to a specified level of competence. There is a government training establishment at Fort William in Scotland, but the government also support courses at other centres.

Accidents make diving a dangerous as well as a dramatic business that is often in the news. There are three kinds of accident: fatal, decompression and physical damage. There is a further difficulty: an absence of doctors conversant with diving techniques. According to the Department of Energy diving fatalities between 1971 and 1977 came to thirty-seven. When an accident occurs the department aims to circulate a memorandum in which it brings out points to be watched in the future.

The difficulty about diving accidents is that they occur underwater and it may take hours to mobilize and pressurize a medical team before it can examine the patient, who meanwhile must depend upon first aid administered by his diving companions. The medical officer will have to decide whether to operate under pressure or stabilize the patient for the five days it may take to decompress him and bring him to the surface. In time pressurized wings may be developed at hospitals.

Of approximately 1,400 divers now operating in the North Sea about 900 are working in the British sector: that is the number who will be out at sea during the peak work period. As of mid 1977, probably less than 20 per cent of the 900 divers in British waters were members of British companies.

Diving regulations have been supported by all the diving companies; every installation and team has to be inspected at least once a year. This is in marked contrast to the position when North Sea operations started. At that time there was no diving legislation. Since then the 1974 Offshore Installations (1229) Act was passed to cover diving from platforms; prior to that legislation only covered diving in ports, harbours and inland waterways. Other acts followed that of 1974: the 1975 Merchant Shipping (116) Act; and then the 1976 Pipelines (923) Act, which between them cover the responsibilities of oil companies, shipping companies, contractors and diving companies for putting a man underwater. Britain is the first country to pass comprehensive legislation for offshore diving activities. Other countries are adopting the British legislation; Norway has done so almost verbatim.

In 1977 a major diving taxation row exploded. Previously divers had been treated as self-employed, but then the Inland Revenue decided to make companies put divers on to PAYE. Divers are paid large sums of money by most standards; when, should PAYE be introduced, it seemed many would be only taking home 18 pence in the pound, a substantial number of divers decided to quit British companies and go abroad. The situation was exacerbated by the fact that foreign divers with British domicile, although working for non-UK registered companies, have only a part of their salaries paid in Britain and receive the rest abroad. The Inland Revenue decision threatened disaster for British diving and North Sea developments. By driving divers abroad—and there was every indication they would go—there would follow a dilution of available experience, a collapse of the growing British industry after great efforts by the OSO to involve British companies in the North Sea, while oil developments would also suffer through lack of divers.

The tax move appeared certain to undermine the ability of British companies to compete with foreign ones, which in any case found themselves in a strong preferential position: for example, Americans are allowed 183 working days in Britain before they are taxed at all and thereafter only 50 per cent of their income is taxable in this country.

Divers themselves, being intensely individualistic, frequently move from job to job and company to company, so that they can advance a powerful case for being treated as self-employed. They earn big money and it was the prospect of this apparently slipping through its grasp which goaded the Inland Revenue into action. An air diver working in the southern North Sea, for example, can earn between £10,000 and £12,000 over twelve months, while a top diver in the North Sea can earn as much as £20,000 in six months. Divers are usually paid a daily rate. Some divers have never paid taxes and foolishly boasted of the fact. Most divers give up the life at thirty-five or forty; when the tax threat became clear, many quit for jobs in the Middle East and the best men, capable of big earnings, signed on with foreign companies.

The tax initiative came just when the British industry was beginning to strengthen; there are twenty-five companies which now belong to the Association of Offshore Diving Contractors. Before the tax storm, out of every twelve divers three were experienced men, four were middling and five were recruits; following the tax storm and the number of men who quit the British industry as a result, out of every twelve men only one was experienced, three were middling and eight were recruits.

Divers claimed that PAYE, as opposed to their self-employed status on schedule D, would greatly reduce their earnings. About 250 divers refused to undertake deep saturation diving. Although by that time thirty-four men had died in the North Sea, the top divers—some of whom could earn £6,000 a month—claimed that the risks were acceptable. PAYE, however, could cut their take-home pay by two-thirds. The threat of strike action by the divers produced talks between representatives of the Association of Offshore Diving Contractors, and the Treasury in July 1977. By the end of September it was claimed that 250 top divers working in the North Sea had either quit the industry or gone abroad and such a wastage rate clearly began to tell in the industry–Inland Revenue negotiations.

One company protested at Treasury tactics and claimed:

My company received a telephone call from the Revenue saying that, in their view, we were outside the law. They said they could take us to law to make us responsible for all the tax that was due to them for five years.

Divers have no more right to evade taxes, as some undoubtedly were doing, than anyone else and the Treasury was correct to try to pin them down. But the problem was not so straightforward. Although it had been decided in 1975 that divers were to be treated as employees and not self-employed, no action had been taken because of government anxiety to get the oil flowing. Then as Tom Earls of the Contractors' Association said: 'It's now 1977 and the oil is flowing. They decided to make an example of the divers.' At the end of 1977 the North Sea Divers' Action Group also launched a campaign to reverse the Inland Revenue decision to end their self-employed status: not only had 250 divers left Britain for more lucrative work elsewhere but if the PAYE ruling were applied it was suggested a further 700 would be lost to the industry by the time the new season started in April 1978.

By February 1978 the divers had won their case. The government announced a reversal of the Inland Revenue decision. In Parliament Mr Robert Sheldon, Financial Secretary to the Treasury, said:

After a careful examination of their particular circumstances, I recognize that there are certain distinctive features about their work, such as the danger it entails, their vulnerability to long-term health hazards, the exceptional travelling difficulties and the shortness of their working life.

All this was undoubtedly true; so, too, was the fact that as a group the divers were in an exceptionally strong position to resist the Treasury, since their withdrawal from the North Sea could bring its development to a standstill. Another group would almost certainly have lost such a battle.

There is growing realization that in the long run the biggest spin-off from the North Sea will be the maintenance industry. Analysts already say that for every £1 million spent on platforms the equivalent must be spent on offshore maintenance. When all the fields are in full production, the maintenance bill could come as high as £1,000 million a year, although at present the Department of Energy is talking of an annual figure between £400 and £500 million. Most maintenance work is contracted out; possibilities for British companies are endless even though a majority of North Sea operators are foreign. The Americans, for example, will not set up maintenance yards of their own but will use the local companies. The platforms are a 'one-off' job, but they will stand on the seabed producing oil for about twenty-five years and the maintenance required will become proportionately greater for each one as time goes by. And so far almost everyone has been taken by surprise by the speed and extent of corrosion.

By 1977 the repair and maintenance aspect of North Sea oil was becoming apparent. Under the Offshore Installations (Construction and Survey) Regulations 1974, all offshore structures must be re-certified at least once every five years; but apart from such government regulations companies must be sure of their structures for reasons of both safety and efficiency.

Estimates by OSO suggest that maintenance and repair costs will run between £175 million and £400 million in 1980; that they will rise further up to 1985; and thereafter will continue to rise for at least a decade until the serious decline in oil production really sets in towards the end of the century. For at least twenty years there will arise new commercial opportunities for subsea inspection, maintenance and repair; for the modification of structures; for the maintenance of production equipment—well-workover activity; as well as routine work such as painting. These activities are obvious now; others will occur.

Thus, for example, the warmth of risers in the wells produces far more rapid corrosion than anyone had expected. There is the problem of splash zones—a 20 foot to 30 foot area of the platform structure which is in and out of the water depending upon sea conditions; original estimates had suggested no more than 6 feet. There is the extent to which salt spray in the winds corrodes the platforms. After the Ekofisk disaster it has been accepted that firefighting ships should cover all the main fields.

When North Sea production really declines, maintenance of all the structures could become proportionately far higher, for by then some of the platforms will have been standing on the seabed for as long as twenty-five years.

The Offshore Europe Conference of 1977 devoted one of its workshops to maintenance. While it is not expected that there should be any significant costs within the first two years of a platform's life, thereafter they are expected to increase. Every production well, for example, could require a workover costing about half a million pounds every three to six years so that this item alone could come to £60 million in 1980.

The estimated maintenance figures for 1980 which range between £175 million and £400 million represent between 3 and 6 per cent of capital costs. By that year, however, the industry should have discovered a good deal more about corrosion and other special factors which could well mean a far higher maintenance bill. As the Minister of State, Dr Mabon, said in Aberdeen in 1977:

. . . by the early 1980s a new rapidly expanding inspection repair and maintenance market in the North Sea is expected to be worth in the region of £300–£400 million annually.

North Sea oil has given rise to a new body of laws: to delimit national sectors, and to protect and regulate the lives and safety of offshore workers. International laws controlling the North Sea largely stem from the 1958 UN Conference on the Law of the Sea, which produced three conventions covering Territorial Sea and Contiguous Zones; the General Regime of the High Seas; and the Convention on the Continental Shelf. Differing, though similar, laws govern British, Norwegian, Dutch, Danish, French, Belgian, German and Irish activities.

In Britain petroleum rights are vested in the Crown, as are rights to explore and grant licences to produce oil and gas. The key acts regulating activity in the North Sea are the 1964 Continental Shelf Act; the Petroleum Production Regulations of 1966; the Mineral Workings (Offshore Installations) Act of 1971; and the Petroleum and Submarine Pipelines Act of 1975. Although the legislation exists, test cases of various kinds are bound to occur before some at least of the responsibilities or working conditions and rights are clear. The Continental Shelf Act, for example, lays down:

> A constable shall on any installation in a designated area have all the powers, protection and privileges which he has in the area for which he acts as constable.

The Mineral Workings (Offshore Installations) Act of 1971 lays down that the Secretary of State, 'may make regulations for the safety, health and welfare of persons on offshore installations . . .' which covers people whether or not employed on such installations; transport to and from them; or vessels concerned with work on or near them.

As yet there is less than clarity as to the degree of power exercised by companies on platforms. The problems are complicated. The general assumption of British law is that it does not operate for British subjects beyond territorial limits, while there is also the difficulty of applying the law to foreigners. As the Sea Gem disaster showed, it is essential to have a single person in absolute charge on a rig: this means a formal command structure.

Sooner or later the question of sex discrimination will be raised: at present women do not appear to have a role of any kind on any rig. And there are unresolved questions of jurisdiction: not simply between Britain and France or Britain and Ireland over median lines, but also about what is known as 'creeping jurisdiction' as rigs are placed farther out to sea in ever deeper waters.

Trade union activity in the North Sea is as yet unorganized, but that state of affairs is unlikely to last. The Mineral Exploration and Investment Grants Act empowers the Secretary of State to make grants up to £25 million to help in exploration, while the Industry Act of 1972 is designed to help companies obtain equipment needed for exploring on the continental shelf. Other laws concerning the North Sea will be enacted as problems become clearer.

The North Sea is producing an area of law which contains some awkward grey patches. Thus, when the Grampian police were asked to track down a fireraiser on a rig, they got their man —only to be obliged to hand him over to the captain of the support vessel to which he belonged. Although the vessel was operating off a British rig it was then more than 500 metres from the rig and so beyond British jurisdiction. In any case the vessel was Dutch-owned, Panamanian registered and chartered to an American company. British police are not responsible for the safety of offshore installations although the Norwegian police are. The law, like everything else, has to catch up with North Sea developments.

6

Gas

It was the discovery of gas, not oil, that sparked off the North Sea scramble, and once the discovery had been made there was quick European agreement to divide the area between Britain, the Netherlands, West Germany, Denmark and Norway. It is an odd aspect of the North Sea story that the contribution made to the British economy by gas has been largely ignored. This is partly because oil is more spectacular; yet natural gas has revolutionized the role of gas in Britain's energy economy. Gas sales have increased fourfold, primarily at the expense of imported oil, to save £1,000 million a year and gas has taken over the largest share of the domestic energy market, contributing 40 per cent of this in 1975. In that year the southern gas basin of the North Sea supplied 97 per cent of Britain's total gas consumption.

In 1976, 39·4 billion cubic metres of natural gas from the North Sea was sold to the British Gas Corporation (BGC); in 1977 gas from the huge Frigg field began to be delivered. Otherwise—at present—only the Brent oil field has sufficient quantities of associated gas to justify a separate pipeline.

At the end of 1976 British North Sea gas reserves stood at 809 billion cubic metres, while the year's consumption had been largely offset by fresh finds. As a result of new gas developments (associated gas from the northern oil fields and Frigg) the southern gas fields will fall from supplying 100 per cent of Britain's gas in 1976 to about 50 per cent in 1982. According to law all gas that is recovered has first to be offered for sale to BGC. BGC has a great advantage over oil or coal in its price: long-term contracts arranged with the oil companies in the mid 1960s allow it to pay about 2 pence a therm for gas landed from the southern North Sea fields—the exact price BGC pays the oil companies is a closely guarded secret. Oil now works out at 14 pence a therm.

The first discovery was by BP (West Sole) and at that time the price was fixed at 5d a therm, which BGC considered high. The Gas Board hoped—up to the signing of the contract—to get the gas for only 2½d a therm. The Minister of Power had to arbitrate between the Gas Board and BP and settle the price at 5d a therm. BP had wanted 6d or 7d.

The contracts for the supply of gas to the Gas Board (later BGC) arranged before June 1975 are not affected by Petroleum Revenue Tax (PRT); this means all the fields in the southern North Sea. There is a formula for price escalation dependent upon inflation but, like the price, this is a close BGC-oil company secret. These escalation clauses controlling the price BGC pays to the oil companies have meant that gas prices have risen less than those for other energy sources.

BP's West Sole field, discovered in 1965, was forty miles from the Humber estuary; production started in 1967 and the gas was piped to Easington. Three more fields were found in 1966: Hewett, Leman and Indefatigable. Shell-Esso's Leman Bank is the sixth largest offshore gas field in the world. When by 1967 these four major gas fields had been discovered, the decision was taken to convert the entire British system to natural gas. It was then estimated that natural gas supplies could be increased to 4,000 million cubic feet a day by 1975, which would quadruple the Board's gas sales. This figure turned out to be an extremely accurate forecast. By 1976, before Frigg or associated gas from the northern oil fields was flowing, natural gas from the six southern fields (West Sole, Leman Bank, Hewett, Indefatigable, Viking and Rough) coming ashore by pipeline to Bacton, Easington and Theddlethorpe supplied 98 per cent of the country's requirements, equal to 30 million tons of oil. Shell, Amoco and Phillips between them from Leman, Hewett and Indefatigable brought ashore 77 per cent of the gas consumed in Britain in 1977. This was all processed in their plants at Bacton and then piped into the BGC grid system.

There would appear to be many more smaller gas fields whose size has not yet been ascertained, although at present the companies do not wish to investigate them further. This is because there is currently enough gas available, because the companies will be obliged to use the associated gases from the northern oil fields, because the price offered for the gas is too low and because oil is more profitable.

In the Irish Sea there are prospects of more gas. A field has been established in Morecambe Bay about thirty miles from Blackpool. The discovery lies in shallow water of between 70 and 110 feet, which is far less than the 300 to 400 feet in the southern North Sea. Hydrocarbons Great Britain, a wholly-owned subsidiary of BGC, is responsible and may develop the field for use during the winter periods of peak demand. It is near to huge industrial markets as well as domestic ones. By early 1978 Hydrocarbons GB had drilled a number of successful wells and despite BGC caution it appeared to be a

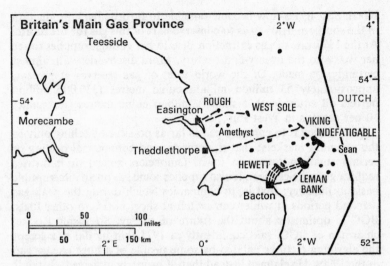

Britain's Main Gas Province

worthwhile discovery. Already in mid 1977 BGC had been searching along the north coast of Wales for a possible terminal site.

The Frigg field in the northern sector of the North Sea is the largest gas find there; it straddles the median line between the British and Norwegian sectors. Unlike gas from the southern fields, Frigg gas will cost far more, the price being indexed to competitive fuels; the field will also be subject to PRT. At a rate of 1,500 million cubic feet of gas a day, Frigg will increase British supplies by 40 per cent.

It will be seen that Britain's natural gas resources are now substantial. By 1970, only five years after West Sole had been discovered, proven reserves stood at 27 million million cubic feet, enough to sustain a daily production flow of 3,500 to 4,000 million cubic feet for twenty-five years. The supply of natural gas in 1975 was three times the total consumption for 1968, while estimated recoverable reserves then stood at 45×10^{12} cubic feet in British waters; 75 per cent of these reserves lay south of latitude 56° north. Other additions will come from the more northern waters and the Irish Sea and could raise the reserves to a possible 84×10^{12} cubic feet. Associated gas such as that from the Brent field will be in addition to this. The sudden acquisition of these huge reserves allowed British consumption to increase from 2 per cent of total energy in 1960 to 15 per cent in 1975. Norway and Holland also have huge reserves in Europe.

By the 1980s the amount of natural gas consumed will be equal to 60 million tons of coal a year, although more discoveries will be needed to maintain that level of consumption for ten or more years. As a result of the associated and other gas discoveries in the northern

North Sea, it has now become possible to throttle back production in the southern fields so as to conserve part of this gas for the future. At the 1977 rate of gas extraction Britain has enough supplies to see her well into the twenty-first century. More discoveries will, almost certainly, be made. Of the world total of gas reserves at present, approximately 53 million million cubic metres (330,000 million barrels oil equivalent), 5 million million cubic metres (just under 10 per cent) is in West Europe.

BGC policy is to conserve gas as far as possible by selling only to the premium markets: that is, domestic and commercial heating or certain small industries in towns (smokeless zones) or industries requiring smokeless heat. It also supplies some gas on an interruptible basis to industry: that is, to companies which during the peak gas demand periods in winter can switch at short notice to other fuels. BGC is optimistic about the future of energy. Sir Denis Rooke, chairman of BGC, said confidently in 1977 that he did not accept the alarming pictures painted by some people of a huge energy gap in the 1990s. He claimed instead that, if properly managed, Britain's primary energy resources—oil, gas, coal and nuclear—should provide the country with the range of energy supplies it required into the foreseeable future.

Gas production will soon reach 6,000 million cubic feet per day (cfd)—the oil equivalent of 50 million tons a year. Local factors control the rate of gas production, but the share of the market has increased dramatically since the mid 1960s and could well increase further. This will depend upon price, further discoveries and political pressures to maintain the monopoly position now enjoyed by gas— a position deeply resented by the other energy producers. In the early days following the North Sea discoveries there was a bitter struggle between the Gas Board and the oil companies over the price which should be paid for the gas the oil companies had found: it was all the more bitter because the oil companies had no option. BGC is the monopoly buyer: at least it has to be offered the gas first. As Tugendhat and Hamilton say in their book, *Oil: The Biggest Business*:

> ... it was not until two years of negotiations had gone on and the companies had already invested in the development and subsea pipeline systems that the issue was finally settled in agreements and at a price which the companies never quite forgot or forgave.

The result of monopoly power has been low price gas. As an anonymous civil servant in the NCB argues, the result of a low gas price is that people think gas is a less valuable commodity than it really is; more gas is used in the industrial market than should be, and this in turn means that the oil companies producing the gas from the North Sea are in favour of the most rapid depletion of the fields since they get a low price and want a maximum return. This last claim is not borne out by the facts. Oil companies appear just as ready to deplete the oil fields as fast as possible, for which they get a high return.

BGC has been vested with monopoly powers to purchase all natural gas found in the North Sea or British continental shelf waters. Licensees are required by law to offer gas to the Corporation at a 'reasonable price'—the Department of Energy is the final arbiter of what this might be. Since under the 1965 Gas Act BGC also possesses powers to supply gas to area boards, it in fact controls the purchase price, the distribution and the final price to the consumer. BGC would prefer only to use gas for the premium market: by 1977 this accounted for 5,000 million cfd. The market could be satisfied (at greater cost and inconvenience) from other energy sources such as coal. For the domestic and small industrial market—that is, up to 100,000 therms a year—gas is supplied according to a published tariff; larger quantities are negotiated by contract.

At present between 18 and 20 per cent of gas sales are 'interruptible' and can be stopped at short notice when BGC has to meet peak demands upon production. Companies that take interruptible supplies, therefore, need to be large and able to switch over to an oil system at short notice. Normally they will carry thirty days' oil supply for the cold season.

As the Frigg field was preparing to come on stream in 1977 to produce 1,400 million cfd at peak for the BGC, so the corporation was accused of 'raping the market' in its efforts to sell Frigg gas. The oil companies said that BGC was offering Frigg supplies at 1 or 2 pence per therm below oil prices, thus making it difficult for the companies to consider raising the oil price to the true level of cost supply. However, one can be quite certain that the oil companies won't make a loss whatever the 'true level of cost supply'. It is one of the more exasperating aspects of the whole energy question that the oil companies constantly complain that they are not allowed to charge an economic rent for their product; they are all fiercely for free enterprise, yet they will almost never enter into a real price war and bring costs down for the consumer. Rather they will complain—as in this instance—that gas has an unfair advantage and undersells them. These claims against BGC, it is true, were advanced in 1977 when the market was depressed, yet one would have to search into the dim past of the oil industry to discover a time when they strove to reduce prices on any kind of permanent basis.

Although it claims to want only the premium market, BGC negotiated some major gas contracts with industry in 1977 for the disposal of Frigg gas. One contract was with British Steel for the supply of more than 100 million therms of gas for two direct reduction plants at Hunterstone on the lower Clyde. The contract is the largest negotiated by BGC in Scotland and represents 2 per cent of the output of Frigg. There were also lengthy negotiations between the corporation and ICI for a change in the conditions under which BGC supplies the giant chemical company with gas for fertilizer production. ICI has been able to undercut its competitors in producing fertilizers because it enjoyed the advantage of a fifteen-year contract for gas at very low rates.

The ICI case is interesting because it reverses the role of the oil companies in their dispute over prices with BGC. ICI entered into the fifteen-year contract with BGC for 250 million cfd of gas in 1969, when the corporation was only too anxious to find customers for its new North Sea supplies. By 1977, however, BGC could sell all the gas it obtained to other fertilizer companies at 9 pence a therm. Its contract with ICI allowed the latter to pay only 2·7 pence a therm. The Gas Corporation went to arbitration over this price, alleging hardship, but the arbitrator ruled against BGC.

In principle there was no difference between the BGC complaint that the contract had been entered into under conditions which had subsequently become unfair, and the oil companies' complaint that their contract to supply gas to the corporation from the southern North Sea gas fields (they in any case had no option) had subsequently been rendered unfair by higher prices all round resulting from inflation and the events of 1973.

As it happened, a number of major contracts came up for renewal during 1977 and BGC greatly increased prices on the grounds that customers should be made to pay the equivalent of alternative fuels. These contracts, however, were overshadowed by the ICI row. Following the five-fold oil price increases in 1973–74, ICI had emerged with one of the most valuable possible bargains since its gas was pegged at pre-1973 prices. BGC considered that its contract was becoming less viable by the month.

The consequence was to give ICI a virtual stranglehold on the fertilizer market, since none of its competitors could buy gas as cheaply or had supplies guaranteed over fifteen years. The fertilizer industry lobbied the government to break the ICI-BGC contract, for whereas the world market price for ammonia ranged between £68 and £80 a ton, ICI could charge its own operations at the low figure of £30 a ton as a result of its deal with BGC. Other fertilizer producers were actually going out of business. Huge pressure from the industry and from BGC—although in its case for totally different reasons—were mounted to force ICI to pay more for its gas than it had contracted to do. Once more, to a bemused public looking at the complications of the energy industry, here was yet another instance of demands for the price of energy to be raised—never lowered.

Despite the failure of its arbitration attempt, BGC continued negotiations with ICI to change the contract. The government clearly wanted a change too, since it was opposed to ICI enjoying a monopoly position and wanted more than one fertilizer producer on the market. Government pressures may not have been enough to move ICI but the threat of no renewal of its supply after the contract expires in 1984 certainly was, and so ICI and BGC worked out a new formula. By October 1977 they had come to an agreement; although no details were released, it seemed clear that ICI had accepted a substantial price rise for the gas it purchased from BGC—possibly up to 6 pence a therm so as to add £30 million a year to its gas bill. One result was that a company which had been forced to close early in the year—Thames Nitrogen of Rainham in Essex—could start fertilizer production again.

BGC has been a good deal more successful than other British nationalized industries. It possesses assured supplies of gas for all purposes into the foreseeable future. It enjoys a double monopoly position: not only must North Sea gas be sold to it, but the corporation also controls the downstream market of all outlets that must use gas. As a result it has been able to keep its prices down and so has obtained a far larger (and growing) share of the industrial market than otherwise would have been the case, despite its avowed policy of only wanting the premium market.

Although there was increasing talk of the huge contribution that oil was about to make to solving the balance of payments problem throughout 1977, there was little or no talk of the contribution which gas had been making for a number of years. The balance of payments benefit of gas to the Treasury in 1985 (in 1977 prices) will be £4,000 million. The government take, in tax terms, is relatively small; rather it is BGC and the consumer who do well, the former taking the economic rent and the latter a subsidized price. According to the Department of Energy, the overall contribution of gas to the balance of payments over the period 1975–80 works out as follows: 1975, £1·8 billion; 1976, £2·3 billion; 1977, £2·7 billion; 1978, £3·2 billion; 1979, £3·5 billion; and 1980, £4·0 billion.

North Sea gas has made the British gas system a closed one under a monopoly buyer. The British gas price (at 2 pence a therm) is low in relation to the world price. The parallel price for oil is 13 pence a therm. The effect of this disparity is that the economic rent of North Sea oil goes partly to government in royalties and PRT, while the economic rent of gas goes far more to the consumer. The public, at least, should be happy about this.

The oil companies produce the great bulk of the natural gas. At the time the huge Dutch find was made at Groningen there was little fear that gas would compete with oil and, indeed, when gas was exported from Holland to the rest of Europe the price at the Dutch borders was kept sufficiently high to ensure that its ability to compete with oil was limited. This was managed by the Shell-Esso partnership of NAM. As far as Britain is concerned, however, the main oil company role is to sell the gas to the state enterprise. BGC is then in a position to use it in competition with the oil products of the companies. It is, in consequence, not surprising that the BGC relationship with the oil companies is a less than happy one.

At least to some extent gas monopoly power restricts oil monopoly power. By 1975 Britain was producing the gas equivalent of 40 million tons of oil and will double this amount by 1980. The fact that the price is not controlled by the oil companies means it will replace at least some fuel oil which until now has been used in preference to coal. As Odell says in his *Oil and World Power*:

> This will have the effect of significantly slowing down the growth of the oil industry in Britain over the next ten to fifteen years, as gas moves up to take a position of providing as much as one quarter of the total primary energy requirement.

The oil companies are ambivalent towards gas. Of course they are happy to find it; at present, at least, they are less than happy to develop it since it competes so well with their more profitable oil sales. There are, for example, other gas prospects in the southern North Sea, but a programme of drilling is needed to uncover them and the companies are inhibited from doing this by the low price which they would expect to get for it from BGC. More exploration work for gas is only likely to be embarked upon when the oil companies see the prospect of obtaining better returns for any gas they find.

During 1977, however, the companies did negotiate new prices with BGC. The result was announced in February 1978: the companies had agreed to spend large additional sums of money—Shell and Amoco about £100 million—on new facilities to extend the life of their fields. A dispute between BGC and the oil companies had been dragging on for a long time, BGC demanding the installation of new facilities to ensure that the underwater reservoirs were properly drained of maximum gas resources. The companies had argued that they could not afford the new equipment—compressors—without first obtaining a boost in the price they received from BGC for their gas. Once the compressors are installed they will allow the platforms to produce greater amounts of gas during the winter peak demand periods. While these compressors will prolong the life of the fields, the companies are still not prepared to embark upon further exploration in their area unless first they receive a higher price for their gas.

As the oil companies admit frankly enough, why should BGC increase the price it pays them for the gas when the Corporation can get all it needs from them at the present low prices and they cannot sell it to any other customer anyway? As long as this is the case, BGC can satisfy all its premium customers and with new sources of gas coming on stream—Brent, Frigg, Morecambe Bay—it remains in a winning position. For the time being, BGC has no need to pay prices simply to induce the oil companies to search for more fields, though that may happen in the future. According to BGC, gas hardly competes with coal at all. The premium gas markets are those which otherwise would have to use a light clear fuel such as gas-oil. These are mainly small factories in built-up areas, potteries, steel processors who need a clear flame as well as food factories and factory, office and domestic heating. This BGC claim of non-competition does not accord with the views of the NCB or the Electricity Authority.

In February 1978 the chairmen of these two energy bodies mounted a concerted effort to force BGC to raise its prices. The complaint of Sir Francis Tombs, chief of the Electricity Council, and Sir Derek Ezra, chairman of the NCB, was that chronic under-pricing by gas was robbing them of markets. Once more the public was treated to the curious spectacle of two major public bodies demanding that a third should put its prices up, rather than down, and this at a time of high inflation when the government claimed to be doing all in its power to reduce inflation from a two-figure to a one-figure level.

The NCB and the Electricity Council were especially angry following the announcement that gas prices were to be frozen for a year until April 1979—a piece of news which the country at large might have been expected to welcome. This meant that gas prices would have been frozen for two years altogether at a time when coal prices had increased by 10 per cent and electricity by 8 per cent. The row dates back to the fivefold oil price increases of 1973–74 from which gas was largely insulated because the contracts for its supplies from the oil companies had already been concluded. The electricity and coal industries argue that cheap gas prevents them from planning new investment since it is undercutting them and so removing their markets. They also claim that the public will get a huge shock in a few years' time when the cheap southern gas has been used up and it has to face the higher priced gas from other sources. This is a truly curious argument to advance. If prices have to go up (a phenomenon that the public has come to expect from bitter experience) so be it; but the longer they can be kept down, the better for the consumer. To argue that the public should be made to pay higher prices now, when it is unnecessary, on the grounds that this will prepare them for the time they must pay such prices is to preach a form of *Alice Through the Looking Glass* absurdity.

They also argue that the low gas price encourages speedy depletion: that as soon as the companies have exhausted the southern gas fields they will be able to get more profitable prices elsewhere. This is at best a dubious contention, witness the reluctance of the oil companies to install compressors until the price had been renegotiated.

Sir Denis Rooke replies for gas that prices should reflect real costs and not some artificial heat equivalence—in other words, as long as a low price is possible it should be maintained. The only way for Tombs and Ezra to win this argument appeared to be through government ordering a gas price rise or a gas tax, neither eventuality appearing likely at least during 1978, an election year.

The battle between British Gas and the Electricity Council in February 1978 was fierce. BGC accused the Electricity Authority of using misleading figures when Sir Frank Tombs had claimed in a paper to the Energy Commission that if the electricity supply industry had been able to purchase its fossil fuels at the same price as North Sea gas, it could have reduced the price of electricity by about a third. Then the chairman of the Central Electricity Generating Board, Mr Glyn England, told the House of Commons Select Committee that gas should reflect the longer term costs of bringing in more expensive gas supplies from the fields in the northern North Sea. Why, one is tempted to ask, should it do anything of the sort if it does not as yet have to? In order to make life easier for less efficient or less lucky competitors? The arguments between these energy giants consistently seemed to miss the most important reason for their existence: the public welfare.

BGC answered these attacks first by disputing the figures used; then by saying that the full cost of conversion would have been written off by 1979, and that the cost of writing off obsolete plant would also have been met while the interest burden would have been reduced. BGC said that planned future price rises should be gradual when substitute natural gas is needed to supplement North Sea and other supplies and finished by saying: 'Gas is indeed less expensive than electricity, but it is not cheap. Certainly our 14·2 million customers do not think so.'

BGC is unpopular with the oil companies, the NCB and the

Electricity Authority for one simple fact: it sells gas too cheaply. It is accused of 'raping the market', of unfair competition, of depriving electricity and coal of their economic share of the market, of not paying a fair price to the oil companies for North Sea gas. The oil company antipathy is understandable. They are, after all, private enterprises for whom all state activities tend to be anathema anyway; when they find that by law they are obliged to sell gas to BGC at prices they cannot fix themselves and thereafter that gas undercuts oil on the domestic market, their anger is to be expected. This is not the case with coal or electricity. After all, like gas they are state enterprises whose object in theory is to supply the public with a service. When, however, one observes the inter-state energy corporation squabbles, then concern for the public appears to be the last thing they have in mind; rather, they behave like private enterprise bodies whose only concern is to make profit for their shareholders.

At present it may be said that coal and electricity are dear while gas is moderately cheap. Thus the consuming public does at least get one out of the three state-controlled sources of energy at a reasonable price. If coal and electricity had their way, gas would be made as expensive, relatively, as they are and the consumer would be deprived of even one reasonably priced energy commodity. There is moreover a fallacy contained in the argument that gas is raping the market at the expense of the other fuels: since all three are public bodies producing energy for the public good, it has to be asked whether it matters that one of the three undercuts the other two, especially when the only alternative offered by the other two is for gas to become more expensive to the consumer. After all, when cheap gas has been exhausted coal and electricity will then be able to come into their own, and until gas prices have to go up, the public can enjoy one source of energy that is not too costly. There is only one tenable argument for dearer gas: to impose greater conservation by forcing consumers to take less, and this is the one argument that has been noticeably absent from all those used by BGC's opponents.

After more than a decade of North Sea gas, it is possible to evaluate the role of gas in the economy. Gas sales over this period have increased fourfold, mainly at the expense of imported oil. Gas has saved substantial sums for the balance of payments—£2,350 million a year according to 1977 Treasury estimates. Gas now has the largest share of the domestic market—approximately 40 per cent—and accounts for over a fifth of total energy consumption. It is an impressive record.

BGC does not share the general view of the energy world that there must be some form of energy 'gap' in the 1990s. The gap in the past has been filled by imports; North Sea oil and gas now mean the country will be self-sufficient in energy at least to the end of the century and probably a good deal beyond then. Despite the Cassandras of the energy business, the chances of significant further discoveries in gas are perhaps even better than for oil.

By 1980 Frigg and Brent gas will have almost doubled the available supplies coming ashore; the question will be how best the gas can be used for the nation. By then gas will supply about a third of the country's energy requirements on a heat supplied basis, and a quarter of total energy requirements. More gas will result from the gas-gathering pipelines to be built to tap the associated gases of a number of oil fields in the northern North Sea.

The most important premium market will remain domestic heating and this area of gas consumption is in any case markedly increasing: in the twelve-year period since 1965 the number of households has increased by 2,700,000, and the percentage using central heating from 11 to 49 per cent, much of this heating increase being taken up by gas. Thus the impact of gas can be seen as one of the greatest of any industry upon the country as a whole in recent years. According to BGC, gas should still supply a third of total energy consumption and a quarter of primary energy in 1990. Therefore caution should be exercised before embarking upon new energy policies such as that of expanding coal beyond the level at which costs are competitive. This statement from BGC's *Plans for British Gas* is clearly designed to infuriate the NCB.

Part of BGC's long-range plans concern storage: rather than sell gas to non-premium buyers, the Corporation would prefer to store its surplus for later use in the premium market. There are various methods of storage in existence or being developed such as aquafer storage, and BGC expects to be able to satisfy the premium market at least up to 2000. At present when the demand for gas is lowest in the summer, BGC makes LNG and stores it against peak periods. LNG shrinks to one six-hundredth of its normal volume at this time.

BGC leads the world gas industry in terms of its work to develop SNG (substitute natural gas). It is technically possible to make gas from oil and several plants to do this exist. Plants based upon the British process are being built throughout the world, especially in the USA. British Gas has also developed a process to produce SNG commercially from coal and this, too, is being adopted in the USA: BGC earns royalties. The fact that Britain leads in SNG technology should also mean that there will be a reasonably smooth transition from natural gas to SNG when the former fields begin to run dry.

A gas pipeline map of Britain now shows an astonishing network of pipelines and terminals zigzagging over much of the country. During 1978 crucial pipelines will be laid across the Forth so as to link the Frigg gas which comes ashore at St Fergus terminal in Aberdeenshire into the southern network. A further pipeline across the Forth will bring Brent gas south into the main grid. When both Frigg and Brent gas is being piped south this will represent 2,000 million cfd, half of 1977 consumption.

The impact of North Sea gas has been substantial; the changeover of gas fittings in thirteen million homes to enable them to use North Sea gas was itself a major feat. There have inevitably been accidents and blow-outs and one result was the earmarking in 1977 of £400 million by BGC for the replacement of old cast-iron gas mains and there is to be a publicity campaign on gas safety. Conversion for Scotland was only completed in 1977; then the first gas came ashore from the giant Frigg field and this meant a reversal of the south–north flow of gas to a north–south flow of gas from Frigg, later to be augmented by gas from Brent. Three gas trunk lines carry gas south-wards from St Fergus to the main marketing areas. BGC has already surveyed a fourth and fifth possible gas route southwards in case further major discoveries are made in northern waters.

It is a fact that will not be lost upon the Scottish Nationalist Party that northeast Scotland was only linked into the natural gas grid in 1977 and this was some years earlier than might have been the case without Frigg coming onstream. Scotland was the last region to be converted. Further pipeline work in Scotland will follow the gas-gathering projects designed to link the northern oil fields which do not warrant individual pipelines, and there are likely to be other projects to land Norwegian gas in Scotland rather than Norway, ready for re-export to European premium markets.

Associated gas—that is, gas found in conjunction with oil—is central to the question of conservation and depletion. From an oil viewpoint a company faces several alternatives if substantial amounts of gas are present in a field: the gas can be piped out; it can be lique-fied *in situ* although this process is both dangerous and expensive; it can be pumped back into the field to increase pressure and so push up production from around 40 per cent to perhaps 42 to 45 per cent; or it can be burnt off. There are wide variations in the amounts of associated gas to be found in oil fields. The Forties field has the equivalent of 330 cubic feet of gas to every barrel of oil; Brent has 1,750 cubic feet per barrel. Some of this gas is used on the platforms, some is re-injected and some will be taken in the gas-gathering schemes. It may only be flared with the permission of the Secretary of State for Energy. Gas production from the Brent field, which has by far the largest quantities of associated gas, is to begin in 1979 and will rise to a peak of 600 million cfd between 1980 and 1982. It will be piped to the St Fergus terminal through a 36-inch 300-mile pipeline.

The question of flaring is a contentious one. If gas is associated with oil, it has to come up so that it must first be flared; then it can be used for power on the platforms, sold or re-injected. The companies regard the options open to them from a strictly economic point of view; others may consider flaring as a matter concerning conservation. When North Sea oil first got going, Britain wanted the oil so desperately—in this instance government and companies were at one—that flaring was at first acceptable. Now the legal position is that flaring is only allowed if there is no practical alternative and provided the permission of the Secretary of State has been obtained. In June 1977 however, as the *Sunday Times* said, Britain came of age as a major oil power and entered a new phase in its economic history when the Department of Energy ordered Shell-Esso to shut down platform B on the Brent field until equipment had been installed to conserve the gas which up to that point had been flared.

A project of major importance is the gas-gathering scheme for the northern fields. Gas Gathering Pipelines (North Sea) Limited consists of a study group composed of BNOC, BGC, BP, ICI, RTZ and Elf-Total. The project, costing £2,000 million, would provide a common pipeline to bring ashore annual quantities of gas of up to 15 million tons of oil equivalent (mtoe) of methane; 2 mtoe of ethane; 2·5 mtoe of propane; and 1·5 mtoe of butane from the various fields which have associated gases but insufficient to justify individual field pipelines. The gas-gathering scheme would greatly increase gas availability over and above the northern supplies that will in any case come from Frigg and Brent.

If the gas-gathering scheme is implemented, the most likely landfall would be in the Cromarty Forth which, with the Nigg yard and coming refinery, could become a major industrial area since a petrochemical industry based upon the gas could be developed there. This area could, therefore, become a major industrial beneficiary of North Sea oil and gas. Communications in that part of Scotland need improving. The A9 is being rebuilt at a cost of £110 million and the railway is being improved between Perth and Inverness so that between them they can ensure more adequate handling of industrial traffic.

By the end of 1977 the joint state-private enterprise study team looking at the gas-gathering project had increased its estimate of costs to a possible £5 billion. GGP (North Sea) will advance several schemes and a small one to start with could cost between £250 million and £300 million, although eventually the huge £5 billion network would be developed. Associated gas from the Piper and Tartan fields is to be pumped into the main trunk line that carries gas from Frigg to St Fergus. The Occidental Group was given permission to raise the oil

production of its Piper field only on condition that it built a link gas
pipeline to the Frigg line. This is due for completion in the autumn
of 1978 and will carry 90 million cfd. In the course of the field's life
Piper is expected to produce 90 billion cubic feet of gas altogether as
well as some gas liquids.

The quantities involved in this one field give an idea of the total
amounts of gas that can be gathered if the full scheme goes ahead.
Other spur lines ought to be built from the Brent field so as to include
in the overall network Thistle, Magnus, Dunlin, Cormorant and
Murchison. These fields are all due to come on stream shortly so that
the links must be completed at speed to avoid flaring when they go
into production.

The major scheme presents more complex problems, while its cost
raises at least a query as to whether it would pay. The Department of
Energy regards the full scheme as a sure means of preventing further
flaring and waste. It would involve pipelines to Forties, from thence
north to the group of fields which include Brae, Thelma and Maureen
and then along the British–Norwegian median line using a number of
branch pipelines. The system could be linked into the Beryl and Bruce
fields though these might instead be linked to the Frigg field.

The technological problems would be immense: not so much those
of laying the pipeline system though these would be formidable
enough, but because the different fields contain different kinds of gas.
The major network—if it is built—will not come into being until the
late 1980s at the earliest. By then, however, other discoveries could
have been made while some existing gas fields will be approaching the
end of their life, so that the need for new sources of supply will be
commensurately greater.

On the one hand BGC fears being swamped with too much gas and
so GGP (North Sea) is also looking at the possibility of a new gas
trunk line through Britain and across the Channel into France or
Belgium. This, however, is likely to be opposed by BGC as the Corporation does not want to see its supplies being sucked into Europe.
Once linked to Europe BGC fears that the usual immediate economic-
political pressures would be applied so that North Sea gas would
have to be sold there and supplies would as a consequence run out
just as world supplies were also diminishing, instead of enabling
Britain to make hers last somewhat longer. Sir Denis Rooke believes
that domestic gas supplies could keep Britain going well into the
next century, while on current predictions world supplies will run
short before then. This happy situation would not be the case for
Britain if she were linked into Europe and so under pressure to sell a
proportion of her gas there.

The problems are by no means easy ones to resolve. There are, however, more than twenty fields with gas for collection by some means and the estimated amounts of gas available for gas gathering are enormous:

Estimated Amounts of Gas Available for Gas Gathering
(m. cu. ft. a day)

Year	1980	1981	1982	1983	1984	1985	1986	1987	1988	1989
Total quantity	469	702	1,365	1,675	1,680	1,680	1,649	1,622	1,608	1,670
Year	1990	1991	1992	1993	1994	1995	1996	1997	1998	1999
Total quantity	2,192	1,977	1,759	1,543	1,524	1,327	1,040	735	664	581

Total discounted quantity (m. cu. ft.)	4,599,140
Total discounted energy yield (m. therms)	62,100

Source: Williams-Merz.

BGC is looking at various long-term possibilities, not just natural gas from the North Sea, but what in the next century will almost certainly become common practice: the production of gas from coal. It is less wasteful and less energy is lost when turning coal into gas than into electricity, and it can be done at only a seventh of the cost. In 1977, for example, BGC expertise in producing synthetic gas from coal was adopted for a project in the United States. A contract was concluded between BGC and Conoco, as a result of which the Corporation is designing a plant to produce 60 million cfd of synthetic natural gas from 3,800 tons of coal. In this case BGC technological developments can be tried out in the USA against the day when British natural gas supplies run out.

The fact that BGC is now helping with technology in the USA is valuable from an economic point of view; it also enables the Corporation to examine at first hand the American gas scene where supply is becoming critical and where over the next few years a wide variety of technological expedients will probably be tested to fill the growing gap. Britain may well ponder that her position now—one of plenty—is akin to that which prevailed in the USA in the 1950s when that country also had ample supplies.

In 1978 North Sea gas should save the country £3,000 million in balance of payments, while the figure for oil will be £3,400 million. In 1977 BGC reported an annual profit of £32 million in a year when to the general public's considerable surprise a number of the nationalized industries turned in handsome profits. There then followed one of those curious public rows that delight the hearts of politicians, bureaucrats and the press alike. BGC was accused of dishonesty in its accounting and concealing much larger profits—which at least is an unusual accusation to level against a state enterprise. Under the 1972 Gas Act (Section 16) the Secretary of State has the power to siphon off excess profits from the industry. The kernel of the accusations was that BGC had successfully concealed its real profits to avoid any such government take. Moreover, during the period 1975–77 the Corporation had changed its accounting system and, its accusers suggested, this was in a deliberate attempt to avoid having to hand over excess profits to the government.

The published profit of £31·5 million after depreciation and interest payments did not represent the real profits the Corporation had made during the year. First, the vast sum of £563·5 million had been charged for various depreciations. Apart from this new accounting methods had been introduced such as a 'fixed asset maintenance account'. According to its critics—and it has many—BGC's real profit for the year ought to have been shown as in excess of £200 million, while on current performance this should be in excess of £1,000 million by 1979–80.

As a result of the low price it pays for North Sea gas BGC *is* making large profits. The Corporation is government-owned. There ought to be no objection to it making profits, even high ones. What is important is its accountability and what is done with such profits.

The most interesting aspect of this attack upon BGC is the fact that the low price is resented. Britain has for years been experiencing constantly rising prices, yet BGC has managed to keep gas much lower-priced than many other essential commodities. The fact that it has also had enormous luck seems beside the point. One might have expected a reaction of relief: that it does not matter whether BGC is the monopoly buyer of North Sea gas, that it is in control of the market, that it is a nationalized industry, or even that it makes large profits. Rather, that here is one organization providing the public with an essential commodity relatively cheaply.

Prospects for 1978 were for a record profit. BGC's chairman, Sir Denis Rooke, told the House of Commons Select Committee on Nationalized Industries that the industry should achieve a 4 per cent turnover which should be the annual target. The fact is that of all the nationalized industries—with considerable luck—gas is efficient and doing exceptionally well. This may be resented by some of the other state enterprises; the price of gas is at least welcome to the consumer who all too often is simply overlooked.

PART TWO
Policies

7

Energy Policies

There will be argument for many years as to whether or not Britain should have developed her North Sea resources as quickly as she did; given thirty years of declining power, depressingly poor economic performance and an increasingly desperate need to find a new role for herself, it is understandable—even if it does not constitute the best policy—that once the oil was found the government of the day should decide upon rapid development. This meant too much American involvement and insufficient government control. Even so, it is still far from easy to work out just what government oil policy ought to be. The Mackays say in *Political Economy of North Sea Oil*: 'The trick is to ensure that the State captures the economic rent without discouraging further exploration and production.' The latter continues to take place; the former seems more problematic.

The companies' approach to oil is essentially one of maximum production. As Shell claims in a briefing paper:

> The United Kingdom needs all the oil it can produce in order to lessen the financial drain caused by oil imports and to increase export earnings, to generate revenue and to lay the foundation for an improved economic position.

In reaction to that apparently simple proposition on behalf of the nation, one must pause to reflect what policy might have been pursued had only half as much oil (or indeed no oil) been found.

A question that has yet to be resolved is whether Britain is going to become a major oil exporter. According to the Department of Energy's *Brown Book*, production in the 1980s will lie in a range of 100 million to 150 million tons 'but in some years may be higher'. The most 'bullish' view, however, is that, discounting conservation measures and development delays, output in the mid 1980s could be 200 million tons and at that level Britain would be a major exporter. Britain, in any case, will certainly be in energy balance by 1985; one result could be that she will have difficulty in using the assumed annual coal production of 130 million tons. Present projections also suggest that from a 1990 energy export potential, Britain will change

back by 2000 to an import situation. Assuming these forward projections are correct (and a great deal could happen in the next few
years to alter them), they do mean that the government now has some
reasonable parameters within which to conduct long-term planning.

It is no doubt pleasant for the much battered British ego to be
able to claim a place among the world's top ten oil producers by 1980.
Thus Mr Benn, writing about his chairmanship of the EEC Council
of Energy Ministers in the *Coal and Energy* quarterly in 1977, could
claim that Britain's unique energy strength underlay all the discussions. The EEC is certainly conscious of Britain's oil resources,
and whatever policies are worked out in Whitehall these will have
to take account of powerful EEC pressures for sharing—which means
Britain selling at least some of her oil to her partners. Another factor
to be taken into account is the more or less universally held view
that there is a coming energy crisis on a global scale. Policies, therefore, can be based upon the assumption of a continuing rise in oil
prices.

There are four obvious lines for British policy to pursue: conservation; an increase in coal production; a quick determination of the
total extent of North Sea resources; and an immediate decision
about a nuclear policy. There is a considerable area of vagueness,
however, in relation to energy matters, despite much activity and
numerous committee reports. Both of the major political parties
have indicated that they want production to be set at the rate at which
Britain has previously imported crude oil. If this is to become policy,
it will entail significant control of the companies and their overall
rate of production. It raises the further question of whether such
control is desirable. According to one dour civil servant, public
opinion may have got the impression that because of North Sea oil
we can keep our energy options open longer, but this is not true. The
energy policy must include coal, nuclear power, gas, electricity and
conservation—and it should deal with them now. As the Mackays
say: 'The key question is whether the rate of production of North
Sea oil should be determined by private or national interests.' To
answer that question one has first to determine what the national
interest in this regard may be.

The government has to take into account an astonishingly wide
range of views and interests before it can come up with policy
answers, and this is true even for a potential left-wing government,
which at least in theory would know where it stood in relation to
private enterprise. In terms of production, for example, Professor
Gaskin of Aberdeen says:

There is no rational basis for regarding 'self-sufficiency equivalence' either as the point at which we should aim or as the limit beyond which we should not go in production from domestic reserves.

The long-term question must concern the best use of the resources of the North Sea. If the oil age 'peaks' in the 1990s, it may perhaps be less important for Britain to hoard oil (except for the use of the petrochemical industry) than to develop the next generation of energy sources—that is, coal and nuclear power. This can be done while oil provides the country with a present energy sufficiency as well as the wealth—part of which might come from substantial exports—to invest in the next energy generation. According to BP:

> In the United Kingdom as a whole, trends will soon be set by which the rising benefits which oil production will bring to the Exchequer in the next ten years will either be dissipated for general purposes or committed to the regeneration of the rest of the productive economy. If these commitments are not made then, when in the mid 1980s oil production ceases to rise, and probably begins to fall, the rest of the U.K. economy may follow it.

This is an industry view.

Lord Kearton, on the other hand, says he is not an 'energy gap' man and suggests that the concept of an energy gap to be faced some time in the 1990s is a bogeyman deliberately set up by the energy world. Then again, George Williams of UKOOA argues that even though Britain is in a better position than most industrialized countries, the energy gap will still come, so what—if anything—are we now planning in order to cope with it when it arrives?

According to Department of Energy forecasts, Britain will need 600 million tons coal equivalent (mtce) in 2000. Of this, coal (now contributing 130 million tons annually) will then contribute 165 mtce or 23 per cent; oil and gas (based on ultimate North Sea reserves of 7,000 or more mtce) will then produce 160 mtce or 27 per cent; nuclear power will account for a further 60 mtce or 11 per cent. If this forecast is accurate there will be a huge shortfall of 39 per cent which will have to be filled by imports, 'renewables' and conservation. In terms of such forecast figures Britain will be in deep trouble.

It is, indeed, one of the more remarkable aspects of our North Sea oil and gas finds that before they existed we managed not too badly, though, it is true, with cheaper oil; since the finds, however, with a sort of masochistic pleasure at which the British, including government departments, are past-masters, we have discovered a future that looks infinitely more gloomy with oil than without it.

One factor of great importance to energy policy planners is the security North Sea oil will give to Britain: as long as it lasts Britain will not be dependent upon Middle Eastern or other sources of supply. It is probably, though by no means certainly, a majority view that once self-sufficiency has been achieved the balance of the resources should be conserved rather than the country embarking upon a major export programme. Such a policy of conservation, however, should be subject to certain criteria: there ought to be enough flexibility to enable Britain to barter with the EEC and the USA, both of whom will exert powerful pressures upon her to produce more for their markets. It will also be necessary to get the oil companies to agree to a conservation policy which will affect them all equally.

Even if one does not believe in a coming energy gap, oil and gas are exceptionally important but finite resources; they should be treated as such and conserved for the future whenever possible. Government, therefore, must look at all the ways of controlling their use. There are fiscal weapons which can be used to change consumption patterns, such as a differential road tax to discriminate against big cars. Attention is now being devoted to housing insulation as a long-term means of conserving energy.

If one accepts the view that we ought not to extract more oil than we absolutely have to, then this provides a starting point for an energy policy. There follows the question of price. Although for perhaps a generation Britain is going to be self-sufficient in energy while others are not, this is no reason for adopting a low price policy of the kind that bedevils President Carter's attempts to impose an energy strategy in the USA. North Sea oil and gas reserves are a major gift: the temptation to squander them as an easy answer to national problems must be resisted.

Government could control North Sea resources by nationalizing them, and though this has been ruled out of court for the time being it could be resurrected in the future. Government could create a monopoly buyer for oil comparable to the BGC, but this would be more difficult to bring about because of the extent of foreign (mainly American) companies involved and because downstream control of the industry is not in government hands. There is the tax system which can be altered at short notice. And there is the system of state participation through BNOC which has now been established, though it could well be altered following a change of government.

Up to mid 1977 the overriding consideration of the government was the balance of payments; the result was a desperate determination to get the oil flowing. By 1980 the value of British crude exports on developments as they stood in 1977 is likely to exceed the cost of crude imports by as much as £2,000 million, which represents a turn-round in balance of payments in the region of £6,000 million. Whether thereafter Britain will go for high exports or not is clearly a policy question yet to be resolved.

Roughly, the impact of oil on the balance of payments can be seen as £2,000 million in 1977, £5,000 to £6,000 million in 1980 and £7,500 million in 1985. In the first half of the 1980s, oil-related payments benefits could be equivalent to between 3·5 and 5·5 per cent of GNP.

In 1975 British consumption of oil came to 87 million tons, imported at a cost of £3,100 million. By 1980 North Sea oil will account for between 100 million and 130 million tons, which will cover all British needs and provide some surplus for export. If this oil is worth the lower figure of £5,000 million to Britain, then after allowing for imports and the outflow of interest, profits and dividends to foreign (again mainly American) companies, the real worth to the country should be half that amount. At the same time Britain will face the huge repayments on its massive IMF and other borrowings.

Throughout 1977 as North Sea oil began to flow with increasing rapidity, the balance of payments guessing game got under way. It was a constant of press speculation how much or how little oil would affect the balance of payments. The British have developed a national distaste for any abiding economic stability, so they changed their estimates repeatedly. Thus, euphoria of calculation turns to gloom as international debts are remembered; these in their turn are dismissed when another field comes on tap or the resources of a functioning field are upgraded. The conventional wisdom is hardly helped by the financial writers of most newspapers, who appear in many respects to be the worst speculators of all: to add spice and variety to their columns they must week by week and sometimes day by day change their assessments of the economic outlook. Such an approach does not help to clarify the economic position or the role in it of oil.

It has also been argued periodically that the pound should be allowed to float freely, while exchange controls should be relaxed. By early 1978, indeed it had become one of the ironies of a harder pound (still worth only $1·93) to give rise to a different complaint: Britain's exporters were finding it even harder than usual to sell goods on the international market.

Labour was in power in the crucial period 1974–78 when the extent of the oil impact really became apparent. Two broad aspects of policy emerged during these years: first, that British industry should gain from North Sea spin-offs (see OSO in chapter 8); and second, that government should take a greatly increased slice of the oil profits which has largely been achieved through the tax regime introduced in 1975. The Labour approach to controlling the oil industry has been participation and the creation of the state oil corporation, BNOC.

The Tories would certainly not disagree with the first objective; indeed, OSO is perhaps the least controversial of all developments arising out of the oil. Its role is accepted and welcomed by both political parties. Nor would the Tories disagree with the extent of the tax take though they may alter the details when in power. The greatest divergence, however, comes over what they would consider to be the role of BNOC; they certainly regard a lessening of its powers as desirable—in principle. Just what the party might do in practice remains to be seen.

Certain broad considerations have to be taken into account. There is the question of gas as distinct from oil. BGC is in a monopoly position, and gas is the cheapest energy resource available to the consumer. There is the vexed and highly contentious issue of nuclear energy and what kind of reactor to develop. Decisions taken now will bind the country for a generation. There is the long-term question of the petrochemical industry and the extent to which it makes sense to conserve oil for that industry, however much the supply of petroleum products is cut back elsewhere. Then comes the problem of the Americans. In the first place American companies dominate the oil industry in the North Sea as elsewhere in the world. With nearly 60 per cent of North Sea enterprise in American hands, decisions about future nationalization or greater taxation and government control must be taken in the light of this American participation and the possible repercussions that a policy unpopular with American interests might produce, for example, in relation to BP's Alaska oil stake. Also there is the quite different matter of exports. As the energy gap approaches—at least as far as a US shortfall is concerned—and the Americans continue to use more oil while producing less at home, so they will become increasingly anxious to obtain supplies and will exert great pressures upon any producers who possess a surplus to their own needs. Britain could cope with such pressures, perhaps, if she were to maintain a 5 million ton a year flexibility margin in production for exports. This, however, would not satisfy the EEC.

As Mr Walter Clegg, Conservative MP for Fleetwood in Lancashire, said in 1976: 'There is no doubt the Community would like to get a grip on some of our oil.' He was certainly correct. He was actually talking to fishermen and went on to say: 'Perhaps we are soft-pedalling on the fish question to prevent that situation arising. There must be some good reason why we haven't taken a stronger stand in support of the fishing industry.' The EEC will increase pressures upon Britain, once she has achieved self-sufficiency, to induce her to produce at least a partial surplus of North Sea oil to meet some EEC requirements. As a member of the Community Britain will find such pressures difficult to resist entirely.

Already in 1976 European Community officials were considering charges that, while fostering British industrial involvement in the North Sea, the OSO had discriminated unfairly against companies from other parts of the Community. On the other hand, when Mr Benn addressed the International Energy Authority (IEA)—the OECD's answer to future energy crises—he was detected as adopting a somewhat patronising attitude towards the other less fortunate members. Britain is clearly determined—and this applies equally to the two major parties—that neither the EEC nor the IEA shall dictate British energy policy.

Government policy decisions have also to be taken in the light of the fact—anathema though this may be to the left—that Britain is still a largely capitalist society, while the Labour Party (despite the pronouncements of its more leftward inclined members) is a state interventionist party and in no true sense socialist. Until that situation changes, private business has to be induced on reasonable terms to take part in the continuing exploitation of North Sea resources and production. This means that there has to be enough profit in the business to make it worthwhile.

One is bound to ask whether the average British government is capable of being more long-sighted in its policies than the average major company seeking profits. Looking at the political performance of the major parties in the last twenty years, the answer would appear to be a resounding 'no'. Since it takes between ten and fifteen years to bring an oil field on tap, the private sector wants to know now what the taxation policies of five or ten years hence are going to be. They can then gauge whether or not it is worthwhile opening up a small field. They are, of course, asking for the moon in political terms and even if one party were to give some sort of vague general assurance, like the Varley guidelines of 1974, a new party coming into power, another energy crisis or a host of other possibilities will ensure that any such forward guarantees are at best tenuous.

Government now has wide-ranging powers of control over exploration operations and the development and production of oil and gas covered by British licences. Powers under the Petroleum and Submarine Pipeline Act cover exploration, development, depletion, offshore gas disposal, royalties, the transfer of licence rights, government access to information and the use of submarine pipelines including access to them of third parties. Thus the legislation provides government with the means, in theory, to exercise more or less total control—if it wants. As Shell points out: 'This legislation applies to all production licences and introduces explicit controls over the depletion of oil and natural gas resources to provide a framework for a national depletion policy.'

The issue therefore is how such powers are going to be used. Two other vital aspects of government powers concern small fields and where the oil goes. Government has the power to remit royalties due from small fields so as to encourage development. BNOC has options to buy 51 per cent of the oil produced in all the fields covered in the participation agreements. This means the government can prevent North Sea oil being shared out around the globe or even in the EEC by the international oil companies in the event of a crisis. The role of BNOC is fundamental to state participation and the exercise of reasonable control over Britain's oil. The role of OSO is to help British firms compete in the lucrative North Sea hardware market.

Speaking at the Labour Party Conference in 1976 Wedgwood Benn was able to tell his hearers:

> We have massive resources of coal, gas and nuclear power, and oil around our shores. These resources give to Britain a strength which should be noticed more abroad by those who are commenting on our economic prospects. We must control these resources ourselves.
>
> It is the intention of the Government and the party that we should do that by the development of a policy that allows the country as a whole to share in and control the resources nature has put at its disposal.

A problem for the Labour Party, which receives such vital political support from the major trade unions including the coal miners, was highlighted at the same conference when Mr Arthur Simpson of the National Association of Colliery Overmen, Deputies and Shotfirers said bluntly that Britain should use more coal and export North Sea oil.

An Energy Commission was set up in 1977 to advise the government. In its first paper it set out a flexible strategy for the years ahead. It suggested three objectives of policy as follows: adequate and secure supplies, which should be efficiently used, at the lowest possible cost. Energy policy must concern itself with energy use and a key to this, inevitably, is price: 'Energy prices give both consumers and producers reasonably accurate signals about the costs of energy supply.'

Under the Oil Taxation Act of 1975, the Exchequer expects to take approximately £5 billion to 1980 and £3·5 billion a year thereafter. The take works out at about 70 per cent from fields developed under the first four rounds; from the fifth round of licences onwards with BNOC having an automatic 51 per cent share, the take should be in the region of 85 per cent.

On the question of depletion and conservation the paper says the first aim is self-sufficiency, but draws attention to the assurance of the Secretary of State in 1974 that there would be no cuts in production imposed before 1982 and no delays in development of finds made to the end of 1975. The result affects between one half and two thirds of estimated possible reserves. The paper further suggests that commercial and technical considerations would probably limit cutbacks to 20 per cent of a field's capacity production. Once all these factors have been taken into account one is left wondering whether any depletion control is to be exercised at all. The paper goes on to make the remarkable statement that whatever depletion policy is adopted there will be substantial oil for export in the 1980s. There need not be; there certainly ought not to be any such automatic assumption. In fact, the paper gives the impression that a secret determination has already been arrived at between government and companies to go for a major export policy.

On nuclear policy the paper makes three points: that we need an established reactor system; that we must ensure the technology is available when required; and that we must find satisfactory answers to problems. In other words, there is no nuclear policy.

On research and development the paper alludes to work being done on renewable sources of energy—wave power, solar, tidal, wind and geothermal energy. Most forecasters seem clear that coal should come back into its own over the next thirty years as oil resources do begin to dwindle, and that for a country such as Britain a vastly expanded nuclear power programme will be essential.

A number of questions need be asked to clarify what oil policies have been established or perhaps, what is often more accurate in the British political context, what policies have emerged. How much, for example, have government activities changed the relationship between state and companies? The best means of direction lies in controlling the volume of production. So far little real attempt to do this has been made.

In a brief monograph upon British oil entitled *Six Myths of British Oil Policies*, a Norwegian observer, Petter Nore, asks some pertinent questions from slightly left of centre. He claims that OPEC provides the example for the British government: that control of volume means control of price, and control of price means the maximization of government take. From this he continues: 'Therefore, for the state to maximize its long-run oil surplus in *social* terms, volume control may be necessary if the social rate of discount differs from the private one.' The social rate of discount almost certainly will differ from the private one.

To maximize the spin-off effects of North Sea oil for British business and industry, a slower rate of extraction would have been more effective. Britain went for fastest possible development—for reasons of balance of payments and party advantage—with the result that a great deal of the associated work which could have been done in Britain, given more time, went instead to American and European industry.

It is easy to pose *post-facto* questions. It should be remembered that when the government allowed such easy terms to oil companies in the early stages of opening up the North Sea, this was at a time when companies had a number of alternative exploration and development possibilities open to them. Even so, Nore describes the period 1964–73 as the 'nadir' of British oil policies. It might be more accurate to say there wasn't a policy at all.

It is a fact that once a resource such as oil has been found in any quantity, there will automatically follow a tightening of government controls: in other words, a rewriting of contracts. There is nothing especially radical or 'left' about this; rather, as Nore claims, a government 'that does not engage in such re-negotiations is simply incompetent'.

The question most likely to recur in the years ahead relates to depletion policy. All depletion arguments between companies and government are based upon a false assumption: that companies have a duty to extract oil for Britain, and if instead of such a high-minded approach they only extract for reasons of profit, then they are to be controlled by a government which does have Britain's good at heart. Neither assumption about company behaviour nor government motive is correct. Companies are in the business for profit. Governments are in the business for power; and so they will do what they hope will keep them in power, not what is good for some abstract concept of the country at large.

Should the Tory Party win the next general election and pursue a somewhat less interventionist policy towards the North Sea, it will then be almost *de rigueur* for their Labour successor government (assuming a continuing two-party pattern which is by no means certain any more) to go for a further bout of more stringent controls, especially if such a government comes to office when the oil resources have begun seriously to decline.

The policy of participation has been much misunderstood. The word sent shivers down oilmen's spines when it was first coined. According to the Department of Energy, it is a policy to secure, through voluntary agreement, majority 51 per cent state participation in existing fields. From the fifth round of licences onwards, BNOC is in any case the automatic co-licensee in all awards. NCB holdings which BNOC inherited gave the corporation interests in the Thistle, Dunlin and Statfjord fields and it purchased the Burmah interests in Ninian.

It is, however, both naive and misleading for government and members of BNOC to claim that participation was voluntary. It may have been designed to give the impression of voluntary accession to the policy by the companies, but in fact they had little option. If they resisted, as Amoco did, they were penalized; they therefore came to accept that participation was a necessary price to pay for their right to obtain new licences in the North Sea. Curiously, after a great deal of public argument and anguish from the companies, Shell could state blandly in one of its briefing papers that government participation was not expected to affect returns on capital, and that government had said participation would leave the companies no worse off than if it had not occurred. Shell, with Esso, was one of the toughest opponents of participation, but they finally dropped their opposition to the idea when they extracted assurances from the government that the 51 per cent of the oil they produced which BNOC would be entitled to take would be sold back to them, to ensure a continuous supply from the North Sea for their extensive British refining and marketing operations. This deal, therefore, undermined the whole point of participation in their case.

Amoco learnt its lesson when it held out against state participation in the Montrose field; the result was its exclusion from any fifth round licence award. Amoco was the last company with major discoveries in the North Sea to concede the principle of participation; it objected especially to those sections of the participation agreement which gave the government, through BNOC, the right to information about its future refining and marketing plans. All the companies feared that BNOC would take an unfair advantage and compete in downstream sales. This Lord Kearton denied.

BNOC can exercise a number of options: it has the oil from its own share of fields; it has the right to take 51 per cent of the oil, at full market price, from fields of the first four rounds that have agreed to participation; and it can take oil in lieu of royalty payments to government. As Lord Kearton said 'we intend to exercise all our options'.

The two really important aspects of the 51 per cent deal are: first, that Britain controls enough of the oil to ensure that the companies cannot in emergency siphon it off elsewhere—although this vital condition was invalidated in the case of the participation deal with Shell and Esso; second, that if big oil shortages occur in the 1980s,

BNOC will be in control of major oil supplies which will give it a very strong bargaining position in the world oil market, so that major companies will have to come to it for supplies.

The biggest policy question of all remains that of conservation. Oil is arguably the most valuable world commodity in the present age. It can save the country huge sums in balance of payments while—even if only used at a rate compatible with maintaining British self-sufficiency—yielding substantial returns in tax, so that governments in the 1980s and later will be able to employ a degree of choice that has not been open to them since before the second world war. This situation can be achieved even if a policy of rigid conservation is followed: that is, no exports except for 'mix' purposes. Against such a policy, however, formidable pressures are likely to be mounted.

In the first place, Britain's principal western allies will demand—that is probably not too strong a term—that she produces more than her own requirements in order to supply them. Then the oil companies themselves would, broadly speaking, prefer to work a field to its maximum extent. When all the fields are on stream—if the companies get their way—then, inevitably, the North Sea will be producing more oil than Britain alone can consume.

So far no conservation policy has been enunciated. It is true that only those discoveries made up to the end of 1975 have the right to build up to whatever rate of extraction the companies want. These fields, however, represent a sizeable part of the whole. Thereafter the government reserves the right to control the level of development. The export of oil, moreover, requires government consent. It is possible to argue two ways: if the price of oil continues to rise, why sell it to the EEC or anyone else when it will appreciate in the ground? Alternatively, if Britain is pressurized by her allies to sell, she may agree to do so—but at a higher price than OPEC, so that the country gets a return commensurate with selling so vital a resource.

Conservation policies need to be made now since it is technically difficult and, the companies would argue, economically disastrous if at the British self-sufficiency stage they are then asked to throttle back production to that level only. Efficient conservation must be worked out well in advance. There are two basic ways to conserve: to develop a field and then limit the flow; to find a field but not develop it until the oil is required.

By mid 1977 the first seven fields had gone into production and were then meeting about half Britain's needs. Probably at some point in 1979 all Britain's needs will be met from the North Sea, although in value, as opposed to volume, terms Britain should make the break-even point earlier. Her light crude sells at about $1 more a barrel than imported heavy crudes and we shall always export a proportion of light North Sea oil for imported heavier crude to achieve the right industrial mix. Nine more fields were under development in 1977 and another dozen were being evaluated. 1977, therefore, was the time for both the government and the Tory opposition to work out conservation-depletion policies for the 1980s. This certainly should be done before the twelve fields under evaluation are given the go-ahead for development.

Maximum conservation in the 1980s makes sense against the predictions of an energy gap in the 1990s, since the conserved oil will then be of greater value. Mr Benn, however, has already told the oil companies not to fix long-term contracts which could preclude oil selling options for the 1980s. He wishes to prevent BNOC's position being undermined by engagements entered into by the majors; BNOC will have large amounts of oil available for sale in the 1980s, and if all overseas contracts had then been taken up by the companies, BNOC would be forced to provide the British market only—one ironic aspect of participation not perhaps foreseen at the time. This does not appear to be part of any conservation policy. Secondly, the Secretary of State wanted to ensure that Britain does not run short of crude as a result of long-term export contracts. The oil reaction to Mr Benn was unfriendly: companies see his directions as one more encroachment on their power and think that he has already taken more than enough of their freedom to manoeuvre away from them.

The one area where conservation measures have been taken concerns gas: the order to keep the Brent platform shut until gas handling equipment had been installed by Shell-Esso; and the refusal to allow Occidental to increase production from the Piper field until it had arranged to pipe its gas ashore. Without these orders, it seems, the companies would have continued to waste the gas—at least for the time being.

Sir Derek Ezra argues (no doubt with his coal market very much in mind) that once present home requirements have been met, oil should not be produced above these or a glut may develop on the market in the 1980s. And Professor Colin Robinson of Surrey University says the general government purpose appears to be to reduce production below what the oil companies would wish to see— although not before the 1980s.

Conservation covers a far wider field than oil or gas. During 1976 local authorities in Devon, Cornwall and Jersey were looking at plans to set up a south-west energy group to study the possibilities of the region in which there is particular scope for developing alternative sources of energy such as wind power, wave power, solar and geothermal energy.

According to an official of the Department of Energy, savings from energy conservation between now and 2000 could equal the total production envisaged over the same period in new plans for coal. There are probably few areas in which there is as much waste as in the energy industry as a whole. Conservation measures such as proper insulation in houses are also a form of alternative energy. The government's *Save It* campaign—a result of the energy crisis—was designed to make people conscious of energy waste. But the money devoted to it—£5·1 million initially—was very little compared with the vast sums that go into the various energy producing programmes. France claims to have a more aggressive *Save It* campaign than Britain, one which sets targets for industry. The French claim a 5 per cent saving rate as opposed to a 2 per cent rate in Britain.

And according to the WAES report (referred to earlier):

> Our studies lead us to believe that much energy can be saved. Indeed, energy conservation may well be the very best of the alternative energy choices available. Its advantages and benefits are substantial.

Calling energy conservation the fourth 'prong' of an energy policy of which coal production, nuclear power and research on alternative resources to oil and gas were the other three, the President of the Royal Institute of British Architects said in 1977 that £1,000 million should be spent on conservation over the next ten years. A starting point for such a programme, he said, would be to improve and insulate the fabric of 20 million homes which were responsible for about 30 per cent of the country's primary energy consumption. Then should follow the upgrading of public buildings.

At the end of 1977 Mr Benn announced a ten-year conservation programme to cost about £321 million in the first four years. It is expected to save the country about £700 million a year by the end of the decade. The programme includes better insulation for two million council houses; better heating systems in schools and colleges; the consideration of new building regulations; talks with the car industry to raise mileage per gallon of petrol; and the establishment of a conservation division within the Department of Energy.

Many conservation suggestions are likely to be forthcoming as the energy debate continues. But it would be foolish to imagine that more than a certain minimum can be achieved this way. In the first place, it is in human nature to use resources rather than save them; it is easier to burn oil or coal than to build insulation into existing houses. And since on the whole there is more money in oil, gas or coal than in insulation or other savings, governments will find it difficult to limit energy resource use beyond a certain extent.

The second argument in this respect concerns posterity: the present generation, it is argued idealistically, have an obligation to see that some of this resource is available to its grandchildren rather than squandering it all themselves. Most people would subscribe to the theory; in practice few people do anything to preserve resources for future generations. And as one key man in oil circles, who on this at least would prefer to be anonymous, asked: 'What did posterity ever do for us?'

Conservation also features in the oil pricing argument. For years Britain has lamented the weakness of the pound: yet when at the beginning of 1978 it at last became stronger, the complaint was at once advanced that this would upset our oil bonanza because oil is priced in dollars. North Sea oil is price-linked to similar grades of the main African crudes from Algeria, Libya and Nigeria and top grade North Sea crude costs approximately $14 a barrel. In early 1978 domestic and export prices for North Sea crude were expected to fall by about 20 to 30 cents a barrel, and huge sums were knocked off both the government tax take and company profits—a lowering of daily revenues in the region of between $180,000 to $270,000 when the country was producing at a rate of 900,000 barrels a day.

At least as far as oil is concerned, the price is unlikely to be reduced for the consumer; it will continue to go up. This reflects inflation: the company desire for profits and the equal government desire for as large a tax take as possible. On top of these reasons comes conservation: people must be dissuaded from wasting a precious commodity *by* the high price. It is, indeed, one of the ironies of the energy question that no matter what arguments are deployed by companies or what policies are put forward by governments, the one certainty will be that the public pays more, never less.

Government income from oil comes from royalties and tax; therefore the weaker the economic situation at any given time, the greater the interest of government in maximizing production so as to increase revenue. According to BP in a paper upon the effects of North Sea oil:

In the particular cases examined, an invarying 83% of the resources available to the U.K. from oil production was passed to the Government as tax and royalty, while the Exchequer share of the increased cost of oil prices was probably around 5%.

In all cases the ratio of government take to resources generated is approximately constant, indicating that the tax structure does not in general provide a cushion for company earnings as prices change. Consequently in all price and exchange rate environments the cases can be ranked in the same order by both the

government and companies indicating that they have broadly
similar interests.

It is a contention of the majors which they consistently overplay
that their interests and those of government are really so similar as
to be synonymous. This is not and never has been the case. The basis
of tax policies has to be measured against the lift to the national
income that is derived from oil and gas. The North Sea benefit to
GNP is considerable—somewhere in the region of 5 per cent. At the
same time North Sea oil is unlikely to add more than 1 per cent to
Britain's long-term annual growth rate even on the most optimistic
assumptions, at least according to stockbrokers Phillips and Drew.
In other words, too many expectations placed upon what oil can do
for the economy in the light of these big figures will be misleading.

Tax is the key government weapon and means of control. In the
early 1970s before the new tax regime was introduced, various ideas
were mooted including, for example, a barrelage tax. This, effectively,
is levelled in the Middle East, but there little difference exists in costs
from field to field. In the North Sea the cost variations are enormous,
so a barrelage tax does not make sense. The present tax is upgraded
according to the way a field is developed: in the early stages there
are allowances which fall away as full production is attained. This
means that the great bulk of the fields now in production or coming
on stream will be subject to the full rate of tax by 1980. The idea of
a ring fence applied to the North Sea has meant a unique government
system: each field is treated as a separate entity for tax purposes. In
addition, the North Sea is also ring-fenced so that a company such
as BP cannot write off losses made in the Gulf or Alaska against
North Sea profits. Corporation Tax will be computed on a company's entire North Sea operation. Thus the ring fence round fields
ensures that only losses and investments made in the North Sea
can be offset against a company's bill. The variation from field to
field can be substantial. According to one economist writing in *The
Banker* in 1977, the return on Auk was 48 per cent and on Piper
44 per cent while that on Heather and Ninian was only 16 per
cent.

A number of questions relating to tax need be asked. The first is,
how many loopholes exist in the system? Second, at what stage
should the oil be valued: at the well-head or when it is landed? Thus,
for example, why should landing costs be included before oil is
valued as is the case at present? Then, when a 'farm-in' occurs (an
outside company buying into a field, usually into a consortium where
a smaller member needs capital), the costs of such a 'farm-in' are at
present acceptable against corporation tax. Should a major 'buying

in' to a profitable field be able to write off its gain against corporation tax?

There is a curious ambivalence about British politicians of the left: they say the oil companies are not being taxed enough which is a reasonably valid proposition for them to put forward. But they are exceptionally cautious about how much more should be taken in tax and how or when this should be. They propound the principle, yet at the same time appear happy to continue working in the environment of a capitalist society.

A normal oil company reaction to the possibility of any serious increase in taxes for their North Sea operations is to warn that these could drive them away and prevent any further investment there. Now this bogey has been put up and flaunted so consistently by the companies as to suggest that it is the reverse of the truth, although government and a wide range of economists and others seem to accept the proposition. Lord Kearton maintains that nothing will drive the companies away from such a bonanza as the North Sea. From a government point of view then—and certainly from one that claims to be of the left—the answer would be to try it: greatly increase taxes and then wait and see what the companies do.

When in July 1974 the government announced that it was going to increase public participation in the benefits of North Sea oil through a state corporation, by altering the licence system and by imposing a Petroleum Revenue Tax, the subsequent delay in revealing the details certainly did have the effect of making oil companies stand off, unwilling to invest or develop further until they did know the details. As the author of *Labour Law and Offshore Oil*, Jonathan Kitchen claims:

> Several major oil companies threatened to reduce their involvement in the North Sea or delayed investment until the argument with the government was cleared up. When it was, it was hailed as a victory for the companies, and share prices rose on the news.

During this period, moreover, the companies tried to keep the size of fields secret until after the announcement of the tax details, while arguing that too much tax would make the smaller fields uneconomic. In fact reserves seem constantly to be upgraded.

The actual tax to be levied on oil depends upon the Customs and Excise estimate of the oil flow. Oil companies have to use reliable measuring instruments—flowmeters—yet the make is not prescribed, although in most revenue matters such instruments would be. Thus at present, in a situation which involves vast amounts of money, only the trader specifies the make of instrument.

In the deliberately dry, almost uninvolved, language sometimes

6

adopted by the multinationals, Shell, in one of its many briefing papers, gives what might be taken as the official multinational view on taxes:

Tax is an important factor in planning the development of new oil and gas resources and the rate at which the tax burden on marginal fields is assessed is crucial to the development of new production capacity. An increasing proportion of future projects are likely to be only marginally commercial, and such fields are worth developing only if incentives exist.

The oil taxation office was set up in 1975 and the Oil Taxation Act of that year set out the conditions of Petroleum Revenue Tax which include special rules relating to oil companies. All the companies operating in the North Sea are dealt with from this office and a company is deemed to have become involved from a tax point of view as soon as it obtains a licence. When a company makes a discovery the 'petroliferous' trade begins, as the taxman says. At first, while the company is sinking its wells and building up production, it will be a question of tax losses. The tax office becomes interested in a company as soon as a discovery is made. Once oil has been found the government may indicate to a company how and when tax will arise. In the early stages—that is, during exploration—it is a statutory requirement for a company to declare a find. A company may then ask the tax office—at its own option—points that may arise. The Department of Energy undertakes the determination of a field: its delineation in geographic and geological terms. Then expenditure on the development programme is fixed. Thus, when a field begins to produce oil the tax office, through the Department of Energy, will already know the size of the field and the person or company to tax.

Under the first four rounds, licences demanded a government royalty at $12\frac{1}{2}$ per cent of well-head value. This has been calculated in terms of landed value: say $14 a barrel, less the cost of transport from well-head to land terminal by pipeline or tanker. This could work out at 50 cents a barrel transport charge, giving a figure of $13·50 upon which to calculate the royalty. This exercise is carried out every six months for each field and company.

Petroleum Revenue Tax is designed to bite fast: it is chargeable every six months and the resulting tax is due four months later. PRT is computed according to receipts for sales of oil by the company at a value negotiated between the company and the tax office. Returns have to be submitted every 31 December and 30 June and the return will be made up of the number of barrels landed multiplied by the agreed value. Once the company has made its return it can then claim for expenditure that has been agreed by the tax office. The return goes in by 1 December; claims have to be made by 1 April; and payment must be made by 1 May unless there is a dispute.

Allowances can be claimed for platforms, plus a supplementary uplift allowance of 75 per cent of capital expenditure: thus, if a company has paid £100 million for a platform before the field starts production, it can claim £175 million before it begins to pay tax. The rationale behind this 75 per cent allowance is in lieu of allowing interest charges so as, for example, to prevent the companies borrowing from their own subsidiaries at exorbitant rates. There are two other sets of allowances to help marginal fields: an oil allowance and a safeguard allowance. The oil allowance permits 1·5 million tons of oil to be taken off each field tax free in each chargeable period of six months up to a maximum of 10 million tons a field, so that this amount may be tax free over a five-year period. The safeguard allowance is to guarantee a company a minimum return on capital expenditure before PRT is applied. Thus, if the profit from a field in any calendar year is less than 30 per cent of the capital expenditure needed to develop it, the field escapes tax. This safeguard allowance means that when the capital cost of a field is £100 million, the field would have to make £30 million in a taxable period before any PRT would be applied. This provision, in fact, is only likely to be important at the tail end of a field's life.

Finally there is Corporation Tax. In this case the company's accountancy has to show the profits from all its North Sea operations. For PRT there is a ring fence round an individual field; for Corporation Tax there is a ring fence round the entire North Sea operation of the company. A typical example of computing corporation tax would be as follows: first, capital allowances; then PRT; then interest for the various fields; finally corporation tax at 52 per cent.

After all allowances have been dealt with, the government tax take on each extra £1 earned will come to approximately 70 per cent. The royalty payment is in addition to that. It is the duty of the tax office to supply the Department of Energy with oil field values for royalties. The Department has the power to remit royalties.

It is probably not a bad system of tax. It is devised first to bring in money fast to government, and second to ensure that all profits from the North Sea are taxed for Britain, so that the majors cannot offset losses elsewhere in the world against their North Sea operations. The tax may appear to be very high; the fact is that after its application the companies still make enormous profits.

8

The Department of Energy, BNOC and OSO

The Department of Energy is the successor to the old Ministry of Fuel and Power. The Secretary of State from June 1975 has been Mr Wedgwood Benn who was, as it were, demoted to the job by Wilson from Industry, where it was thought he would have too much influence upon Labour Party policy. The Department of Energy, as it turned out, provided him (if the pun can be excused) with an especially appropriate power base. He has proved a tough and able minister in a job where some highly controversial decisions, especially affecting the oil companies, had to be put into operation. The job also put him into a key position to present to the Labour Party his ideas about the use of the oil wealth.

Dr Jesse Dickson Mabon, his Minister of State, was appointed by Mr Callaghan in 1976 and has responsibility for what might be described as the 'nuts and bolts' part of the Department's activities. As a team they have managed to get more news mileage than virtually any other department of government excluding the Prime Minister himself and the Chancellor. They have had the luck to run a department which, largely as a result of oil, has given them more reasons than most—often pleasant ones at that—for remaining in the public eye.

As of 1 November 1977, the Department of Energy had a total staff of 1,302, making it one of the smallest ministries. Of this number 333 were members of the five oil divisions: Oil Policy (Home) Division, 43; Petroleum Production Division, 48; Petroleum Engineering Division, 83; Offshore Supplies Office (OSO), 129; and Continental Shelf (Participation) Division, 30. Apart from oil the Department is responsible for gas and the BGC; coal and the NCB; electricity and the Electricity Authority; nuclear energy and the UKAEA; 'renewables' and conservation measures.

The Department has wide powers at its disposal (see chapter 7) and as Esso says:

The Government recognizes the part which the oil industry must play in the provision of energy, and discussions take place between the oil industry and the Government on many levels, to ensure that misunderstandings do not hold up the vital work that must be done.

Mr Benn's predecessor at the Department, Mr Varley, made a policy statement to Parliament in July 1974 about government proposals to take powers of control, and subsequently he followed this with a statement on depletion policy on 6 December 1974. This was of basic importance and came to be known as the Varley Guidelines in which government policy towards the companies and the rate of oil extraction are laid down. It remains a key to energy policy (see Appendix 3).

As more and more oil finds were made through the 1970s, so the Department refined its procedures. Once a discovery has been made and a company wishes to develop, a wide range of information has to be supplied to the Department. There are two schedules (A and B) of requirements. Stringent programmes giving details of field installations, wells, other relevant works, the quantities of petroleum to be produced and the construction schedule must be submitted. For their Development and Production Programme, the Department of Energy requires background information to include an historical introduction to the field, details of the area to which the programme will relate, geological and geophysical data, formation parameters, reservoir fluid parameters and reserves, development and production plans, profiles, transportation of petroleum, pollution prevention measures, shore terminals, costs, construction schedule, process flow diagram and other matters. By the time the Department has all this information it has a fair knowledge about any given field.

The main control over the rate of development possessed by the Department of Energy is control of the rate of licensing; the Department can also delay the development of any discovery. It is a condition of licences that all oil and gas is landed in Britain unless it has been agreed otherwise by the Secretary of State. When it is landed, for example, by an American company and is intended for export, the company must get an export licence.

On the question of foreign companies the British government stipulates that 70 per cent of investment in the North Sea by firms whose ultimate ownership is foreign must come from overseas. And on the extent of foreign participation in the North Sea and whether or not the ratio of foreign to British companies operating there should be altered, Dr Mabon said in 1977:

It has been HMG policy in all previous rounds of licensing that there should be no discrimination on grounds of nationality. All applicants were considered in the light of criteria published when applications were invited. We have no plans to change this practice.

The various divisions of the Department of Energy between them have responsibility for ensuring that offshore activities are in accordance with government policy to maximize the benefits to Britain of its oil and gas resources. Thus it is the responsibility of the Offshore Energy Technology Board (OETB), set up in 1975, to define department programmes of oil and gas technology. The OETB has to acquire data, determine standards and assist the OSO. Through its research and development programme it is examining the following aspects of the industry: safety, assisting British industry, tethered buoy platforms, single point moorings, positioning, mooring and anchoring systems, subsea completions and seabed production, systems for marginal fields, pipelaying, diving, underwater tools and power sources, underwater maintenance and repair, inspection and submersibles.

The Department of Energy is responsible for safety regulations of all kinds: these cover the construction of platforms, fire, safety of platforms at sea. The Health and Safety at Work Act is now extended to apply to offshore installations. The Department has an inspectorate and roughly once every three months a platform and a field will be inspected by mechanical, electrical and petroleum engineers in rotation.

In June 1977 Mr Benn announced the establishment of a twenty-two man Energy Commission to advise on major energy policy issues. The Commission was to be a mix of representatives from the energy industries, the trade unions and consumer interests. Mr Benn was to be chairman; the Minister for the Scottish Office is also to be a member. The seven industry members are appointed from the NCB, the Electricity Council, the BGC, the UKAEA, the BNOC, South of Scotland Electricity Board and the Petroleum Industry Advisory Committee. Union membership comes from the TUC Fuel and Power Industries Committee. When membership of the Commission was announced in October of 1977, one newspaper described the Commission as representative of Mr Benn's commitment to open government. A possibly more interesting aspect of Mr Benn's commitment to open government was his appointment in October 1977 of Professor Peter Odell as a part-time consultant with the Department of Energy. The professor's well-known views on oil and the companies, and the fact that he has been a severe critic of company and government policies, certainly made the appointment an interesting one.

In its short life—it came into being in January 1976—the British National Oil Corporation has been the centre of a good deal of controversy. It is, indeed, a reasonable guideline to most public institutions or individuals that they are often denounced in proportion to their effectiveness. BNOC may well fall into this category.

'The government does not see a case for total nationalization of the oil industry,' according to Dr Mabon, and that being the case something like BNOC was inevitable, at least under a Labour government. BNOC's 51 per cent participation role had both political and regulatory appeal; and it was felt that by involving the state corporation in all aspects of the North Sea it could truly advise the Department of Energy. In a sense the 51 per cent was clearly a political symbol. There are many aspects of BNOC that have to be considered. Oil companies may find the margins unattractive in exploiting fields which, however, are vital for British energy supplies, though not a good source of company profits. Here is one justification for BNOC. Royalties which are paid into the National Oil Account can be used for BNOC's capital spending. As a result of an amendment to the Petroleum & Submarine Pipelines Bill when in the Lords, BNOC can borrow abroad on a commercial basis—a thing it first did in mid 1977. When it was set up BNOC took over all the NCB North Sea interests and so started life with an equity in the Thistle, Dunlin, Hutton and Brae fields and part of the British section of Statfjord. It also took over Burmah's North Sea interests.

BNOC has met with much acrimony from the oil companies, less because they were aggrieved at the idea of a state oil corporation than because they had thought the political will to establish it did not exist. Once it was there they were obliged to come to terms with it. There is in fact no nationalized industry over which such a system of control has been established. There are two civil servants on the board and the Secretary of State for Energy possesses powers for specific direction. It is, moreover, the only nationalized industry that cannot retain its own profits: these go into the National Oil Account and BNOC can then have them back, in so far as it is able to persuade the Secretary of State for Energy that they are needed for the Corporation's tasks.

BNOC exists to keep the control of North Sea resources in British hands. Its key role is to monitor profits and prices. The Corporation may:

   . . . do anything required for the purpose of giving effect to agreements entered into by the Secretary of State with a view to securing participation by the Government of the United Kingdom, or by the Corporation or any other body on behalf of the Government, in activities connected with petroleum beneath controlled waters.

BNOC has to be able to do what an oil company can do so that it can show the government probabilities which are not necessarily oil company interests. It has to supply to government the expertise of a company. And it has to act as the agent of government—that is, it has a responsibility to see that the oil is disposed of in the best interests of the British economy. Since it controls licences BNOC can control the rate of exploration.

BNOC's future role could be of even greater importance; so far it has been a question of the development of the large, commercially attractive fields. Later must come the marginal fields. Then, when companies are uninterested in the marginal fields, BNOC will be in a position to ensure that decisions about extraction are taken in the national interest. BNOC argues that it must be involved to represent government successfully over issues such as depreciation. Thus for example, where a company might bring out oil quickly for cash flow reasons and only 'cream off' 20 per cent, a BNOC presence could ensure this would be increased to, say, 30 per cent. Oilmen argue that BNOC is unnecessary since there already exists the Department of Energy which possesses wide powers. BNOC's reply is that it would simply not work for the Department of Energy to attempt some of the functions assigned to BNOC: the Corporation has stepped into the harsh realities of the oil world and so can give to government practical advice founded upon experience. It has to ensure that the national oil bonanza is maximized for the good of the country.

BNOC can use its strength to help OSO and the Department of Energy get their way. In March 1977, it made certain that a contract for steel for the Murchison field went to the BSC. One view is that BNOC—acting as a super-nationalist—should insist that all sub-contracts for its fields go to British contractors. Its aim is to have oil companies buy British for their North Sea developments and most oilmen would agree with this, if there were no obvious bars (such as price, performance and delays) to adopting such a course.

Virtually the entire share of state oil will pass through BNOC (a small amount belongs to BGC). When the full rate of production has been reached in 1981, this will amount to over 900,000 barrels a day (b/d). This will consist of 133,000 b/d from fields in which BNOC has a direct shareholding; 286,000 b/d under a provision which allows companies to pay their $12\frac{1}{2}$ per cent royalties in oil; and 500,000 b/d from the participation agreements with private oil companies which allow BNOC either to take 51 per cent of their oil at market price or the equivalent amount in foreign crude. There are also further agreements which give BNOC the option to buy another 380,000 b/d, but in these cases the companies have an immediate buy-back right so it is a paper transaction only. All these BNOC entitlements exist apart from anything found as a result of the fifth round: in that case BNOC would have 51 per cent outright of any oil found. In simple terms of volume these holdings and options make BNOC a formidable oil company.

BNOC is split between London and Glasgow: the establishment of BNOC in Scotland was mainly a political face-saving device—a large number of personnel remain in London to deal with government and oil companies. The SNP, always on the look-out for slights to Scotland, claim BNOC advertises its main jobs in England while only the more junior posts appear in the Scottish press. The Corporation has no PR establishment—unlike the oil companies which have large and highly efficient PR departments—and though its Chairman, Lord Kearton, is ready enough to speak, BNOC gives the impression of general reticence in public pronouncements.

When production of the huge Thistle field started in February 1978 (late as a result of bad weather conditions and labour troubles), BNOC obtained its first equity oil. BNOC, moreover, is the operator so this represents a double first for the state corporation. Experience gained in Thistle will prove invaluable to other BNOC fields where it is operator. At peak Thistle will produce about 200,000 b/d. Early in 1978 participation agreements were concluded between BNOC and its Thistle partners—Deminex, Santa Fé International, Tricentrol, Burmah, Ashland, Conoco, Gulf and the Charterhouse Group—so that the corporation gained access to more than half Thistle output. It owns 16·2 per cent of the 550 million barrels of recoverable resources through its equity interest in the field anyway and the rest comes as a result of the participation arrangements. Further, the Charterhouse Group, which only has a 0·96 per cent stake in the field, has agreed to sell BNOC all its oil.

With Thistle BNOC enters an era of selling oil to the companies. The Corporation is going to become a major influence in the oil trading market and so has set up its own unit to monitor world crude prices. By 1980 BNOC will be selling between 800,000 and 1 million barrels a day. This will represent between 7 and 10 per cent of total world output of premium low sulphur crude—oil that is sought world-wide for petrol and chemicals. Ironically, there are growing signs that BNOC would prefer a more flexible selling policy (as it is coming to have so much oil to dispose of) than the Department of Energy so far has shown itself to favour.

North Sea Crude Accessible to British National OIL Corporation in 1981 (all figures in '000 b/d)

Field	Royalty	Participation options*	British Gas Council's interest	BNOC's interest	Total	As % of year's production
Auk	1	4	—	—	5	50·0
Beryl	9	29	7	—	45	56·2
Brent	58	230	—	—	288	56·5
Buchan	5	20	—	—	25	55·5
Claymore	14	54	—	—	68	56·7
Cormorant	6	27	—	—	33	55·0
Dunlin	13	30	—	14	57	47·9
Forties	49	190	—	—	239	56·6
Heather	5	23	—	—	28	56·0
Montrose	5	16	14	—	35	70·0
Murchison	6	—	—	19	25	39·0
Ninian	37	60	—	62	159	47·4
Piper	28	108	—	—	136	56·6
Statfjord	3	—	—	9	12	38·7
Tartan	7	36	—	—	43	55·8
Thistle	22	60	—	29	111	55·5
TOTAL	268	887	21	133	1,309	54·1

* Including buy-back arrangements.   *Source:* Wood, Mackenzie.

Part of the justification for BNOC as advanced by its own staff is its ability to tie down the experts, that is, the oil companies, on the practical side. Comparisons can be made with Norway's Statoil which was founded in 1972 and will act as Norway's main operator. The basis of company opposition to BNOC is simply that the more powerful the state corporation, the more it will detract from company influence and power. If the British government wanted, BNOC (like Statoil) could become the main British operator in the North Sea. Government at present does not want this although it is a possibility for the future. Norway, it must be remembered, has a far less sophisticated industrial base than does Britain: if she can make her state oil corporation the key to her North Sea activities there is certainly no reason why Britain cannot do so too.

The companies objected strongly to the creation of a separate British state oil corporation. The government could have taken over BP (in which it had a majority holding) for the role. It did not. One of the more successful myths peddled in Britain was that to make BP the state corporation would have been to frighten away the company's foreign holdings—Alaska was constantly cited. Elf and Eni are both state corporations with a variety of foreign involvements to their credit and both survive without difficulty in this dual role.

A different objection has been that BNOC could never successfully manage the role of the majors in the North Sea since this would be too difficult for it technologically. That objection has already been superseded by events. Then there is the curious free enterprise objection of the companies that it is unnecessary for the government to find taxpayers' money for BNOC when they are themselves willing to put up all the funds needed to finance developments. Why not put up taxpayers' money if, for once, it will bring the taxpayer a good return?

On a quite different level, the companies argue that BNOC is bound to have conflicting interests. An example of this was in the negotiations between the Heather and Ninian consortia over the use of the Ninian pipeline, when BNOC had an option in the first and an equity in the second. In that case, however, BNOC withdrew from the negotiations. There is indeed no reason why in such cases she should not act thus; at least each such occasion ought to be judged on its merits. A more complicated issue could arise if two consortia with BNOC majority stakes in them both want a block lying between them. In such circumstances BNOC might have an interest to split the block. Consortia agreements, for example, include a clause (made before first drilling) to the effect that no one partner will apply on its own account for areas around the block being drilled. The idea is that the vital knowledge of what is beneath the seabed is common to them all, since all have taken a share in the costs of the field. BNOC, however, refuses such a clause and this has raised company fears that it will gain disproportionate advantage from its part in consortia.

As pointed out in *The Banker* in May 1977, 'A good entrepreneur takes all the chances he can get. Distrust of BNOC stems from the feeling that it will get too many chances.'

One oilman explained his antipathy to BNOC simply in terms of the state corporation being allowed to take 51 per cent of all their early finds. From round 5, however, BNOC will automatically have a 51 per cent stake in all finds and will also carry 51 per cent of the risks. Another oil company complaint is that BNOC offered 50 per cent more for salaries to attract staff. It also does not have to pay PRT. Others say it makes political, as opposed to commercial, decisions—which is true and unsurprising. Another company objection is that even if government intervention is accepted by the industry as inevitable (if not desirable), it is wrong to have an extra adviser that is also an oil company. It is far from clear why this should be wrong—unless the objection is that a state oil company is able to give advice that the other companies would prefer to withhold. The companies fear that BNOC could obtain information from them in its role as arm of government, and then use it in competition with other oil companies. They argue that BNOC is unlikely to act impartially between government and companies. A cynic might reply that it is precisely because the oil companies argue BNOC is unnecessary and its functions could all be done by the Department of Energy, that BNOC should exist. BNOC's information role is crucial: for example, the costs companies claim for North Sea developments are not audited. Again, no one knows how much oil there is or the timescale needed to get it out so that BNOC information on this will be vital to government.

Although the companies complained that BNOC poached staff from them, the Corporation maintains that many were happy to join BNOC since its staff can be UK based. BNOC will pick up its share of development costs from the fifth round onwards and is to be the operator in six fields. By the 1980s when its own oil production will come to 6 million tons, BNOC will rank fourth in the North Sea.

The companies are wary of BNOC entering the downstream part of the oil business because it could provide them with some very stiff opposition indeed. At present BNOC is cautious about any such suggestion, although it is widely expected to enter both the refining and chemical ends of the business eventually. These activities, however, demand a huge scale of investment and so BNOC might go into downstream partnerships with oil companies. The participation agreement with BP, which was treated in a class by itself anyway, included a provision for BP to train BNOC staff in downstream activities although BNOC is to refrain from such activities for five years.

BNOC financing is met through the National Oil Account. This was established under section 40 of the Petroleum and Submarine Pipelines Act of 1975. All BNOC's expenditure is met from the account while the Corporation's gross receipts are paid into it. So also are loans for BNOC from wherever they may come. In addition all royalties, rentals and licence fees are paid into the account which is under the control of the Secretary of State. In 1976, its first operational year, BNOC spent £91 million on development and exploration. The cost of acquiring interests from the NCB and Burmah came to a further £287 million.

BNOC's future will depend upon its ability to raise loans. It came through this test in 1977 with spectacular success. In May 1977 BNOC was seeking a $700 million loan in the Eurodollar market. By June BNOC had pulled off a major loan of $825 million from British and American banks. This was more than had been expected, although Lord Kearton claimed that the corporation could have had more still had there been the need. Citibank acted as BNOC's agents and according to Lord Kearton the loan package proved that

'. . . some of the most influential and forward-looking banks in the world have decided that BNOC is worth backing'. The banks taking part in the loan included Citibank as manager, six other American banks, Barclays, National Westminster, Bank of Scotland, Clydesdale Bank and the Royal Bank of Scotland. Most of the loan— $675 million—was in American domestic dollars. This was another important first for BNOC.

The loan was arranged for BNOC at the same time as the City was arranging the huge sale of government BP shares to the public. BNOC raised its massive loan at far less cost than government spent to sell off its shares. The companies are quick enough to say that BNOC could not stand on its own; so the loan-raising exercise was especially important for BNOC morale, demonstrating that the Corporation has A1 rating on the international money market.

There was also considerable political significance in the loan, mainly of American money. Strong government doubts had been expressed as to whether BNOC could raise a commercial loan without government guarantees, and although Lord Kearton denied it, obtaining a loan with heavy US content does mean that BNOC is in a stronger position to resist future government manipulation. The fact that no guarantee was needed meant BNOC had obtained an international banking seal of approval as a commercial company, while at the same time the loan freed the Corporation from some of the controls which the Treasury might otherwise have exercised over it. The loan can be regarded as BNOC's first step towards becoming a substantial commercial rival of the majors.

The Corporation has four functions: the commercial management of its equity interests; the effective use of the petroleum available to it; the development of expertise and knowledge of all aspects of the oil business; and development of its capacity to give informed expert advice to government. Presenting its first report the Chairman, Lord Kearton, said:

> What we have done is come through a year when the betting of the oil companies was that we wouldn't survive that year. It seems to me that the next six months will see BNOC become an increasing influence, and by the 1980s it will be a very powerful influence on the European oil scene.

The growth of BNOC was rapid: when it started it had only half a dozen staff; a year later it had four hundred. Lord Kearton made his reputation building up Courtaulds as a rival to ICI; if he can now make BNOC rival the oil majors, it will be a major personal triumph. With the prospects before BNOC, 'We will be taking at least 10 million tonnes of oil a year from BP alone from 1979, and that goes on until the 1990s', Lord Kearton can afford to be optimistic about the Corporation's future:

> I believe that North Sea oil is going to give this country the biggest opportunity it has had for many years—although the operative word is *opportunity*.

Oil company suspicion of BNOC remains, since they cannot reconcile themselves to its dual role of company and government adviser. Lord Kearton explains this away, somewhat airily, by saying that it exemplifies 'the English pragmatic way of dealing with problems as they arise'. The ambiguities of BNOC's position are certainly there, as are the uncertainties for the future. At the time of this first report, the *Financial Times* called upon the Tories to abolish BNOC when they regained office, and said the Corporation was developing in such a way that it '. . . can hardly end up as anything other than a powerful spokesman for the very international companies that the Labour Government seems so anxious to control'. But Lord Kearton knows how to defend and justify BNOC:

> What you want is tax revenue. But if you want that, the essential thing is to have information about such matters as estimated North Sea reserves, since it is such information that determines Britain's oil policy. Our participation agreements will give us access to more information than ever before.
>
> If you assume that oil is going to be coming out of everybody's ears in the future, then BNOC is of no value at all. But if you regard it, as I do, as a scarce commodity, it is absolutely necessary for Britain to secure a certain supply. After all, that is the priority that any oil company puts at the top of its list.

If it is not destroyed politically, BNOC probably has a bright future. It will in any case become increasingly difficult to end its life, since its involvement in equity and participation in the North Sea is now so complex as to warrant a massive disbanding operation.

There is undoubtedly more oil to be discovered off the continental shelf and there are few, if any, other areas around the world with equal prospects from a viewpoint of political stability. Again, in terms of government take—70 per cent to the companies' 30 per cent—there are few areas where companies are treated with such generosity. By the time North Sea oil dwindles, BNOC should have moved into other resources. This background added particular interest to the statement Lord Kearton made in February 1978 to the Commons Select Committee. He said that the North Sea bonanza was over unless the price of oil went up in the near future. He argued that all the big fields had been found; that the risks attached to developing the small ones made them far less attractive financial propositions for the companies (oil costs five times as much to drill and get out in the North Sea than in the Gulf) and that companies had under-estimated the complexity of the area. He suggested that a time might come when the companies would lose interest in developing such small fields and would leave this side of development to BNOC. He added that BNOC is now working on a ten- to fifteen-year plan to recruit men from other disciplines to train them, so that should the multinationals eventually leave the North Sea and retreat to their home waters BNOC would be in a position to continue developing the area.

BNOC is certainly controversial. Apart from Lord Kearton, the deputy chairman is Lord Balogh,* a former Minister of State for Energy unloved by the oilmen anyway, who has been a principal target of attack by the opponents of participation. Then there is Ian Clark, formerly chief executive of the Shetland Islands Council at the time when the Council negotiated with the oil companies for the terminal at Sullom Voe. BNOC now has powers to search for oil anywhere in the world.

It was typical of its stormy path as well as the role assigned to it that in early 1978 BNOC was at loggerheads with UKOOA about a standard operating agreement for the exploration and development of oil finds under the fifth round of licences, in which BNOC will be a compulsory 51 per cent shareholder. The main point of contention was the clause which would allow BNOC to go ahead with develop-ment of a find even if its partners felt it was uncommercial. The companies are suspicious that BNOC might be happy to go it alone rather than join them in negotiating a reduction in royalty or tax as extra incentive. This is typical of the sort of clash of interests BNOC must face.

The antipathy towards BNOC appears to be fairly widespread. Understandably the oil companies see it as a menace; it is now sug-gested that the government sees its creation getting out of control, while public suspicion of yet another state body is to be expected. The Tory Party talks of curtailing its powers, but has carefully avoided actual commitment to do so. They, too, see the merits of controlling the North Sea bonanza.

On the other hand, one eminent and veteran oilman, who on this issue would prefer to remain anonymous, said emphatically that it was absolutely vital for Britain to have such a corporation: not only would it provide the government with essential advice but would also control Britain's oil—and that, he said, is as it should be. It is not untypical of attitudes to oil earlier in the decade that the

* Lord Balogh relinquished his post as deputy chairman in January 1978; he remains economic adviser to BNOC.

Mackays, whose perceptive book *Political Economy of North Sea Oil* we have frequently quoted, took a line that has not been borne out by events:

> We believe that it would be extremely difficult to recruit the personnel to undertake such an active policy and there is nothing about British policy in the North Sea, nor in the past performance of the public sector, which encourages us to pin much faith on the expertise, proficiency and dynamism of a state-controlled agency.

They had reckoned without Lord Kearton. The oilmen also assumed BNOC would not be able to master the intricacies of the business—not least because of the mystique with which the oil world loves to surround itself. A member of Shell, for example, claimed unconvincingly that, prior to Benn and BNOC, government was not kept in the dark by the oil industry. By August 1977, after twenty months of participation negotiations, Lord Kearton said that people simply could not realize the complete lack of control the government would have had over North Sea oil, had there not been participation.

In a wide-ranging discussion of BNOC Lord Kearton argues that the Corporation's advisory role is its justification. Unless BNOC is involved in the oil business this role is meaningless; or, put another way, the Department of Energy could not obtain the information it requires except from someone with first-hand experience. Against the company argument that the Department could develop its own expertise is the career structure of the civil service; after two years or less personnel are moved. Thus the Department would have no stable group to deal with the companies. Over a two-year period Lord Kearton claims he has had to deal with three under-secretaries. He asserts that BNOC can ensure there is enough oil for Britain; almost all other countries have expropriated.

Despite BNOC and the other regulations the companies groan about, Lord Kearton claims that the British oil regime is the most benign in the world and far more so—in terms of fewer controls—than even that of the USA. The companies do very well out of it. Moreover they are past-masters at tactics to delay and obstruct. Over the issue of conflicting interests in the various consortia to which BNOC belongs, Lord Kearton suggests that the companies are now coming to see the Corporation's presence as spreading the risks; the companies, however grudgingly, are slowly accepting BNOC's role. One aspect of BNOC which ought to be welcome to the companies is the fact that its existence has possibly taken North Sea oil out of the political arena, in the sense that it will no longer be a candidate for nationalization.

Lord Kearton offers doubtful comfort to the SNP. The Scottish party claims that the BNOC presence in Scotland is a sham. This Lord Kearton denies: BNOC has carried out the biggest real estate deal in Glasgow in years; 60 per cent of the staff are there, with more to come. But all the companies are in London as is government, so BNOC has to have a niche in the capital; in fact, Stornoway House makes quite a niche. He also says, blandly, that when BNOC calls meetings in Glasgow everyone squeals.

Perhaps the real reason for the intense dislike the oil companies bear the state corporation arises from the fact that it is dispelling the mystique about their knowledge. Kearton claims the companies are fallible in quite simple business matters, and cites as an example their estimates of both costs and manpower needs for the Sullom Voe terminal, both of which were far too low. He was right in his criticisms and that of course is a bad sin to commit. On the companies Lord Kearton can be amusing—though they might not agree. He says they will only give advice to government which is to their own advantage; they work on the assumption that a fool is born every minute. They are good-tempered, however, when they lose. His point is simple: it is not the business of the oil companies to watch over the national interest. And this is why BNOC needs a minimum superstructure and maximum entrepreneurial and expertise skill, so that it can conduct an informed dialogue with both companies and government.

Lord Kearton, who has his share of enemies and against whom plenty of stories are told, is quite happy to tell one against himself. When BNOC was formed, he says, no one wanted the job. Then, when his acceptance of the post of chairman was announced, one Tory MP commented 'that's scraping the bottom of the barrel'. 'He had no idea how right he was,' claims Lord Kearton happily; 'I was the forty-sixth person to be approached!'

The Offshore Supplies Office—OSO—was the direct outcome of the government-commissioned IMEG report of 1972. It was set up under the Heath government and adopted by Labour when it came to power in 1974, so it has had a relatively untroubled political life. The Labour government moved OSO from the Department of Industry to Energy and sited it in Glasgow. OSO came into being in January 1973 and was intended to have a small staff of forty. The oil companies were then required to make quarterly returns which would show how many of their purchases were made in Britain. Thus OSO was in existence at the time of the Yom Kippur war. The subsequent oil crisis emphasized the importance of the North Sea developments; the need to obtain a major slice of the business for British industry was becoming increasingly obvious and urgent.

At inception OSO's basic role was to make sure that British companies obtained a full and fair opportunity to compete in North Sea business. From that it has progressed to looking at ways for British industry to expand into other offshore areas elsewhere in the world. OSO now collects and evaluates information from round the world in order to advise on timing and scale of major offshore developments: the organizations which will make the key buying decisions; and the extent to which local business can cope and the consequent scope for intervention.

In the early days OSO obtained sound backing from Chris Chataway, Minister of State under Walker at the Department of Industry. After the fourth round of licences, government ministers made statements to the effect that orders placed with British companies would help when claims for future licences were made—one way of exerting pressure to buy British.

OSO developed slowly at first. Following the October war of 1973 and the three-day week, however, OSO found itself in the curious business of granting licences to firms in order to allow them to work a five-day week: they were allowed power for five days if they were engaged upon priority work for the North Sea. Since no one knew whether or not they qualified for such treatment, OSO found themselves seeking out companies to tell them they did qualify. This odd occupation enabled OSO to build up early some fascinating statistics relating to industry and the North Sea.

OSO began under difficult conditions: there was little knowledge of North Sea requirements or the timescale involved, and so OSO exhorted; unfortunately it did so when industry was in a confused state following the three-day week. The organization held seminars and brought in people from the oil companies or successful suppliers to describe North Sea needs and opportunities. It established representatives in the key industrial centres: the main areas of blue-collar employment related to the North Sea are in central Scotland and the Tyne-Tees area.

OSO now produces its own *Blue Book* which is a guide to its activities. In its first three years of publishing this report (1974–76) the British share of the offshore market increased from 25 per cent to 57 per cent. To judge OSO one has to ask how well British industry would have done in the North Sea had OSO not existed, and the answer is far from clear. First, it has been working in a largely new industrial sector and though OSO played an important part in alerting companies to North Sea opportunities, it is difficult to quantify this. Second, there are powerful political elements to contend with in offshore work; much of it is so large in scale that government will go to considerable lengths to secure projects for British firms when otherwise tenders might be won by foreign firms. Neither the French nor the Dutch are happy with OSO, which probably means it has succeeded in enabling British companies to get work that otherwise would have gone to industry in those countries.

In certain areas which were identified in the IMEG report, British industry has a long way to go before it becomes competitive, especially in such activities as pipe supply and rig hire where the Dutch tend to dominate the market. OSO has worked hard to improve the British rig hire record. Other sectors of British industry also have a poor record. BSC only began to look at subsea pipe tenders rather late in terms of North Sea developments. Should the huge gas-gathering pipelines project go ahead, the government would find it difficult, no matter how uncompetitive its tenders, to pass over BSC.

OSO is concerned with growing markets. In 1977 Britain won approximately 75 per cent of the inspection, maintenance and repair market, then worth £30 million. The size of this market will increase dramatically to around £300 million by the 1980s and one of OSO's tasks is to ensure that British industry keeps its high percentage of the whole. OSO's 1976 report showed the extent to which British industry was increasing its share of the offshore market. In 1974 this was 40 per cent; it increased to 52 per cent in 1975; and then to 57 per cent in 1976 for a total of £591 million worth of orders out of £1,041 million. There were considerable variations between sectors: the British share of offshore capital goods supply rose from 63 per cent in 1975 to 70 per cent in 1976, while that for the provision of services from only 41 per cent to 45 per cent.

OSO has five objectives: to ensure that British industry is given a fair and full opportunity in the North Sea; to help British industry identify needs and help offshore operators identify British companies that can meet their needs; to maintain pressure on firms to overcome delays in delivery; to promote new ventures that will supply the offshore market; and to assist British industry find new offshore outlets elsewhere in the world.

The North Sea market is worth something like £1,000 million a year and no British government could allow this to be lost to foreign companies. In the next few years the world offshore market will reach an annual value of £6,000 million; it would be a major indictment of British industry if, with the North Sea on her doorstep, it does not both obtain a major part of that market as well as capturing a fair slice of the remainder.

In order to maximize the share of British industry in North Sea developments, OSO has a secondary role of 'policeman' on the oil industry to see that companies try British industry first. Inevitably this means an element of blackmail. A great deal of oil business is government to government and, where appropriate, OSO advises about British industries which could meet oil company needs. This position gives it considerable power.

After identifying offshore opportunities for British companies and interrelated onshore projects, OSO advises and assists industry to respond to them. OSO aims to break into the closed circle of the oil companies on behalf of British business. The organization sponsors research and development proposals to the Offshore Energy Technology Board and works on the assumption that offshore technology will be a growth area for a long time to come. As Norman Smith, its industrial director, says, it is appropriate for the government to help research as 'otherwise new technology and technological leadership will continue to come from the established American companies'. This role of sponsoring research and development is of growing importance. Proposals submitted to OSO are subject to a number of criteria: relevance, necessity, novelty, credibility, exploitability, dependence upon support, Britain's competitiveness and the need for further work.

Although host countries are expected to go for their own equivalents of OSO, nonetheless opportunities to supply expertise and equipment will increase as the offshore market expands. When offshore business reaches an annual value of around £6,000 million as it is expected to do in the 1980s, with work off Brazil, Venezuela, Argentina, Mexico, India, Indonesia, Malaysia, West Australia, West Africa (Nigeria, Cameroon, Gabon, Angola), the Baltic, the Caspian and the Black Sea, expertise developed in the North Sea should have given sectors of British industry some commanding leads in this field.

OSO has a particular role to play in the development of overseas offshore business. It is establishing close contact with state oil corporations such as Pertamina in Indonesia or Petrobras in Brazil where there are major offshore possibilities. Its aim wherever practicable is to demonstrate British offshore capabilities. Since 1976, OSO representatives have visited a wide range of countries in this connexion.

OSO can be described as a group of corporate counsellors to industry. In its short life it has built up some formidable expertise and knowledge about North Sea operations. It believes that British offshore industry could outdo the Americans at deep sea efforts, and the huge 'software' market of offshore installations such as telecommunications should be a natural for British firms. Certain equipment such as turbines or pumps have long been provided by British industry anyway and Bookers, for example, claim that one of their pumps is to be found on most North Sea platforms.

Apart from the USA Britain now has the widest range of offshore expertise. A fact of additional importance to the British industry is that for political reasons Brazil and East European countries would prefer to buy British rather than American. OSO can only take industry so far; thereafter it is up to the companies.

One problem for OSO is the oil company blacklist. Thus when a major oil company talks of the inadequacies of industry, the latter feels it cannot answer back for fear of being blacklisted for future orders. There are the problems attached to dealings with the Americans and Europeans. In the USA the Jones Act and the Murphy Amendment protect American industry working in the Gulf of Mexico, and the EEC has suggested that OSO uses unfair tactics to help British industry at the expense of European rivals. The Canadians and Norwegians, however, are both considering establishing their own form of OSO, perhaps the best compliment that the organization has been paid.

The OSO works closely with the TUC. The unions back the 'full and fair opportunity' policy. In November 1975 there was a 'Memorandum of Understanding' between the Department of Energy and the UKOOA aimed at increasing the chances for British industry in the North Sea:

> Members of UKOOA have undertaken to give UK industry a full and fair opportunity to manufacture and supply the goods and provide the services necessary for the programme of exploration, field delineation and the development of a field and associated facilities to full production and beyond.

A code of practice was annexed to the memorandum.

When it returned to power in 1974, the Labour Party accepted the argument for OSO, put it in Scotland and quadrupled its size. OSO headquarters are in Glasgow and it has a branch in Aberdeen. It has a man in Whitehall, but is the only policy division of the Department of Energy which is not in London. Some of its senior members look askance at the political decision which sited OSO in Scotland when they have to spend so much of their time commuting to London. The Director General is Alan Blackshaw, better known to the public as a mountaineer. A number of businessmen have been drawn into OSO. The first Director General was Peter Gibson, formerly of ICI, while its present industrial director, Norman Smith, came to it from Baring Brothers. As he says, if other countries are annoyed at the activities of OSO, it must be making an impact.

PART THREE
Finance

9

City Operations: the Banks

North Sea oil has opened up a new range of financing activities for the City of London and produced forms of lending which cut across traditional methods, although they have been used in the American oil world for years. During the 1970s a number of British banks developed special oil sections to enable them to offer suitable expertise to the wide range of companies involved in the North Sea.

When BP developed its huge Forties field it already faced enormous cash commitments in Alaska; in order, therefore, to minimize the impact upon its balance sheet, it decided to raise a loan against the project itself: this meant the 'oil in place', a now familiar phrase in banking circles. After the Forties loan which might have set a pattern came the 1973 Middle East war, the fivefold increase in the price of oil and general inflation which between them raised doubts about future North Sea profitability. Then came the new Labour government which stated its intention of introducing participation and major oil taxes. A period of uncertainty followed until the government had actually spelt out its oil policy and this uncertainty produced financial hesitations.

Despite these problems two financial deals at this period broke new ground: that by the Thomson Organization to finance its share of the Piper field; and that by LASMO and SCOT (later merged) to raise £75 million loan stock to finance their share of Ninian development. Both deals represented 'firsts' in British oil financing.

Most small companies operating in the North Sea find their activities dominated by the problem of raising enough finance to cover their development commitments. Tricentrol, for example, had to obtain a guarantee from government to cover a loan for its share of Thistle development. The major factor in raising finance for oil is the risk involved; oil has always been regarded as a high risk business, though when it pays off it does so handsomely. Many of the financial risks encountered in the early days of opening up the North Sea have progressively lessened as more has been learnt about the area. The risk potential of particular ventures can now be more accurately gauged; it is still high.

Apart from risk there is the very high level of expenditure required for offshore oil production especially at the depths involved in the North Sea. It takes two to three months at a cost of up to £1·5 million to drill an exploration well. Rig hire is also a major cost item. One estimate suggests that over the next ten years the continuing cost of exploiting the North Sea will come to between £20,000 million and £40,000 million, while if the search goes north of latitude 62° and west of Rockall—that is, into really deep waters— costs could reach an astronomical figure in the region of £400,000 million. From a financial point of view money on this scale can be found; but only if the risks are properly evaluated.

North Sea investment has to be made sufficiently attractive to produce these large sums. According to the May 1977 issue of *The Banker*, $15 billion had been spent on North Sea development up to that time, of which $10 billion had been found by the major oil companies and $5 billion by the banks in which $2 billion was project finance. Traditionally the majors are self-financing. But the North Sea has absorbed up to 80 per cent of annual investment outlays by some companies. On the other hand, by the late 1970s and into the 1980s some of the majors will be reaping huge cash flows as a result of their earlier investments and so will be able to use this money to finance their next round of developments.

As City banking has got into its North Sea stride, it has encountered some major American influences since the American banks remain pre-eminent in the business of oil financing. Even so, half the oil money needed has been raised by British banks. The three main Scottish banks have each established an oil division and are now represented in the USA.

There are two groups of borrowers: the oil companies and the service companies. And there are a number of types of loan: corporate, project, special facility, leasing. Oil is of course highly political and with the size of the development projects involved—the giant platforms, the pipeline systems and quantities of steel required— foreign governments have provided export credits to their firms participating in North Sea developments. The result, for a time, was to place British firms at a disadvantage, since the North Sea was not overseas for them and they did not therefore qualify for comparable government assistance. In order to compensate British industry, the government created the Interest Relief Grant Scheme so that a company could qualify for assistance from this if it were to build a platform. Such assistance meant a 3 per cent reduction on 10 per cent interest charges on loans. An interesting balance of payments sideline arising out of North Sea developments has been that much of the money needed was raised in dollars, and much of this again was used to buy American goods, while the balance was converted into sterling at a time when the pound was falling.

Almost all North Sea development costs are front-loaded: that is, the investment has to be outlaid before any returns come from selling the oil. Some of the loans have so many participants and are so large that, as one banker says, 'the international banker putting together a financial package running into many millions, with complicated documentation, may take a year or longer'.

The scale of North Sea impact needs to be measured against the country's financial position as a whole. According to BP: 'It is estimated that the net resources generated and available to the U.K. economy in the period 1976–85 will be between £20 and £25 billion in 1976 £'s.' Of this return to the economy BP estimate that the government take will be approximately 83 per cent, while the balance of payments benefit over the same period is likely to amount to between £30 and £35 billion, again in 1976 pounds.

Estimating development costs is a complicated business. According to one oilman, for example, the cost worldwide of producing new oil—that is, the replacement cost per barrel—is $2·50; therefore, on the present North Sea tax basis, he argues that all profits have to go back into exploration. The cost per barrel can be worked out by dividing capital expenditure and operating costs by the total output over the expected life of the field. In *Political Economy of North Sea Oil*, the Mackays worked out the capital costs per barrel of four North Sea fields as follows: Argyll, $0·16; Auk, $0·88; Piper, $0·58; and Forties, $0·95.

The main items of expenditure are the platforms and pipelines. In 1975, for example, a semi-submersible rig cost £25 million to build and the daily operating cost to an oil company came to £30,000. According to Shell, their exploration and production activities in the North Sea cost £13 a second. A further unique aspect of North Sea operations is the fact that capital investment and production capacity has to be concentrated to an extraordinary extent into single engineering units—the huge platforms. So far the average capital costs for North Sea oil have worked out eight times as expensive as those for Middle East onshore oil. Another estimate suggests that the cost of a barrel at peak capacity flow is £1,400 to £1,500 for the North Sea, £900 for the Gulf of Mexico, £400 for Nigerian waters and £40 for the Middle East. What is certain is that the North Sea represents the most costly oil and gas producing area in the world. As BP says:

Production costs in the shallow accessible fields of Kuwait in 1975 averaged about 12¢ per barrel compared with some $3 per barrel for the North Sea. Each well in the North Sea presently costs about £3 million. The largest field in the UK sector—Brent—is estimated to cost about £2,900 million to develop.

National Westminster claimed that to the end of 1977 approximately one third of North Sea expenditure was raised from external sources. At the same time, according to BP, about '40% of capital costs are assumed to be incurred in foreign goods and services, priced in dollars'. It is because of these huge sums that oil companies regard a field of, say, 250 million barrels recoverable oil as marginal if it costs $400 million to develop; and according to Ivory and Sime, the Edinburgh financiers, it would not be much more profitable to develop than one which costs $1,000 million.

The rate of expenditure as a result of these costs has been on a scale that few oil companies have had to face before; for Britain it represents something like a 25 per cent increase in private capital expenditure. On present estimates the industry will invest about £1·7 billion a year in the North Sea between 1977 and 1983. By 1980, for example, Esso alone will have spent about £2,500 million and the industry as a whole about £12,000 million. What these cost and expenditure figures mean is that the City has to find enormous sums of money for each new North Sea development. The result has been new levels of financing and the introduction of a number of new techniques.

There are a variety of ways in which companies can raise the money they require. They can do so through an equity operation: the issue of shares, although this is expensive. Similarly bonds and debentures can be issued to obtain money from institutional sources. The amount to be raised in this way is limited by the size of the issuing company. Bank lending is the cheapest source of finance; a fair amount of North Sea capital has been found this way. Such money, however, is only available to 'acceptable credits' as the banks describe them. Cash can also be raised by leasing. The oil companies will frequently, if they can, produce the money required from their own profits. Some bankers now think that by the early 1980s there could be a world shortage of capital for oil developments. In Britain, at present, the government seems determined that major funds should be directed into oil.

So far Britain has produced between 30 and 35 per cent of the total finance needed for North Sea developments. Where the financing has been in sterling, British banks have been in the lead as, for example, in the sterling part of the Forties loan for BP; the Tricentrol loan of £60 million for Thistle; the ICI loan of £75 million for Ninian; or the Deminex loans of £75 million for Thistle and £12 million for Statfjord.

A great deal of money has been raised in the USA—apart from the funds of the American majors operating in the North Sea, which have come largely from their American or other world wide sources anyway. The sheer size of North Sea projects has forced companies to look to external financing. The European Investment Bank has shown great interest in oil developments, since these slot into its function of lending for projects of general interest to the EEC. Since 1973 the bank has lent 350 million units of account (£220 million) for North Sea projects that have included Sullom Voe and installations on Beryl, Frigg and Thistle. French banks have played a major part in providing funds for Elf and Total activities in the Frigg field; the German banks for the Ekofisk pipelines.

One City banker explained that had there been no North Sea but major developments off the shores of Brazil instead, it is highly unlikely that British banks would have come to play the kind of oil financing role which they now do. As it happened, the North Sea operation grew at a time when Britain was already involved in more and more foreign borrowing. Oil led to foreign capital inputs. As the North Sea was opened up, British banks also became involved in financing arrangements for the Dutch and Norwegian sectors as well as the British one. Through BP they were providing finances for its North Slope Alaska activities so that it was natural for them to look farther afield for other oil ventures such as those in Australia. Thus North Sea activity has provided a major impetus to get British banking involved in oil worldwide.

The steep rise in oil prices in 1973–74 favoured North Sea development—in the long run—since it brought income more into line with the rapidly escalating costs that were in any case occurring. The 1974 change of government meant also a change of attitude towards North Sea operators. During that year there was considerable oil company apprehension over prospects for individual fields. The British balance of payments strategy meant that the government was concerned about the pace of development and did not want it to flag behind in contributing to solving this problem. The government wanted to concentrate first upon a taxation framework for the North Sea, and while this was being devised some companies held back on further commitments to development. The government asked the Bank of England for help in putting a number of ingredients together to give the right weight to its taxation: it wanted to establish sensible parameters for a rate of return that would commend itself to an operator. This meant minimum government take while the operator was recovering his outlays; thereafter the rate of return was to come into full effect. There was uncertainty during this period as to whether enough finance for future North Sea activities would be forthcoming.

Government strategy was to involve the clearing banks in the process of finding the necessary finance for the North Sea. This meant some radical new thinking in banking circles, since oil developments required more than the conventional lending techniques. In fact, until the opening up of the North Sea the City had had little experience of project finance. One result of oil was to give the banks something of a private line to government, a development they welcomed. Like the oil companies, the banks were concerned about the effects upon their business of the various government policy decisions, such as the new PRT and participation.

In 1974 an informal working group was set up which included members of the Bank of England, the big five clearing banks, the three Scottish banks, the Department of Energy and the Treasury to look at ways of financing North Sea oil. There were at first two areas to talk about: Whitehall's interest—that there should be no shortfall of finance to keep the North Sea going; and the banks' interest—to identify and elaborate the obstacles to the provision of finance. Such obstacles, in the view of the banks, included especially government obstacles.

As this bank-government liaison got underway, the Department of Energy assembled information on a field by field basis to provide the facts for the Inland Revenue, which was then in the process of working out the taxation system. Thereafter it would be possible to establish the financing requirements of the North Sea so that the banks could play their part in meeting them.

The Bank of England invited the banks to build up a picture of their existing exposure both in the North Sea and in related offshore activities, though these latter activities mainly applied to the Scottish banks. In this way the Bank of England could monitor what was happening. As demand for finance for North Sea operations grew, cash availability was helped in the mid 1970s by the weakness of financial demand in other areas. Furthermore, non-British companies such as Esso have to find 70 per cent of their capital for development from abroad. They are also allowed to repatriate their current earnings.

A number of brokers have attempted to play a special role in the oil business but without achieving any major breakthroughs. Different banks have specialized in particular aspects of oil. The Scottish banks, for example, have been especially concerned with the service side of oil, an obvious role for them since most North Sea servicing activities are carried out from ports such as Aberdeen or Peterhead. National Westminster led BP's Forties loan; Barclays and the Bank of Scotland were instrumental in establishing the International Energy Bank (IEB). According to National Westminster in 1974:

The exploitation of North Sea oil is politically and economically highly desirable and there should, in consequence, be a good banking market for the syndication of loans for this purpose.

This followed.

One result of North Sea oil with its huge cash requirements was to make some of the banks aggressive in their pursuit of the business; there was a fairly rapid build-up of bank energy sections. According to National Westminster, the North Sea is indeed a bonanza and if owners of licences could keep the full proceeds of their discoveries it would make them immensely rich. Instead, the bank said,

> . . . a great proportion of the income will be retained for the benefit of the UK community generally, and not be the privilege of a few, or transmitted abroad for the enrichment of others.

Another point made by National Westminster about North Sea oil concerned British financial difficulties and loans from overseas:

> . . . and these friends are happy to assist the UK over its difficulties, but it is very doubtful if they would have been quite so forthcoming, had they not had the confidence that within a few years we should have a much stronger economy.

How much North Sea oil was mortgaged in the 1970s for international loans to the government will only become obvious during the next decade as repayments are made.

National Westminster's Terry Green, a key figure in oil banking, set out some of the factors that make North Sea oil an attractive lending proposition in a speech of October 1977: the industry is strategically essential and politically desirable; oil is an internationally saleable product and so not subject to the cyclical problems of any one country; if there is a two to three year expenditure period with a two to three year pay back period, this is better than almost any other industry which could call for comparable capital outlay; the industry is led by very large and successful multinational corporations which have proven ability and the muscle to see their projects through; the industry—worldwide—is still profitable. He went on to say that: 'the North Sea could be one of the best bankable situations available in what is generally a very gloomy market for lending money today'. This is the view of a major British bank now heavily involved in the oil business, although it was not first off the mark.

Banking expertise in oil is one of the many spin-offs to come from the North Sea. At the beginning of the 1970s the experts were the Americans: the Bank of America, Chase Manhattan (a major supplier of funds), Morgan Guaranty, Citibank; and from Texas the First National Bank in Dallas, the Republic National Bank of Dallas and the Texas Commerce Bank. Between them they possessed wide experience of lending on a project basis as also did the Royal Bank of Canada. The American banks were anxious enough to move into North Sea activities and of course had among their clients the American majors.

However, a wide range of British banks soon became involved in North Sea activities, the Scottish banks in particular. The Bank of Scotland became a founder of the IEB in which it holds 15 per cent of the stock, and has been a participant in almost all field development financing schemes. The Royal Bank of Scotland has specialized in the business of equipment leasing. The Clydesdale Bank has pursued business in the traditional banking sector as new yards, such as Nigg, have sprung up over Scotland. The Bank of Scotland was in fact one of the first British banks to see North Sea potential. It has built up the largest oil department of any European bank and invested in a number of technical people. It relies upon attracting business because of the special knowledge it can make available rather than its size. In a far-sighted move the bank took on as advisers a number of oilmen in 1972: they knew what was to be done when the bank was approached for finance. The bank now holds a 5 per cent equity in some fields. It was also the first bank to exhibit at the Offshore Technology Conference in Houston and the first to open a branch in that city. It claims to be the first British bank to see the importance of North Sea oil developments especially as they would affect Scotland. Its oil division now has fifteen members. To date it has participated in financing some of the biggest fields including Forties, Claymore, Ninian, Piper, Thistle. It holds equity in the Viking pipelaying barge and has as customers some of the new service companies such as Seaforth Maritime.

Of the major English banks, Barclays' oil interests grew rapidly following their participation in financing Forties and their help in setting up the IEB in 1973. Between 1973 and 1977 the bank was involved in a total of eighteen oil-financing operations which covered sixteen different companies and spanned seven fields. By July 1977 Barclays had a £375 million commitment to North Sea developments. Peter Lunn, one of the bank's general managers, said: 'The financing requirement is vast. We estimate that by 1980 the oil companies will have committed more than £20 thousand million, a major part from their own internally generated funds. But a number of companies will also be substantial borrowers. . . .'

Barclays set up its oil department in 1973. Its shareholding in the IEB (including its 35 per cent holding in the Bank of Scotland) comes to 22 per cent. The Group Oil Department regard the prospective borrower's partners and the size of the possible cost overruns as the key to any decision to lend. Barclays was the lead bank in the Tricentrol loan which was guaranteed by government. When mounting a loan the onus is on the lead bank (whichever that may be) to check the field; thus any bank in a loan group will look at the technical reports of the lead bank and its consultants. Barclays have their own petroleum engineer and their man, for example, would supervise any independent oil consultants engaged to check a field.

When a company strikes oil, the bank prefers to have a running dialogue with it about the eventual financing of the field as the appraisal is carried out, rather than simply receive a report when the appraisal is finished, followed by a demand for cash. Thus along the way the bank can discuss structures and how the financing can be arranged with the borrowers. It may then take three or four months to draft the documents covering the loan; sometimes it takes considerably longer.

Apart from National Westminster, Barclays is the leading English bank in North Sea developments. As it happened, when they became involved in oil, there was a low cash demand in the USA so that plenty of money was available for North Sea investment. This, however, could change in the future and then British banks would have to find a greater proportion of the money needed. The money is available both in Britain and elsewhere. Because lending rates were good during the period 1974–75, some banks are quite happy to let loans made at that time run their full course, so that they can continue to get better interest than is now possible. Other banks would prefer a quick return to release funds for new ventures.

The banks tend to regard North Sea money as a catalyst. The cash flow—rate of return—from the North Sea is enormous. Banks are wary of projects such as platforms, which they consider should either be fully insured or that covenants should be made with the borrowers to cover the possibility of a disaster. They will not take any risks in relation to such projects that the insurance companies will not take. The banks may consider that their approach to North Sea possibilities is well-balanced and they have a reasonably good relationship with the larger operators. On the other hand, one small operator without the muscle of the corporations said he found one of the Scottish banks lethargic and British banks generally backward in their approach to North Sea possibilities. He thought there had been a diminution in the pioneering instinct of the merchant bankers as well. Certainly his small company had experienced difficulty in raising the backing it required from the banks.

The merchant banks claim that the smaller companies have offered

7

a way into the North Sea for them. Kleinwort Benson have secured
a 2·5 per cent stake in Argyll and a smaller stake with others in two
of the fifth round blocks. Charterhouse Petroleum owns 1 per cent
of Ninian and 8 per cent of a block near Claymore which is to be
explored with Tricentrol. Morgan Grenfell have taken a leading role
in North Sea oil developments and have more general oil involvement
than other competing merchant banks. They were responsible for
syndicated loans for the Frigg field worth approximately £100
million; raised $12 million for American companies; and partici-
pated in the BP Forties loan. The oil and chemical sector is the largest
of ten sectors in industrial categories for which Morgan Grenfell
raise money; it represents about 8 per cent of their business. Their
total balance sheet as a merchant bank is about £1,000 million; the
bank's expertise lies in its ability to get a syndicate together. It will
then put in some of its own money.

Participation in oil financing depends upon the size of loan required: a loan in the region of $30 million to $40 million would be a
likely candidate for syndication by a merchant bank such as Morgan
Grenfell. If the figure required were $100 million or more, this would
require an involvement by all the banks. The big oil companies
syndicate their own loans and have their own experts.

Morgan Grenfell was responsible for the LASMO rights issue of
January 1976: in effect, how to finance 9 per cent of the Ninian field.
This was the first example of North Sea financing which was done
entirely in terms of taking 'oil in place' as collateral.

Bankers prefer to raise funds against company balance sheets of
the previous five years of a prospective borrower. If, however, a
company has a small interest in a field and no balance sheet to show,
then the bank requires a number of steps to be taken: first, a field
appraisal followed by a sensible development plan; then a match-up
of expenditure and income. The bank must be certain the operator is
competent and has good relations with the government. And further,
that all the other participants in the field are also capable of raising
their cash requirements so that the bank's own borrower will not be
forced into the position of picking up the liability of a defaulter as
well as his own. If a bank then lends in such circumstances it will
expect a return close to equity.

The closer banks put up to equity position the more they take. The
perceived risk in the North Sea as of 1977 was far less than in the
early days, so the banks had come to accept a lower return on loans.
If they are providing a loan for a big American oil company, they
expect to take $\frac{5}{8}$ per cent over LIBOR (London Inter-Bank Offer
Rate); for the LASMO £30 million operation through Williams &
Glyn's Bank in 1977 the charge was $2\frac{1}{4}$ per cent over LIBOR.

By 1977 it had become harder for a newcomer to raise finance for North Sea exploration purposes: because of risk there was a low limit on lending, while those who took the big risks had entered the business earlier. Further, by then the topside reward had become lower with the introduction of PRT and participation. In fact by 1977 North Sea oil had become a good risk—double or lose—as opposed to something like the tenfold possibility that it had been in the early days. It is now a business for equity money, say the bankers, although some of the small operators or companies would not agree: that is, for professionals and those with a cash flow who want to invest in ongoing exploration. There is no longer any opening for gamblers' money. In 1974 there was a gambler's chance, but since then the costs have gone up, the oil price has risen, the parameters are changing and the government has introduced its oil tax regime as well as participation. Moreover, government has become increasingly restrictive as to whom it will allow to take part in North Sea activities anyway.

The International Energy Bank was established to further North Sea developments. It is the creation of a consortium of banks: Barclays Bank International (15 per cent), Société Financière Européene (SFE Luxembourg) (20 per cent), Canadian Imperial Bank of Commerce (20 per cent), Banque Worms (10 per cent), Bank of Scotland (15 per cent) and Republic National Bank of Dallas (20 per cent). It came into being in September 1973 and has a staff possessed of technical skills in the energy field. It claims: 'Opportunities for finance in the energy field are abundant.' In its 1975 report the IEB stated:

> The mandate of this bank, originally outlined in 1973, has now been applied through two full years of operation. Its energy basis is adequately justified by the range of credits within our portfolio. IEB is now associated with medium-term investments including the most sophisticated oil field development finance, oil tied equipment, drillships, tankers, pipelines, energy and hard mineral extraction, nuclear fabrication, electrical generation and the provision of comprehensive finance to international state energy agencies.

The bank has an authorized capital of £20,000,000. In February 1976, for example, it structured and financed two North Sea loans to the value of $275,000,000.

One way in which money has been raised for North Sea operations is by putting together a syndicate. Thus in 1976 Charterhouse Japhet —for an undefined field or fields—put together an investment syndicate with institutions such as pension funds and assurance companies, each subscribing £1 million. Onshore—although this has mainly concerned Scotland—a number of companies have been created to speculate in land and development in areas, for example, where yards have been built. In Shetland came Norpoint, in Aberdeen and the northeast came Peterhead and Fraserburgh Estates, in Cromarty Firth appeared the Cromarty Firth Development Company. A great deal of land speculation and buying went on in these areas during the early 1970s. By March 1973 the Cromarty Firth Development Company had spent £3 million and purchased 3,500 acres. Some of the activities of these companies backfired upon them. They were often tactless, Scottish Labour MPs began asking awkward questions about them and the phrase 'the Edinburgh Mafia' did them no good.

It became clear early on that North Sea operations would break new ground. As a result competition grew up between the banks to be given responsibility for a small number of high risk—although well remunerated and publicized—financing ventures. Further, a number of companies such as Bishopsgate Offshore Services (London) or James Findlays (Glasgow) set themselves up in order to provide capital for small offshore business operations. One of the most successful such companies is North Sea Assets, an investment trust set up by the Edinburgh merchant bankers, Noble Grossart. It was launched in October 1972 with a capital of £20 million in order to provide institutional investors with an opportunity to participate in a specialist investment company, which would seek significant minority shareholdings in companies operating offshore and onshore in service and support sectors of the North Sea, and elsewhere. Its investment managers are Ivory and Sime. North Sea Assets has holdings in Northern Offshore which operates mini-submarines and submersibles for surveys, structural inspections and underwater work of all kinds. It also has a fifth share in the $100 million Viking pipelay barge. About 80 per cent of North Sea Assets funds come from major British institutions and the balance from some 200 individual investors. It was Scottish initiative which financed both the Viking pipelay barge and Ben Ocean Lancer—a dynamically positioned drilling ship—the only ones of their kind to be financed in Britain.

Another such company, Viking Resources International, was incorporated in July 1972:

> To provide a medium through which investors may participate in the growth of companies connected with the development of natural resources, particularly those of the North Sea, and other European offshore areas.

The long-term outlook for such companies is good since there is a supply-demand imbalance in oil as well as an artificial pricing structure. A key point made by this company is that the oil price will remain high 'as the responsible exporters seem prepared to cut production in periods of softening demand', which means OPEC.

As a result, oil companies have had more money to spend on capital projects and so have stepped up their exploration activities:

> This has encouraged the development of high cost areas, such as the North Sea where activity began in 1964, and has continued at a high level. In addition, the success rate in the North Sea has been consistently above the world average.

The North Sea is highly profitable for the oil companies both in relation to other areas and past history. Viking claim that 'Even for a field such as Argyll where there are problems of water flooding, and where the recoverable reserve estimates have been lowered, the rate of return is excellent.' The marginal oil fields, this company believes, will also yield a good return to the operators. They say: 'There is one major misconception about the North Sea which has to be dismissed: the capital cost of developing the fields is not increasing, but decreasing.' It has to be remembered that Viking Resources International is in the business to make money and their estimates are designed to attract investors. Their propositions are based upon an accurate appraisal of conditions.

No general rule can be applied to the vast operations mounted to finance North Sea development. Each field has a different technical history and a different set of companies responsible for it; these latter have different financial backgrounds and needs, so that the bankers have had to produce new criteria for every operation. Examples of half a dozen financing operations show wide variations. In 1972 BP borrowed $468 million and £180 million for nine years for its Forties field at a margin over LIBOR of $1\frac{1}{4}$ to $1\frac{1}{2}$ per cent from a financing syndicate of sixty-six banks, lead-managed by Lazards, Morgan Guaranty Trust and National Westminster. This was a limited recourse loan in a forward oil production agreement and represented the first example of North Sea project financing in which the banks agreed to take the resource risk of their being sufficient oil in place, and BP agreed to take all risks of recovery. It was a new exercise at that time both to the banks and to BP, although in fact it was 'off the balance sheet' because of BP's strength and the consequent certainty of completion.

In 1974, for the Piper Field, Occidental borrowed $150 million for nine years at a margin over LIBOR of $1\frac{1}{4}$ to $1\frac{1}{2}$ per cent from a syndicate of fifteen banks, lead-managed by Republic National Bank of Dallas and the IEB. This was a full recourse loan with optional conversion, although conversion of a proportion of the debt could only occur after certain levels of production and other criteria had been reached. The same two banks, with twenty other banks participating, also lead-managed another loan for Occidental in 1975 of $175 million for its Claymore operation. Again, that year, Occidental raised $30 million in the form of sinking fund notes on the Eurobond market.

In 1976 LASMO-SCOT raised £75 million for its Ninian operation: this was 14 per cent unsecured loan stock 1981–88 which was raised on the stock exchange together with 7·5 million oil production stock units, which entitle the holders to receive 8·75 per cent gross yield interest in net income from the field. Also in the case of the Ninian field, ICI arranged its own syndicate of ten banks to manage two loans of $100 million and £75 million for seven years; these were full recourse loans on the forward oil purchase agreement.

Tricentrol borrowed £60 million for its Thistle operation in 1976 for four years at $1\frac{1}{4}$ per cent over LIBOR from a financing syndicate of sixteen banks lead-managed by Rothschilds and Barclays. It was a full recourse loan to a third party guarantee with optional conversion. In this case the security during the development phase was provided by the Department of Energy guaranteeing the repayment of the loan by the end of 1980. The Department receives a minimum royalty of 5 per cent. If production and/or development delays are experienced and/or Tricentrol fails to meet its repayment targets, then the royalty can increase. Up to £30 million of the loan can be converted to a production payment, once production criteria are met.

The fifth round of licences is liable to produce a number of 'farm-ins'. Ten of the twenty-six members of Brindex—the small operators' association—are involved in consortia granted licences. Until 1975 the government was wary of farm-ins and licences changing hands, but it changed its mind so that the small operator could have a chance. Brae, a complicated field anyway and likely to prove expensive to develop, has seen a number of farm-ins and direct take-overs. Pan Ocean is the only minor company to discover a big field. Siebens Oil and Gas had an 8 per cent interest and sold half to Marathon in exchange for Marathon meeting all costs of development. As a result Siebens simply had a cash revenue equivalent to a 4 per cent share. Pan Ocean wanted someone else to become the operator—it would cost $1 billion—and Marathon again moved in to take over Pan Ocean for about $250 million. Also in the Brae field Bow Valley Industries held a 28 per cent interest—the second largest share. Then in February 1977 Louisiana Land & Exploration

Company and Ashland Oil farmed into Bow Valley's share providing the cash to meet its share of development costs.

It is the small exploration companies which are the customers for the banks: the difficulty from a banking point of view is that they are often insubstantial customers and there is also a great deal of ignorance and speculation. Small companies, so bankers claim, find the North Sea very difficult: the risks are high and the costs great. But it is when they find oil that their problems really start. This is the point when the majors come along to farm-in.

This may be true, yet one small operator complained (he prefers not to be named since he is still trying) that City thinking is arcane. He said the City would not provide development finance for a small consortium even if it had found oil and was offering the oil in place as its collateral.

When oil is found, the weaker members of a consortium, through the sale of partial interests in development or through the sale of royalty interest, raise the funds they require without disposing of their entire stake. It is likely that the big oil companies will increasingly become the bankers for the small companies. The alternatives facing most of the small companies are: to bring in government; to raise their own loans; to sell out to the big companies. Since oil has now started to flow in a big way, the majors will soon have available large funds for reinvestment purposes. In both the Thistle and Brae fields there were two consortia where the required spending was beyond the means of some of the members.

The most impressive of all the equity finance operations was the £75 million loan stock issue for LASMO-SCOT in 1976 (see chapter 10). A sizeable part of this loan stock was taken up by Scottish institutional investors. Thus LASMO (London & Scottish Marine Oil Company) and SCOT (Scottish Canadian Oil and Transportation Company) raised the money for their share of Ninian development costs by means of public issues of a new type of listed security. Within a year of its issue the stock stood at 308 pence when LASMO again went to the market for a further £30 million medium-term loan.

When an offshore project is presented to the City for finance there are a number of factors that have to be evaluated: the financial strength of the borrower; the level of oil reserves or the production profile of the field; future oil and gas prices; the project development plan; the consortium structure; the political environment; the legal system of the country where the loan is to be made; the condition of the financial markets. The art of financing is largely that of accurately evaluating risks. Since much North Sea finance has been raised in dollars, one of the problems for the lenders has been that if a failure does take place, would the banks then be in a position to control the extraction of the oil? This was something that had to be worked out with the Secretary of State for Energy. There are seven major categories of risk that the banks associate with North Sea financing. The first is the reservoir risk: here great technical resources and expertise can reduce the risk of estimation, but there can be problems in the difficult fields such as Argyll or Brae and the more difficult the geological structure, the greater the risk.

Second is the construction period risk when additional costs can occur. There may be capital losses that are wholly or partially uninsured (such as the Frigg jacket which sank while on tow and had cost between $70 million and $100 million to build). Or there can be delays on completion which affect the cash flow: according to the Department of Energy, between October 1973 and April 1975 development costs escalated at an annual rate of 80 per cent. Lenders will try to incorporate completion guarantees from the borrower in their loan-financing agreements.

Third is the consortium structure risk. There are risks attached to the competence of the operator: he may, for example, be changed as in the case of the Ninian field where Chevron took over from Burmah. Usually there are severe penalties for members of a consortium who do not meet their obligations.

Fourth is the product marketability risk: North Sea oil is expensive because of its development costs, and though it is at a premium for its low sulphur content and lightness, the City and indeed the British oil world generally has never quite overcome a lurking fear that OPEC could reduce prices at some future date and so undermine Britain's oil position.

Fifth is what bankers call the political-fiscal risk: this can come with a change of government and, for example, a subsequent alteration in the tax regime. Uncertainty still surrounds long-term government policy over refineries and depletion.

Sixth is the legal risk: problems can arise out of new legislation, or from fields that are outside territorial waters. To date, all agreements for lending have been built on *ad hoc* solutions to legal problems.

Finally there are unforeseen risks: *force majeure* and war.

The four main risks however are: the extent of the reserves; the commercial risk (will the product produce enough cash?); the operator (co-licensee risk); and the completion risk (the possibility of high cost overruns). When these risks have been evaluated, the type of financing operation to be adopted can be determined. To Shell, this was a loan against the balance sheet; to ICI, against corporate credit; to the Frigg consortium, against guarantees from the parent companies. The main financing structures are project loans, advance purchase of petroleum and public issues (of the LASMO type).

There can be mortgage loans secured on the project and its revenues; leases (not so far used in the North Sea) and only appropriate if a field is 100 per cent owned by one company. Throughput—take or pay contracts—is the method used for pipeline financing. On advance payments in lieu of oil in place, the repayment will be geared to the receipt of a percentage of the take.

The simplest of these various forms of financing is a loan directly geared to a company's balance sheet; however, when the sums involved run to hundreds of millions, this is only possible with the largest companies. Throughput loans are geared to a pipeline: the banks will lend for its construction against the assurance that a minimum amount of oil will pass through the pipeline at an agreed price so as to meet scheduled repayments. Project financing can use both this method and buying the end product when the oil comes on stream.

In one case Chevron, operator of the Ninian field, which has the biggest North Sea consortium, guaranteed a syndicated bank loan of $120 million to Ranger Oil in return for which Chevron was to take an 8 per cent royalty on Ranger's 5 per cent take of the field. In the case of two giants, Shell and Esso, they plan to finance the bulk of the development of their Auk, Cormorant and Tern fields with the cash flow from their huge Brent field.

Project loans are among the most widely used to finance North Sea activities. The loans are geared to expenditure and repayment is geared to anticipated receipts; they include an allowance for delays which are a common factor in North Sea operations. In fact payment depends upon recoverable oil, and in most cases the producer probably has no assets other than his interest in a field, while there are unlikely to be any guarantees available. Normally banks require an undertaking from a parent company that a subsidiary will carry out its covenants.

As a rule agreements are highly complex, since companies want to ensure that if there is no oil, or no oil forthcoming, they will not be regarded as in default. As a result there are substantial risks to banks including the possibility of damage to platforms which are a prerequisite for the oil being brought out. Project loans represent a radical departure for British banks. They may be of several kinds: the banks may lend a corporation the money it requires against its balance sheet. Then there may be indirect recourse to balance sheets: in such a case the 'full faith and credit' of the borrower are involved, but the credit is indirectly secured and there is no specific charge on

7*

the project as security. This was the case with ICI's Ninian loans. Thirdly there is convertible lending, when an opportunity is given for the borrower to convert part of his 'full faith and credit' loan to a loan secured on the project itself. This was the case with Occidental's Piper and Claymore loans and Tricentrol's Thistle loan. In such instances the banks will take over a part of the risk once development is complete and a substantial production has been achieved.

There is also limited resource finance: that is, a loan is made available—even during the development stage—only on the oil to come. The banks were prepared to do this with BP for Forties and Thomson for Piper because of the very high quality of the fields. There are unsecured loans: LASMO's stock for Ninian, an issue made direct to the public, falls into this category. And finally there is farming-in—the selling of all or part of its interest in a field by a small company to a large one. This, so far, has been less common in the North Sea than in the USA, since permission to transfer licences has to be obtained from the Department of Energy; but it has occurred, for example, when Deminex obtained 41 per cent of Thistle by buying in to United Canso and Chaplin.

Roughly, it will take ten years to pay off an investment: that is, from the start of the development stage (but after exploration) until the loan is repaid. This, for example, will be the case with Brent. A major such as Shell or BP will use the cash flow from its first field in operation to develop a second field and so on.

As of 17 August 1977, the London Clearing Banks had extended total facilities to the tune of £600,382,000 and $1,203,128,000. At the same time the Scottish clearing banks had extended total facilities to £47,313,000 and $154,000,000. The Accepting Houses, other British Banks and Consortium Banks (excluding the subsidiaries of the Clearing Banks) had extended facilities to £74,772,000 and $219,389,000; American banks to £304,255,000 and $1,692,460,000; and other overseas banks to £131,527,000 and $769,551,000. At that date, the total facilities from all banking sources extended for North Sea operations came to £1,158,249,000 and $4,039,028,000.

Perhaps nothing could so drive home the effects of North Sea oil upon the British economy generally, or the City and financial world in particular, than the way in which by the late 1970s share prices and City reactions were increasingly geared to oil operations. Constant speculation about tax cuts, the effects upon other aspects of industry or upon the balance of payments followed each oil move while the returns of the majors had an instant impact—'cheer or gloom'—upon City calculations. And, of course, oil was responsible for the decision to float the pound in 1977.

There are two myths about North Sea oil: that as capital costs rise, so the business becomes less profitable; and that because of PRT the profitability of a high yield field is as good as that of a low one. Although costs have been vast and borrowing on a huge scale, Forties had been paid back by the end of 1977 ,Thistle will have been paid back eighteen months from January 1978, and Argyll in little more than a year.

Money was and is being pumped into the North Sea because it pays—and pays handsomely. This simple fact of attraction should raise some awkward questions about any so-called regeneration policies: will money pumped into an industry which is in any case in trouble make much difference? As long as oil is at a premium, North Sea investments will pay off and finance for the companies will be forthcoming.

10

Newcomers to Oil: Insurance

The North Sea bonanza has attracted such a wide range of interests that companies not normally associated with oil have become involved and new companies established in order to take part in the oil boom. P & O, a name normally associated with shipping although it does have Middle East and American oil interests, has become engaged in North Sea exploration through its membership of several consortia, such as the MESA group. Further as an established company with sea repair experience it has gone in for North Sea support work and operates a huge service base at Montrose.

Although ICI uses petroleum products for its petrochemical operations, it is again a name not normally associated with oil though it has had petrol station outlets in the northeast for years. In the early days of oil excitement, however, ICI, as one of its executives put it, went for 'a flutter' of £1 million a year in the North Sea. It was a flutter that paid off handsomely.

ICI has in any case benefited from the North Sea in other ways, earning something between £1 million and £2 million a year, for example from the supply of explosives for North Sea operations. Far more important is its 16 per cent holding in the Ninian field. Though ICI sells petrol, this has always been strictly a by-product of its petrochemical business. In 1974 the consortium of which it was a member made its rich Ninian discovery. Altogether ICI estimates that it will have to spend about £235 million for its share of Ninian development and up to the end of 1976 had already spent £73 million on the field. As another by-product of its North Sea involvement, ICI sanctioned £50 million for oil concessions, exploration and development in the USA. The firm's petrochemicals division is one of the world's largest so that ICI is a huge customer for oil anyway, and it made sense for it to have its own equity holdings in a field.

Thus P & O and ICI, major British companies associated in the public mind with activities other than the production of oil, both decided to go for an actual holding in the North Sea, while both are also taking part in aspects of the service and supply industry.

A quite different profession that has substantially expanded as a result of North Sea developments is insurance. There are five Lloyd's syndicates and the Indemnity Marine (part of the Commercial Union) dealing with oil which together form the London Drilling Rig Committee; these six underwriters are the leaders of what is known as the Master Rig Cover.

The huge costs involved in North Sea operations—the rigs, platforms and modules, and the complicated business of 'spudding in' these monsters—mean a risk area where the demands for insurance run to millions of pounds a year. Capacity to cover platforms, which was of great concern, has now risen remarkably and amounts of up to $700 million can be placed, although this is still not enough to cover a $1,000 million platform. Insurance capacity has expanded faster than thought.

At present, insurance cover for the first three phases will normally be provided as a single policy: that is, construction of the rig onshore (fabrication), the tow-out to position (tow-out) and the putting into place (installation). There can be discussion as to when installation ends: usually that will be at the spudding in of the first well. Then, when production begins, the fourth phase of insurance—for the rig in position—will come into being.

As a rule during construction a single insurance package will be arranged by the operator of a field who will take the responsibility for this on behalf of his partners. Sometimes a consortium of brokers will cover a consortium of oil companies. Insurance brokers will be approached to arrange cover for a particular operation. If it is a major platform, for example, then one underwriter might take up to 5 per cent of the risk. Each aspect of the insurance of a huge operation such as putting a platform in place may be rated separately and then packaged to become a single premium—tow-out will differ from construction and so on. One field installation insured for £90 million carries an annual premium of £900,000, but $1\frac{1}{2}$ per cent to $1\frac{3}{4}$ per cent is more normal and cover will often attract nearly 2 per cent.

The London Master Rig Cover, which is led by six underwriters, had over a hundred separate insurers in 1977. This number of insurers under the master rig may change each year; at the beginning of a year, however, the underwriter agrees to take a share which might range from 1 per cent to say 5 per cent, but whatever they agree is accepted for the entire year and binds any business that comes in that percentage proportion. When the agreement comes round for renewal, they may increase or decrease the percentage they want to take on or drop out altogether. In effect this master rig covers the world. Although, in 1977, there were over 100 insurers, these in turn are extensively reinsured so that the total number of insurers involved would be much higher with few if any reputable insurance companies anywhere in the world not having some part of the risk.

OIL (Oil Insurance Limited) represents a complication for the insurance world. In 1972 a number of middle level oil companies set up OIL of Bermuda. These companies, which were mostly American, considered that the insurance market was reluctant to grant pollution cover and was too expensive, so OIL was formed as a mutual. OIL's members have to give five years' notice to quit and they each pay an annual premium on the basis of turnover. OIL covers physical damage on and offshore from oil refineries to pipelines and structures; the cost of controlling blow-out pollution liabilities and clean-up. The limit for any occurrence is $100 million, to be shared between the members. In the case of the Ekofisk blow-out, for example, 85 per cent of the members of the consortium were members of OIL and so Ekofisk cost commercial insurers under $10 million. The insurance market tends to charge higher premiums than OIL but comparison is complicated.

The 1977 limit of the Master Rig Cover is $400 million. Such a limit would be for a single separate structure and certain related interests up to that total; thereafter extra cover may be obtained but outside the Master Rig Cover. In the event of a claim, it would either be all the $400 million first and thereafter from the extra cover up to the limit, or, depending upon how the insurance had been arranged, a claim could be on a pro-rata basis against both the Master Rig Cover and the extra cover.

Customarily the Master Rig Limit is for each structure on a field although two such structures might be deemed to be connected, as is the case on Frigg where two platforms are exceptionally close together. Once a Master Rig Cover insurance has been made, the insurers will reinsure round the world so that the ramifications of one major cover policy can be enormous. For example, if the 100 syndicates or company groups which make up the Master Rig Cover were broken down into the companies or partners belonging to each one, there would be a total of some hundreds of insurance companies and thousands of Lloyd's members involved altogether.

The six brokers who combined to place the Master Rig Cover which is now a key to North Sea insurance are Bland Payne, Sedgwick Forbes, C. T. Bowring, Bain Dawes, Stewart Wrightson and Willis Faber. At present North Sea insurance comes to about $200 million a year—a sizeable new slice of business for the City. A breakdown of North Sea premiums might show that approximately 50 per cent are with the Master Rig Cover, 30 per cent with OIL, and the remaining 20 per cent have been placed elsewhere round the world. This latter category would include self-insurance, done mainly by the large oil companies.

In practice an insurer could take 0·35 per cent of a cover and then reinsure with other smaller companies but the first company—taking the 0·35 per cent—is in the 'front line' and remains fully liable if, for example, one of his reinsurers goes bankrupt.

There are separate London placings by the big companies such as BP, Shell, Esso or Elf which would be of significant additional premiums to the market. Many North Sea oil majors are part self-insured, but most buy cover in respect of platforms. This is not possible for new or smaller companies in the North Sea. For purposes of comparison Lloyd's Marine premium income was £604 million in 1974, while in 1976 it included perhaps $200 million of North Sea and other offshore oil premiums.

A key role is played in the insurance business by classification societies; there are twenty of these round the world. Lloyd's Register have roughly 800 surveyors for ships and every four years a ship has to be given a major classification survey. Then the surveyors will say whether it can keep its class or what needs to be done. The Department of Energy now demands that a rig or platform be classified. Underwriters also employ technical experts to inspect and authorize towage arrangements both for mobile drilling equipment such as jack-ups or semi-submersibles and also for towages and lifting arrangements during the construction phase.

One group of specialists in this line are Noble Denton Associates: effectively they carry out the functions of an engineering department for the insurer. Noble Denton have about eighty salvage-towage experts.

The Department of Energy has laid down minimum safety requirements for platforms and co-opted certain classification societies and others to work as its agents as certifying authorities. The Department has approved eight such societies to work for it; one is Lloyd's Register. In fact, this is an area in which the Norwegians were quicker off the mark than Lloyd's Register and, for example, Det Norske Veritas is responsible for a larger total of platforms.

The extent of oil's impact upon insurance can be gauged by the fact that at present a typical Lloyd's marine underwriter could find that between 5 and 10 per cent of his premiums are derived from North Sea activities. Insurance can be arranged for any of the risks arising out of the energy programme: yard fabrication, transportation of structures, offshore installation, equipment, political risks, costs of control of gas or oil blow-outs and consequential losses as a result of accidents.

A typical company of City-based insurance brokers, Bain Dawes, have a specialist team in energy, handling premiums of £300 million in all annually, and the team includes companies and departments capable of providing every facet of cover required by the energy industry. They are, of course, deeply involved in the North Sea.

Offshore insurance is now big business; the profession has constantly to deal with casualties to oil rigs and platforms, fires, platforms sinking, collisions with supply vessels, cranesnaps, blow-outs, fatalities to divers and so on. North Sea activity is still in its early days and many of the risks that are likely to increase with the age of platforms have yet to be fully identified. Even so the cover now provided is very wide and effectively deals with every aspect of North Sea work and the equipment being used.

Two newcomers to the North Sea as oil companies, LASMO and Thomson, are both especially interesting because of the different ways in which they became involved and the methods they used to raise large sums of capital to cover their field development commitments. Both may be described as highly successful.

The London & Scottish Marine Oil Company came into being as a result of a visit to Britain in the early 1960s by the President of the Canadian company, Ranger Oil; he was attracted by the prospects for the UK Continental Shelf and interested in extending his oil activities outside Canada. During the 1960s Ranger tried unsuccessfully to obtain a licence for North Sea production; by 1969 it had become clear that Ranger's chances would be greatly increased if it took on a British partner. At the same time it had also become obvious that there were British investors anxious to subscribe for North Sea exploration.

One result was the formation in January 1970 by Cazenove & Co. of the Scottish Canadian Oil & Transportation Company Limited, whose shareholders were mainly British insurance companies and investment trusts. Subsequently, in association with Ranger Oil, SCOT was granted three exploration and production licences for the North Sea; by 1975 SCOT's total issued capital came to £5·4 million.

In April 1971 LASMO was incorporated for identical purposes to SCOT, since the same shareholders were prepared to put up additional money for North Sea activities. As a result some of the SCOT shareholders who wanted to venture further with other newcomers formed LASMO. In 1972 LASMO, also in association with Ranger Oil, was granted three licences to explore for oil and gas and, developing along parallel lines to SCOT, LASMO had a total issued capital of £7·4 million by the end of 1975.

In January 1974 oil was discovered in Block 3/8 (which now turns out to be 30 per cent of the Ninian field) in which both companies—SCOT and LASMO—had a share. BP held 50 per cent, Ranger UK 20 per cent, LASMO 15½ per cent, SCOT 7 per cent and two smaller companies—Cawoods Holdings Ltd and National Carbonising Co. Ltd—3¾ per cent each. Ninian extended into the neighbouring block 3/3.

The significance of the find to the two companies was that development of the field was going to cost in excess of £1,000 million and they would soon be called upon to provide their share. LASMO and SCOT in combination represented just over £12 million of capital and they had no other resources apart from their shareholders. They had little chance of raising the sort of loans that would be made available to major oil companies.

Moreover, when the decision to develop Ninian was taken in May 1974, Britain was recovering from the three-day week, the economic situation was depressed and the minimum lending rate then stood at 12 per cent. Further, at that time no oil field in the deep northern waters had yet been developed, so that risks and production problems for Ninian were difficult to assess. And the country was just entering a period of uncertainty as to the government's North Sea policy which was to last until the tax regime had been announced as well as the government's intentions over participation. None of these facts made major borrowing easy for a small new company with minimum assets.

At first, all the participants in the Ninian consortium explored whether they could raise the finance they needed on a joint basis; but after two years investigation this possibility fell through. A joint agreement could not be worked out because of the differing financial needs and ratings of the participants. Meanwhile the members of the consortium had been obliged to put up money as they went along to meet the operator's cash calls.

The Ranger Group, including LASMO and SCOT, then tried to obtain a loan syndicated through the Royal Bank of Canada, but in the end the bank withdrew from the operation because of the risks and political uncertainties that existed at the time. Next the group tried to find a guarantor from among would-be purchasers of its oil, but no guarantee was forthcoming that would not take, as part of the price, an equity interest in the field and this the group were unwilling to concede.

By early 1975 both LASMO and SCOT had exhausted their cash resources; both kept going by floating a short-term unsecured loan followed by £12 million Floating Rate Unsecured Loan Stock which was privately placed and subscribed mainly by their shareholders. This £12 million was due to be repaid by 31 December 1975, at which time it was hoped a long-term financing arrangement could have been completed.

During this difficult period, it was felt that LASMO would be strengthened if the interests of Cawoods Holdings and National Carbonising in Ninian could be acquired for LASMO shares and this was done in July 1975. At that time LASMO and SCOT appointed Morgan Grenfell as their financial advisers and commissioned them to find the money they needed. Part of the difficulty at this time was that government had still not stated its terms of participation. In October 1975, for example, the two companies almost concluded a participation agreement with the Department of Energy whereby for 51 per cent the state would provide that equivalent of financing; but government then decided that participation should be through rights and options to buy oil and not through a financial contribution to a field. So LASMO decided that it had to raise all the funds needed for its share of Ninian and enough over to enable the company to continue exploration elsewhere in the North Sea while Ninian was being developed.

LASMO had less than three months in which to find the money before its loan stock became due for repayment; there was intense activity in the City and during this operation LASMO had to go to its shareholders and ask for an extension of the loan for a further three months into 1976. The operation had developed into something of a cliff-hanger.

The eventual plan that the companies, Morgan Grenfell and their brokers, Cazenove & Co., came up with had to take account of the fact that they would need £100 million or more for their development share of Ninian, although exact forecasting was not then practicable. They had to attract to their support shareholders other than those they had already; and the whole package had to be arranged at extraordinary speed. It was decided to make a two-part offer: firstly of Loan Stock and secondly of Oil Production Stock (OPS); successful applicants for Loan Stock were given preference in the allotment of OPS to a maximum of ten units for every £100 of Loan Stock.

It was decided to raise £75 million this way; the issue covered both LASMO and SCOT and a combined prospectus of 30 January 1976 presented the issue which consisted of £75 million 14 per cent Unsecured Loan Stock 1981/83 at a price of £100 per cent and 7.5 million units of Oil Production Stock at 10 pence each. The issue, a first for North Sea operations, was considered a success by the City. There were 11,319 applicants for a total of £87,285,000 Loan Stock and 11,619,255 units of OPS. As a result of this operation LASMO could pay off the Floating Rate Loan Stock at the end of February 1976.

LASMO and SCOT then decided to merge; as far as Ninian and

this financial operation were concerned, they had in any case been acting as one, and the merger took place in January 1977 on the basis of four LASMO shares being offered for every seven SCOT shares.

Consolidation of LASMO's position took place during 1977. It was necessary to obtain a listing for LASMO shares, but under Stock Exchange regulations a part of the share capital had to be offered to the public. It was not, however, deemed advisable to do this until LASMO's entire share of Ninian development had been fully covered and only £75 million had then been raised; a further £30 million was required. LASMO had also been advised that neither a public offer nor further Ninian financing could be raised until the first Ninian platform was in place and LASMO had made satisfactory arrangements for the sale of its oil. The middle period of 1977, therefore, became an exceptionally busy one for the newly merged company.

During May and June 1977 the first Ninian platform was towed out and put in place and while this was being done, LASMO concluded agreements for the sale of its oil which satisfied the bankers. As a result of these two operations, Williams & Glyn's Bank was able to form a consortium of banks to provide a further cash facility of £30 million for the balance of LASMO's Ninian expenditure. The bank also provided the company with overdraft facilities of £5 million to cover any overrun expenditure. That July, Morgan Grenfell put on offer 8,500,000 LASMO Ordinary Shares of 25 pence each at 155 pence per share: of these 6,600,000 were new shares acquired by Morgan Grenfell from the company while the balance came from the existing shareholders. The Stock Exchange had required a minimum of 8·5 million shares to be offered to the public. LASMO had set 6·6 million new shares as the number needed to raise further funds for exploration. The offer was over subscribed ten times.

The LASMO story showed how well a small newcomer to the North Sea could do with sufficient determination when it had almost no capital and was obliged to work against time in a particularly difficult period of financial uncertainty, exacerbated by political uncertainties as well. In this case the North Sea gave birth to a new company: in the few years of its existence the company had a merger, was extensively changed and rationalized and mounted a most daring and successful City share floating operation. Now, apart from its share in the huge Ninian field, LASMO is an oil company with prospects and possibilities in the North Sea and elsewhere.

A second, very different story, belongs to The Thomson Organisation (TTO). At the beginning of the 1970s, no one would have associated

Thomson's Newspapers and Publishing (the owners of *The Times* and *Sunday Times* as well as a host of provincial newspapers) with North Sea oil. Yet by 1977 the City was showing irritability when the half-yearly figures for the Organisation were published, because these did not as yet show the huge expected profits from the North Sea— and by then everyone claimed to have done their calculations as to how much money the Organisation should make from its investments in the Piper and Claymore fields.

Thomson have a 20 per cent interest in the Occidental Consortium which at present has licences for seven North Sea blocks that include the Piper and Claymore fields. Piper came on stream in December 1976 and by mid 1977 was producing 250,000 b/d. On re-appraisal, ministerial approval was given during the second half of the year for production to be increased to a level of 300,000 b/d, a figure that was expected to be reached early in 1978.

Piper crude sells at about $13·50 a barrel, which is the lower price scale for North Sea oil since it is heavier and contains a higher sulphur content than other North Sea crudes. The upper price is about $14 a barrel. A rough calculation based upon a production of 250,000 b/d selling at $13·50 a barrel works out as follows: a government royalty at well-head price of $12\frac{1}{2}$ per cent ($1·69 a barrel) reducing the take to $11·81; production costs including interest and other charges (about $1·81), leaving $10; depreciation (total capital cost divided by recoverable field reserves) $1·30, leaving $8·70; tax at 70 per cent (a combination of PRT at 45 per cent and corporation tax at 52 per cent) on $8·70 would leave a final figure of $2·60 a barrel which represents profit to the Consortium. Thomson's share of this—250,000 × 20% × $2·60, or 52¢ a barrel—gives the company an approximate daily profit of $130,000. This will fluctuate according to oil flow, the prevailing price of oil at the well-head and changes in production costs. With Claymore coming into production at the end of 1977 and Piper production being increased to 300,000 b/d, the City estimated that Thomson post-tax profits for 1979 would be in excess of £50 million. This is big money by any standards.

Thomson's undoubtedly had luck. They were not the first choice of partner to be approached by Occidental; indeed, two other groups, who in terms of their apparently dynamic reputation might have been expected to leap at the chance, turned it down. Occidental Petroleum had only come on to the international oil scene in 1966 when it became involved in Libya. At the beginning of the 1970s its creator, Dr Armand Hammer, was being investigated by a Congressional Committee—nothing subsequently came of this—but the the fact of the investigation deterred Ivory and Sime, the Edinburgh financiers, from accepting an invitation to join the group. Slater

Walker were then approached and they too decided against North Sea oil ventures. Had they gone in with Occidental, the whole Slater-Walker saga might have turned out very differently.

Thomson's were then approached and, surprisingly perhaps for a newspaper empire, said yes. That decision, however, had to be backed up by money on a scale that the Organisation simply did not command. The other members of the Consortium—Occidental itself (36·5 per cent), Getty Oil (23·5 per cent) and Allied Chemical (20 per cent)—controlled financial resources that dwarfed anything that Thomson (20 per cent) could produce. Moreover, Lord Thomson determined that however the Organisation did become involved, it would not do so by using its publishing side as collateral for any North Sea venture. Effectively, this decision meant that Thomson's had to raise large sums of money on the strength of its share of oil to come.

When Thomson joined the Occidental Consortium in March 1971, it had no oil experience of any kind. TTO did not see the high risks of North Sea activity as something it could carry against its newspaper interests, especially as it already had a high debt-equity ratio and profits from the Organisation as a whole went in part to carry losses on *The Times*. In order to take part in the consortium, therefore, the Thomson family decided to put its interest in Thomson Scottish Associates (TSA), a family company which holds 66 per cent of TTO equity, whose cash flow came from TTO dividends. From the start TSA gave to TTO the option to buy 90 per cent of its oil interests at cost.

Thomson made certain decisions at the start of the association about their participation in the consortium which were to be crucial to the way TSA subsequently operated. The company decided not simply to be a silent partner, but to develop a capability as a producer of petroleum and seek a long-term involvement in the industry, maximizing its contribution within the consortium. Having determined not to put the newspaper empire at risk, finance had to be found from sources other than TTO. At the same time, it was necessary to limit Thomson family exposure and not allow its resources to be overcommitted. In what was rapidly becoming a feverish atmosphere of boom and risk in the North Sea, these were likely to prove difficult objectives to maintain. What eventually was done proved to be unique in the story of North Sea oil financing.

At first there was little requirement for Thomson to put up much money as its other partners were prepared to do 'a carry' to a limited extent—a usual enough procedure in the oil world. The consortium, however, was blessed with early luck: after two wells had been drilled the third one led to the discovery of the Piper field.

It was agreed early in 1973, while delineation of the Piper field was still in progress, that the consortium would have to construct a terminal in the Orkneys, a 135-mile 30-inch pipeline and a platform in 470 feet of water (then the deepest undertaken) as well as drill a total of thirty-six production and injection wells. The budget for this programme was set at $350 million of which $60 million was to be the Thomson share. Thus, urgently, TSA had to find what (to it) were very large sums of money.

In the early 1970s, the British partner was essential to the consortium and the role to be played by its chairman, Alastair Dunnett (former editor of *The Scotsman* and a dedicated Scot himself), was to be crucial to those decisions which impinged upon Scottish interests as, for example, the terminal at Flotta in the Orkneys. The development went ahead remarkably swiftly: the pipeline was laid in 1974, the platform put in place during 1975 and Piper went into production in December 1976. By mid 1977 Piper was producing 250,000 b/d, although an enhancement project will raise production to 300,000 b/d as well as increase the rate of gas recovery. Recoverable field reserves were upgraded in 1977 to a figure of 695,000,000 barrels. It has to be recalled that when Piper was discovered, the price of crude oil stood at $3·60 per barrel, as opposed to current prices of between $13·50 and $14 per barrel.

Then Claymore, a more complicated field in structural terms, was discovered in mid 1974 twenty miles south of the Piper field in 370 feet of water. In this case there was to be a platform capable of handling thirty-six wells: an 8-mile 30-inch link line to the Piper pipeline; a gas line from Piper to the Claymore platform to transfer surplus Piper gas to enhance Claymore recovery and to provide fuel gas. And the terminal facilities being developed at Flotta had to be increased to take Claymore production as well. When the decision was made to develop Claymore, the Thomson share of costs was estimated to be $75 million.

The way Thomson raised the finance for its Piper and Claymore commitments set a precedent in the North Sea and the oil world. In the dry language of bankers, Thomson Scottish Associates obtained a limited recourse loan of $100 million from a financing syndicate of twelve banks in October 1974:

> The banks accepted the oil in place and other risks as the basis of the credit facility. Thomson were committed to inject a certain amount of subordinated finance. In addition to the interest margin (the loan was for nine years with interest at a margin over LIBOR), the banks receive a $2\frac{1}{2}$% royalty on Thomson's share of the first 642 million barrels produced.

But before this position had been achieved, a great deal of searching had gone on. The financial mastermind of the Thomson fund-seeking operation was their financial director, Michael Brown. He clearly delighted in finding resources on this scale and ensuring that Thomson could continue in the major oil stakes. Now, with its 20 per cent interest in Piper and Claymore, that is considerably easier than it was when they started.

The other partners were not searching for finance; Allied Chemical and Getty were big enough to carry their share of development costs and Occidental had the strength to command the loans it might need without great trouble. Thomson, therefore, needed to raise its share of the finance in a hurry.

Having already decided that the public company could not be asked to take the oil risks, although the private family companies were prepared to do so, the first thing that Thomson did—derided at the time by their advisers as unnecessary and excessively cautious—was to aim at raising double their estimated share of production costs, since they were certain that overspend would be inevitable. This meant finding a loan of $120 million instead of $60 million.

The company rapidly investigated a number of possibilities: raising equity for the oil companies (Thomson Scottish Petroleum and Thomson North Sea Limited) which are oil subsidiaries of Thomson Scottish Associates; supplying crude oil to oil companies in return for finance; obtaining leasing finance from institutions; or getting one of the partners to carry Thomson, although this would have reduced Thomson to the status of an investor with little influence upon the consortium and with no incentive to develop as an oil company in its own right.

Various banks were approached, Thomson's fundamental position being the desire to obtain non-recourse finance: that is, the lenders would only be able to obtain repayment of their loan against Thomson's take of the oil from the Piper and (later) the Claymore fields, and not against any other Thomson assets.

While seeking finance, Thomson made plain that it was after $120 million for Piper, and though consultants advised that even with catastrophic additional costs they would not need more than $90 million, in fact all the sum and more had been spent by late 1977 and Thomson's super-caution proved more than justified.

One of the last attempts to raise the money before a solution was found was through a major British bank; but this fell through at that stage possibly because neither Thomson nor the bank had enough oil experience and their timescale was not quick enough.

Eventually Thomson obtained finance from a consortium of banks headed by the Republic National Bank of Dallas (RNBD) and the

International Energy Bank (IEB). When RNBD and IEB had made their own assessments of Piper reserves, they agreed to a loan to Thomson Scottish Associates as follows: TSA first had to provide a front end of $20 million for development costs; RNBD and IEB would then provide a non-recourse loan of $100 million against Thomson's share of oil in place in Piper; and Thomson agreed if necessary that it would inject a further $30 million into the project. In addition Thomson agreed to pay to the banks a $2\frac{1}{2}$ per cent royalty on its oil take up to the first 642 million barrels. This arrangement received strong support from the Department of Energy while the fact that Occidental—with a stronger base than Thomson—was also arranging a loan from the same banks strengthened Thomson's general position.

When Claymore was discovered Thomson repeated the operation, raising another $100 million through RNBD and IEB. There were complications in this case since there was far greater difficulty in agreeing Claymore reserves, the field being structurally more complicated than Piper. The loan, which had a far greater British banking content, was made with a second charge on Thomson's Piper oil as a further form of collateral. Like the Piper Field financing, the Claymore financing required Thomson Scottish Associates to provide $20 million front-end costs and to inject, if necessary, a further $18 million into the project. To meet its front-end requirements and to provide facilities to meet the $30 million and $18 million obligations, Thomson Scottish Associates raised loans based on crude supply contracts and the general worth of its business—in particular it raised $40 million from a syndicate of banks led by the Royal Bank of Canada. Thus Thomson—mainly in terms of its oil under the sea and with little recourse to other Thomson assets—raised $320 million to finance its share of the development costs of the two fields.

By the end of 1977 with Piper production increasing to 300,000 b/d and Claymore on production, Thomson was then reckoned by brokers to be able to substantially repay all its loans by the end of 1978—nearly $320 million, although the $200 million of project loans for the two fields were negotiated respectively for Piper in 1974 for nine years (due for final repayment in 1983) and for Claymore in 1976 for six years (due for final repayment by the end of 1982). Brokers calculate that the earnings contribution for Thomson's shares from Piper could be 74 pence a share in 1978 and 28 pence a share for Claymore, rising to 81 pence and 37 pence respectively by 1980.

The Thomson story is a remarkable one for a number of reasons. A non-oil company was invited by an oil consortium to become a partner—admittedly because the other three members of the consortium (Occidental, Getty and Allied Chemical) were all American and at that time had to have a British partner—and became one despite having no oil background. This was the beginning. But Thomson determined not to put the parent company at risk and raised the finance it needed by a series of non-recourse project loans that were virtually entirely dependent upon Thomson's oil in place as security. Although unique in their way, the loans were good business for the banks: these, for example, calculate upon a high safety ratio basis (roughly two and a half to one)—that is, that Thomson's oil in place would be worth considerably more than the total value of the loans to be repaid. In addition, for allowing such non-recourse loans in which the banks took all the commercial risks of the project (except the political risk of possible nationalization), they were also paid a royalty of $2\frac{1}{2}$ per cent upon Thomson's oil take —up to 642 million barrels in the case of Piper and 3 per cent for the life of the field in the case of Claymore—plus, for Claymore banks, $2\frac{1}{2}$ per cent of the excess Piper production over 642 million barrels.

Thomson North Sea determined that it would sell its own share of products, independently of its partners where this was felt to be in its best interest, and in spite of the fact that marketing petroleum products is highly specialized, and values will be accounted in billions of dollars over field lives. Contracts have been entered into for crude oil, liquid petroleum gases and a range of other gases. Most notably, ICI has contracted to buy the volumes available to Thomson North Sea from Piper field, which is a large contract even by ICI's standards.

Thomson had great luck (as did the other members of the consortium) in the rapidity with which they found first Piper and then Claymore. And though its American partners had brought Thomson into the consortium in the early 1970s, the part it could and did contribute was very considerable: this was notably through the knowledge and influence of its Scottish chairman, Alastair Dunnett, and the guidance he could give the consortium over the highly complicated questions of the Scottish political and ecological considerations that surrounded the establishment of a terminal at Flotta. The fact that, when the plans for this had been prepared by the consultants in Edinburgh, W. J. Cairns and Partners, only six months elapsed between presentation and their acceptance, was a tribute both to the thoroughness of this particular study (a model of its kind) and the local knowledge that Thomson could bring to the consortium as a whole.

Thomson also had ready help from their traditional clearer, the Royal Bank of Scotland, which both participated in the various loans TSA raised and granted them short-term unsecured facilities for $12·5 million to bridge them over the period of exploration and drilling. Further, they used to the full their excellent relations with their traditional bankers, S. G. Warburg, who were their outside advisers.

The result of a venture with very high costs and risks attached is that Thomson now have a 20 per cent share in two North Sea fields whose total recoverable reserves are 695 million and 410 million barrels respectively; it could substantially pay off all its loans by the end of 1978; and it will then expect to have a minimum annual profit for the next six or eight years of more than £40 million. With this scale of money to plough back, there is no reason why it should not venture further in the oil business. TNS is established as an ongoing oil company with 200 million barrels of reserves, a staff of twenty-one including technical, commercial and financial personnel so that, having been successful in the fifth round in obtaining a further block, TNS is now looking to oil prospects in other parts of the world.

The profits from the Piper and Claymore fields have raised the Organisation up into the top half of the first 100 British companies.

PART FOUR
Onshore Impact

11

Industries and Employment

A major aspect of the oil business consists of onshore jobs and the multiplier effects of North Sea oil activities as these impinge upon regions or particular sectors of the industrial economy. In this connexion some important facts have to be recognized.

First, oil is an itinerant industry which follows discoveries on a global basis. It may be offshore Britain today; in five or ten years it may be offshore Brazil or somewhere else. It is, therefore, especially important that any industries which now become involved in the offshore business should so gear themselves that they may follow oil and continue to pick up offshore business after development moves away from the UK Continental Shelf.

Second, only two of the majors—BP wholly and Shell 40 per cent— are British. Among other things this means that the greater part of the industry is American-based and likely to place its orders with support groups in the USA, with whom most of the oil companies have long done their business anyway. This disadvantage may be overcome by British business; it will only be overcome if such business is willing, after establishing itself in relation to North Sea operations, to become itinerant and follow oil around the world. The need has certainly been recognized by the OSO; whether the organization will succeed in ensuring that enough British firms will also recognize the need to chase oil business round the world remains to be seen.

Third, much of the employment attached to oil is fluid and temporary. There may be no long-term future for a yard building platforms and once a major engineering operation has been completed the actual number of men who can expect long-term employment is often minimal. The gas platforms in the southern North Sea, for example, require permanent maintenance staffs on them of only seven or eight men.

Fourth, oil is a rough business. Many have entered the field, learnt an aspect of the business, set up on their own hoping to obtain support work and have then collapsed.

The difficult nature of the business and the fact that in many cases the majors were followed into the North Sea by their long-standing support companies (usually from the USA or Europe) may be taken as an excuse for poor participation by British business in the early phases of opening up North Sea oil; such excuses cannot continue to be made.

A feature of the early days of oil was an assumption that it would provide a large number of jobs, especially in Scotland. In fact employment is the least important aspect of oil when compared to its contribution to the balance of payments or the government tax take. The Scottish Office listed the benefits from oil as follows: first, the country will have its own oil for thirty years; second, and as a result, it will be more independent in energy than any European country except for Norway over this period; third, the tangible benefits may be seen as balance of payments, tax income for government, industrial development and, at the bottom of the list, employment.

It would be wishful thinking to regard oil as anything more than of marginal importance in taking up the slack of unemployment. It may be of far greater importance in boosting the profitability of engineering and other companies, and enabling them to expand and become involved in providing offshore engineering expertise worldwide. Such a development in its turn will help ensure long-term security for employees in these industries.

Even so in certain places the impact has been substantial. Middle Scotland has benefited particularly from engineering orders, and the Forth Estuary which in any case has a long association with oil has done well; the oil from Cruden Bay is piped overland to Grangemouth and there are other petrochemical developments taking place there. On the west, sites on the Clyde have received huge engineering construction orders.

The effects of one big development upon a rural area may not always be beneficial. When the construction phase comes to an end— perhaps where a terminal has been established—the community may discover it has been badly disrupted without any commensurate long-term gain. The jobs have gone, the temporary rise in cash flow and multiplier effects have also largely disappeared, and the men who have had jobs find themselves out of work with nothing to return to. Further, local impact can be damaging in other ways: if unemployment in an area is low, competition for labour when the oil companies move in will be intense, so that normal activities are neglected while better money is to be earned in connexion with the oil business.

This was often the case with the huge platforms. Not only did they drain off local labour; they also produced strains upon housing and education because much of their labour was imported. Once a platform is completed, a remote yard may find itself without further orders. Moreover, local people who quit their jobs for the higher pay at the yard may find themselves unable to return to their previous employment.

None of this is to argue that such communities did not want the yards and the orders; they did. But afterwards they have been obliged to cope with problems of this nature. By the end of 1977, the large yards such as Howard Doris's at Kisshorn or the Ardyne Point yard of McAlpine Seatank found themselves on a care and maintenance basis hopefully awaiting further orders. McDermotts at Ardesier did better and at least obtained orders to build two small platforms, for Holland and Brazil. Oil is and always has been a volatile business and empty yards today may be full again in a year's time—there are certainly plenty more offshore oil fields awaiting development.

The multiplier effects of oil are very wide though often not in the most obvious places. The banks (see chapter 9) have obtained a large amount of extra business as a result of North Sea developments and there has been commensurate development of banking expertise. British banks are likely to be involved in worldwide oil lending from now on, so that over the long term this activity should contribute substantially to invisible earnings. The case is the same for insurance.

At another level unit holders of Scotbits Securities, for example, were told in a letter from their management in October 1977:

> Overall, however, it is the Managers' view that, with the impact of North Sea oil continuing to grow and a more stable monetary background, share prices should move upwards over the medium term provided that there is no revival in inflationary pressures.

The point here is that the entire share market sees the effects of oil upon the economy generally as a boost to the performance and prospects of many individual companies. Still more important is the extent to which oil may produce a mood of national confidence. Should this happen it would be the best multiplier effect of all.

The multiplier effects of oil will do most good for Britain if they induce firms to capture new markets on a worldwide basis. Land-to-sea telecommunications represent an area where some new break-throughs have been made; these can now be marketed for offshore operations elsewhere.

In the early days of North Sea developments, British companies were generally slow off the mark: to the end of 1974, of £1,600 million of purchases for offshore activity, only £525 million or 32 per cent went to British companies. On the other hand, some companies saw the opportunities early, went after them with determination and seized much of the work. Bristow Helicopters and British Airways for the helicopter business; Seaforth Maritime in Aberdeen for the supply business; Bookers with pumps. British companies did well in module construction or supplying pumps and generators. American, European and Japanese rivals, however, were quick to see North Sea possibilities and grab them where they could, in many cases when British companies ought to have got there first. This was so in the supply of pipelines, steel and supply boats, in much of the platform building and development drilling. Moreover, some of these countries, Norway and Holland for example, virtually operate a closed shop against British companies trying to break into their offshore business, although not for design.

The competition remains fierce. At the beginning of 1978, for example, the order for a £26 million firefighting and maintenance ship to service the Piper and Claymore fields for the Occidental Group was placed with a Japanese shipyard because British yards could not meet the required deadline in mid 1979. Both the Department of Energy and OSO accepted that it was more important for the vessel to be delivered on time than for the order to go to a British yard and be a year late. This was a slap in the face for British performance coming from the right quarters, since OSO exists to promote the interests of British industry and the Department of Energy has never been slow to press the case for orders being placed in Britain.

Between 40 and 45 per cent of the world's remaining oil and gas reserves are now expected to be found offshore, so that for the next decade there will be a steady growth of offshore exploration. OSO claims that British industry has rapidly developed its capabilities to bid for contracts in design engineering, surveying, project management, heavy fabrication, process plant and ancillary equipment, supply and maintenance services and underwater inspection. Much North Sea related equipment springs from a new technology and those British firms which are developing to meet this need could find themselves in the forefront of world offshore activity. Even by 1980 as much as 20 to 25 per cent of world oil may then come from offshore fields.

By 1976 some 300 establishments, many new to Scotland, were wholly engaged in supplying the offshore oil industry. According to the Scottish Office, oil related jobs created in Scotland during the first half of the 1970s worked out at 2,800 by December 1972, 8,600 by December 1973, 16,200 by December 1974 and 23,700 by December 1975. By mid 1976, the same office claimed that a total of between 50,000 and 55,000 jobs associated with North Sea development had been created, and that many of these were in areas of

Scotland in particular need of stimulus. The effects upon Strathclyde have been considerable. As a result of oil, it is claimed, unemployment in Scotland dropped to a figure that was only one fifth above the UK average, as opposed to a previous figure which was double the UK average.

British industry had to break into a field long controlled by the Americans. At first, the oil companies tended to turn automatically to suppliers they had used for a long time. Various aspects of the industry such as project management were in any case dominated by the Americans. In addition to this historical background there is a somewhat different protectionist one. Foreign companies, for example, cannot work in the Gulf of Mexico because of the Jones Act which stipulates that ships working in the US coastal business must be American. Yet American supply vessels were early working out of Aberdeen and Dundee; Britain does not restrict US or other foreign ships in reverse.

The Americans clearly intend to use the North Sea as a proving ground for new techniques; they will capitalize on the experience gained in the North Sea when they come to tackle deeper offshore fields of their own. Then the question will arise as to whether Britain, which will then have developed the technology and capabilities, will be allowed equal opportunities to operate off the USA.

One result of North Sea oil has been a growth of partnerships. In some cases American or European firms have sought British partners, in part for political reasons, to ensure their position operating from a British base. In reverse British companies have sought foreign partnerships in order to marry up with expertise they lacked. A number of American companies particularly have sought British partnerships for the development of modules or platforms—the major offshore engineering works.

As development really got under way, British policy has insisted upon the oil companies providing full and fair opportunity to British companies to compete for orders; this has been reinforced by BNOC which is clearly determined wherever practicable to place its orders with British companies. The result of these practices is to provide British industry with a built-in advantage. It did not have this at first.

In the beginning company attitudes towards the North Sea varied widely. There was a good deal of scepticism in some cases that business would prove to be anything other than a single job, so that the reaction of a number of British firms was one of extreme caution: they were not interested. On the other hand, some new companies were only too eager to break into any part of the work that they could. Established companies like Vickers, which already had a long history of involvement in underwater engineering, took the new North Sea work in their stride.

Poor industrial relations produced their own casualties. Thus a major shipyard was not interested to take a second order for a submersible rig from BP, since they claimed that the men would simply delay and hold the company up to ransom over the job. Such a reaction reveals much about the predicament of British industry and the attitudes of management.

Pressures of time have meant that oil companies want orders completed in a hurry; they have exact shedules to meet and have to get platforms into place during the famous weather window of the North Sea. Foreign companies have penalty clauses in their contracts should they fail to deliver on time; British companies do not. Here is one method whereby greater pressures might be applied to British industry.

Apart from government pressures, there is the natural inclination of the oil companies to be taken into account. On balance BP, for example, would approach British companies first to fulfil its requirements. Non-British oil companies, however, are far more likely to think first of a home company—in Holland or the USA—so that the effort by a British company to capture their orders needs to be all the greater.

A majority of all the servicing operations for the North Sea are based in and around Aberdeen. These include light constructional engineering and most aspect of maintenance. Small companies involved in such work need a good deal of entrepreneurial skill backed by sound finances. Some in fact have tried to start on a shoestring and have then come to grief. Often they have relied upon a series of orders from the oil companies to keep them going, but they have had a rude shock. As one top-ranking oil executive brutally put it: 'We do not want to know of small firm failures; if they can do what we want, that is fine; but it is not our business to help these companies survive.'

Consultancy is a new oil related activity which has flourished. Oil developments have threatened disruption in many areas, most especially in remote regions such as the Orkneys, where huge terminals have been established. Consultants have been engaged by newcomers to Britain, American or continental firms, to enable them to get off to a correct start in their relations with a local community in which they have set up business. The oil business has also spawned a number of associations. There are UKOOA and Brindex but also, for example, the UK Module Constructors' Association which consists of a number of engineering and fabricating companies such as Foster Wheeler and William Press. As North Sea developments have become systematized, so more and more groups have found they had certain interests in common.

Some of the most important developments arising out of oil include the establishment and running of supply bases, submersibles, service engineering, maintenance, transport (both air and sea), telecommunications, cement, pipelines, pipeline lay barges, turbines, the printing industry, and many more. The supply bases are a key to the whole operation. They have to carry stocks of equipment and emergency supplies of all kinds, ready to be taken to the oil fields on demand. Aberdeen now has a huge stock of stores ready for immediate trans-shipment and use. The volume of supplies required and their rapid turnover has necessitated sophisticated warehousing techniques. At Montrose, the P & O Sea Oil Group has established a huge comprehensive base which offers a wide range of services for the offshore industry. The forty-acre base cost £5 million to set up. It includes an oil field equipment division and, for example, one of the many partnerships entered into with an American company operates from the base. The partnership company, Sea Oil Homco, is a joint venture with Homco International of Houston, a leading drilling tool rental company. The base has quays capable of handling the largest of the supply vessels, warehousing facilities, open storage. Such a base has to be secure. It has office facilities and a machine shop, an engineering workshop, craneage and skid-loading facilities. The other major bases at Aberdeen or Peterhead cover the same ground.

Subsea development is also a growth area. P & O Subsea offers a full range of underwater engineering services, which include site surveys, clearance, pipeline and platform inspection, maintenance of offshore structures and cable burial. All such services are carried out by submersibles and diving systems operated from surface support vessels.

Britain has surplus refining capacity, as does the rest of Europe. This, however, does not necessarily mean that she will not increase her capacity—largely for political reasons. Thus the Cromarty Firth is regarded as a natural area for refining activities in view of its proximity to the oil fields. The building and subsequent maintenance of a refinery brings employment and business to the area.

In the long run, service engineering will be one of the greatest beneficiaries from the North Sea. There are many commercial opportunities arising out of platform maintenance. There is the problem of the rapidity of corrosion and how to combat it, and most of the companies that deal with such a problem are engineering ones. There is the more complicated business of subsea maintenance that involves diving companies, underwater television, subsonics, cleaning, spares and repairs which together make up a huge market that will last just as long as offshore oil. All aspects of maintenance will grow, and already there is developing the need for preventative measures to cut down maintenance bills: these include looking again at designs and devising ways of checking on the little things that can cause big disasters.

Everything needed for a ship is needed for an oil platform. Indeed the shipping demands of North Sea oil have increased dramatically. A study published at the beginning of 1978 predicted major growth over the following five years in the repair and maintenance vessel market as well as for firefighting and safety vessels. It also predicted a greater demand for accommodation platforms and suggested that the number of routine maintenance vessels available in 1978–79 would have to double or even treble by 1982 as the peak in demand was reached.

North Sea Vessel Requirements

	Peak demand	Estimated supply end	Forecast peak demand				
	1977	1977	1978	1979	1980	1981	1982
Jack-up rigs	18	17	14	14	14	16	16
Semi-submersible rigs	36	32	30	31	32	32	34
Deck cargo barges	100	90	60	110	90	170	110
Master construction barges	9	9	4	5	4	7	9
Accommodation/storage units	17	17	27	31	35	44	49
Derrick barges	16	15	6	11	9	17	11
Lay barges	4	6	4	2	2	4	6
Derrick/lay barges	8	9	4	2	2	5	8
Trenching barges	7	6	6	4	2	4	6
Fixed platforms	91	91	97	110	122	144	159
Repair and maintenance	38	43	43	52	58	73	81
Firefighters	12	43	13	16	17	22	26
Standby vessels	91	91	97	110	122	144	159
Straight supply vessels	170	280	145	154	158	213	243
Anchor handling supply vessels	164	280	127	164	157	217	192
Anchor handling tugs	158	100	98	109	87	171	157
Pipecarriers	32	30	24	12	12	26	40

Transport to the platforms is a major activity. In some cases normal transport facilities need to be expanded: in 1977, there was only one ferry every other day from Aberdeen to Lerwick in Shetland, clearly by then inadequate to cope with the growth of traffic and goods to the island which had developed as a result of the Sullom Voe terminal. Helicopter services have made Aberdeen into the busiest heliport in the world. Other transport developments have followed; at the end of 1977, British Caledonian Airways opened a new daily flight between London and Houston in a bid to become the British oil trade airline. The flight will link into British Caledonian's regular services to Scotland for the North Sea oil and gas industry, and also into its Nigerian flights; British Caledonian in any case has a great slice of the Nigeria trade and is in partnership with Nigerian Airways. The airline expects that 60 per cent of its business on this new route will come from the oil industry; it also expects a large proportion of its air cargo to be oil industry related freight.

A somewhat different story attaches to the cement business. Although in fact Britain has one of the most advanced cement industries in the world, half the orders for concrete platforms went abroad. Apart from this, however, is the nature of the business. The first platforms were steel; they were followed by the generation of giant concrete structures. Now the industry has turned back to steel again, so that it is by no means certain that there will be further cement structures of any size, especially as concrete corrosion appears to take place even faster than steel corrosion.

Pipelines provide an immense slice of oil related business: as well as the requirements of new fields, there are the plans for the gas gathering scheme linking a number of fields in the northern sector of the North Sea. Apart from fabrication and laying which involves lay barge industry, huge quantities of steel have to be provided. This aspect of North Sea developments ought to act as a stimulus for the BSC, though whether this proves to be the case is another matter. The lay barges cost so much as individual vessels that, once built, they require one major pipelaying order a year to make them an economic proposition. Effectively this means they need access to US waters. So, if the US policy of excluding foreign vessels from its territorial waters continues, there is no hope that a British pipelay barge can be a viable proposition, at least at the present time.

Another growth area which has benefited very substantially from oil is publishing. Company after company—both oil and the whole range of support companies—have produced glossy brochures setting out what they are doing or aiming to do in the North Sea and what support services they offer.* It is a lucrative spin-off market. And there is the growth trade of books explaining every conceivable aspect of the North Sea.

For over half a century Foster Wheeler, giant subsidiary of an American parent company, has been engaged in major contracts for all the leading oil companies; it specializes in processing plants. When the big North Sea expansion came, it had a commanding lead

* In the course of collecting material for this book I must have obtained several hundred such glossy magazines without seriously trying. AUTHOR.

position which it maintained. The company formed Foster Wheeler Offshore. Since 1970 this particular company has loaded out offshore modules which have ranged from 250 to 1,850 tons for many of the platforms in the North Sea; all its loadouts have met delivery schedules—which is more than can be said for some of their competitors. Their Power Products have become leading contractors in the total energy field and enjoy a commanding position in engineering and fabrication of offshore structures, process and power generation equipment packages for the drilling and production operations of the offshore industry. The company operates two large plants at Dumbarton and Hartlepool. As the Foster Wheeler American annual report for 1976 claimed:

> One of our English subsidiaries, Foster Wheeler Power Products, Ltd., has built more offshore deep water platform modules than any other supplier.

Another American subsidiary, Brown and Root, was early off the mark with North Sea contracts, securing a large slice of the business for themselves when the southern gas fields were being developed. They found at that time extreme caution in Britain with regard to the possible longevity of North Sea business, and a consequent reluctance by industries to commit themselves to oil related work. By 1977 Brown and Root had captured approximately 25 per cent of the fabrication business; the company intends to keep that proportion. Highland Fabricators, who have the Nigg yard in Cromarty, are a part of the Brown and Root UK operation.

Ulster, which sadly is too often in the news for the wrong reasons, has an impressive record of offshore related work captured by various of its companies. In 1972 there were seven Ulster firms involved in offshore related work; by 1977 the number had risen to sixty. In 1976 alone, Northern Ireland earned £36 million from activities related to the oil and gas industries, and a large number of its companies have obtained contracts of varying kinds for the huge terminals at Sullom Voe and Flotta. The range of goods being supplied from Ulster covers earth-moving machinery, prefabricated housing sections, precast concrete sections, cattle grids, building design and electrical installation. And though its companies only looked for work in the North Sea or Scottish terminals to begin with, they are now contemplating breaking into the world offshore market.

The ordinary building trade—as opposed to the big contractors—has also benefited from the North Sea spin-off in hotel extensions, new housing or prefabricated units for the various areas of Scotland such as Cromarty or Kisshorn, where the platform yards have been established. The multiplier effects of the offshore oil industry continue indefinitely, and it is often hard to pinpoint just what is new and to what extent an existing company has expanded as a result. None the less, the size of the offshore related industry can be gauged from the *Offshore Suppliers Guide* (third edition) UK 1977, a thick glossy book that lists hundreds of UK or UK-based companies offering some form of service for offshore development.

The North Sea operation as a whole, as well as each individual part of it, entails mammoth logistics. When a platform is in place, for example, thirty welders are needed on the job for a week and these have to be brought on and taken off by helicopter. They will be replaced by a different group—electricians or plumbers—and the logistics of transporting the various work personnel on time, as well as ensuring that all necessary equipment is available where it should be when needed, resemble those of a major military operation.

More than two hundred Aberdeen firms were listed in 1976 as engaged in some aspect of offshore supply and hotel accommodation has greatly expanded. Some effects of the boom are not necessarily welcome to other industries or employers. The Navy, for example, has found that growing numbers of its most skilled sailors have been leaving the service for far more lucrative jobs which also carry greater responsibility, working for oil and associated companies. A naval radio operator responsible for comprehensive equipment and receiving £48 a week in the service can earn three times that amount doing a comparable job for a civilian firm.

As a result of North Sea oil, the oil companies are looking to increase their petrochemical activities in Britain. The range of these is, of course, vast, from insecticides to ballpoint pens to egg baskets. According to the chairman of Shell Chemicals (UK), Bill Thomson, the oil companies are already devoting a larger proportion of their capital expenditure to the chemical industry, and there is every sign that this process will continue for some years. Mr Thomson said in 1977 that the companies were looking to investment in petrochemicals as a means of enhancing the use and value of the crude oil.

It has become part of the Scottish oil game either to lament the extent to which Scotland is being cheated of its due share of oil and related work, or to make wildly extravagant claims for developments. There has been put forward a vision of Scotland ringed with petrochemical plants, and during the 1970s a number of suggestions have been made for new complexes which would turn North Sea oil and gas into other products after coming ashore. These suggestions have been advanced during a period when the industry is in recession and Europe is suffering from refining over-capacity. There will, of course, be a number of substantial developments in Scotland; the pace at which they are started, however, is more likely to be dictated by the state of the world petrochemical industry than by the rate at which the various fields are opened up in the North Sea. None the less, major developments are underway. The most important of these at present is the Shell-Esso proposal to spend £435 million on a gas processing and petrochemical complex in Fife. A natural gas liquids separation plant costing £120 million is to be built by the two companies at Mossmorran to be connected to a marine terminal on the Firth of Forth to the south.

The proposals are subject to the findings of an inquiry, but permission is unlikely to be withheld since government is only too anxious to see such a petrochemical plant established in the area. Esso will also build a £230 million ethylene plant at Mossmorran which will be capable of processing 500,000 tonnes a year. In this case construction will start in mid 1979 and the plant will come on stream in 1982.

Eventually these developments will provide about 400 permanent jobs, although during construction as many as 2,500 could be involved at peak. Depending upon the state of the world industry, Scotland could end up with a serious over-capacity and whether other developments take place must depend in part upon whether or not the huge gas-gathering pipeline scheme goes ahead.

In the mid 1970s it was estimated that an average rig required a crew of approximately 140 (two crews of 70 each), and that for back-up these generated perhaps another 120 jobs onshore. The companies have found that men aged between twenty and forty are best suited to the extremely rugged conditions of work on rigs, and those who are outside this age range very often find they can only stand one shift. According to the *Brown Book* of the Department of Energy, regular offshore employment had risen to 9,200 jobs in 1976. Since then, however, the number of personnel required on a platform has increased. Two men onshore are required to back up every man on a platform. Thus in mid 1977 5,000 men offshore meant a further 10,000 to back them up onshore; if expansion goes as expected and there are 15,000 men working offshore by 1985, they will require 30,000 onshore jobs to back them. Moreover, though the statistics are not clear yet, the older a field the more back-up it will require. On the Forties field it was originally estimated that a regular platform crew should be 72 men, while extra short-term maintenance or other installation personnel could bring the total up to a working average of 96 men. Now, however, BP have found they need a basic crew of 125 men, apart from extra maintenance or other short-term personnel and the same numbers in their replacement crews on shore. In addition they need extra men to cover sickness, training and holidays and these work out at 0·4 of a man to each post. Thus each platform post has come to be reckoned at 2·4 men and roughly 500 men form the total involved in one platform.

At the end of 1974, the Mackays (*Political Economy of North Sea Oil*) estimated that about 19,000 jobs had been created in Scotland as a direct result of the oil: 6,000 in exploration, 8,700 in manufacturing, 800 in production and 3,500 in construction. They also considered that between 5,000 and 6,000 jobs had been created in England, mainly in the northeast where the platform module construction was being done, with some in East Anglia in relation to the gas fields. But during the early 1970s, the jobs created by the North Sea boom were being offset by unemployment in the traditional sectors of Scottish industry. Again according to the Mackays, peak North Sea employment would only offset the equivalent of less than two years decline; in other words the impact of North Sea oil was not sufficient to deal with Scotland's industrial unemployment problems. This fact strengthens Scottish, and especially SNP, demands that a proportion of the tax take from oil be channelled back into Scotland.

A report made in Aberdeen University in 1974 calculated that oil related employment then stood at 11,000 jobs, with a further 5,000 in secondary industries. The report suggested that by 1980 direct employment could have reached a figure of between 25,000 and 30,000 with the same number again in oil induced jobs.

By 1977 the generally accepted figure for employment was 100,000 jobs in Britain as a whole, of which 55,000 were in Scotland. As many as 75 per cent of these jobs, however, were part of the production phase and could later fall away. The 55,000 Scottish jobs might be described as the offshore market; in addition there are more indirect jobs arising out of the multiplier factor.

On this all-absorbing subject of the number of jobs oil has provided for Scotland, Professor Gaskin of Aberdeen University says in *Changing Prospects*:

> If we sum (1976) all the previous components of employment we get a range of 47–49,000, and applying to this a multiplier of 1·4 we emerge with a range of 18–20,000 as indicating the possible level of this secondary, or multiplier-created employment.

Professor Gaskin found that at the end of 1976, 26,000 had employment in wholly oil related firms, 13,000 in partially related firms, 5,000 in the construction of direct facilities and 4,000 in other construction work. In addition 19,000 had jobs in secondary multiplier employment.

Politicians have something of a vested interest in proving that a considerable job spin-off has taken place. Of 100,000 jobs in Britain

8*

as a whole, a half are wholly related to oil, a half are in Scotland and of these half again are wholly oil related. Ten thousand of the jobs in 1977 were offshore, while the remaining 90,000 were onshore in the various support industries.

An especially interesting aspect of oil related employment is the extent to which jobs have been created elsewhere, and most notably in the USA. There the number of full-time jobs—the majority of a skilled nature—for people making equipment for the companies operating in the Scottish province of the North Sea has been reckoned (in a highly confidential report of one of the oil companies) at between 150,000 and 200,000 jobs—that is, three to four times the total of jobs created for Scotland. It is little wonder, in view of Scottish susceptibilities about oil, that these figures have been kept quiet. Thus, talk of what the North Sea has done for Scotland should be measured against what it has done for the USA.

There is no necessary conflict between 55,000 jobs in Scotland and 200,000 in the USA, as those in Scotland (for example, making the platforms) are mainly labour-intensive, while those in the USA are detailed engineering and design jobs for the hardware that is needed. The figures do raise general questions: why more of the hardware cannot be made in Scotland or at any rate in Britain; why British industry was not able to get a larger share of the work; and why the government has been so complacent in permitting so much of the spin-off to go to the USA, even allowing for the large number of US oil companies involved in the North Sea and their natural desire to use their own support companies from home.

A key question for Scotland in the future is the extent to which the oil business will help provide long-term stability of labour. Despite talk of boom over the last few years the largest single employer of labour north of Aberdeen is the Atomic Energy Authority at Dounreay which employs 2,000.

Another vital spin-off from North Sea oil has been in the field of training: universities and colleges in Scotland have devised new oil-related courses while other government establishments have been created for training purposes.

The training provided in British universities and colleges which is relevant to the offshore industry include a wide variety of engineering, geology or physical science courses but there are weaknesses at the post-graduate level. One of the establishments that has moved into this field is Robert Gordon's Institute of Technology (RGIT) at Aberdeen which early pinpointed some of the areas that required courses and training.

RGIT went into oil in 1972 although in 1970 it had started to look at the possibility of offering an offshore diploma. The Institute began by asking what the needs of the new oil industry were likely to be and what the industry would require from a technological institute. A first qualification for oil employment would be in the field of applied science and in this respect the Institute offered a Higher National Diploma (HND) in engineering; RGIT added to its HND in engineering courses in offshore drilling and oil drilling technology.

In 1972 RGIT began one- to two-week courses for oil company personnel and graduates and then offered a one-year post-graduate course to follow the first qualification in engineering. Finance came mainly from government though the oil companies made token grants to the Institute. In 1970 the RGIT had 1,300 students; by 1977 it had 2,400 at a time when educational institutions were being obliged to cut back. In 1977 there were forty students at RGIT doing post-graduate work directly related to oil. Some 2,000 personnel a year pass through the Institute's safety and survival course which is run by six instructors.

In addition to its regular courses oil companies have asked RGIT to do specific research or run special courses for them. The Institute runs a consultancy service: this means either straight consultancy by members of the staff; or undertaking projects which will involve the students. In the latter case the students will work on a problem for the industry and the project will form part of their course work. If a quick answer is required the job will be undertaken by the staff; if there is more time available the problem is made into a student project.

In 1976–77 post-graduate work at RGIT included: problems affecting marine riser tension control; measurement of wave profiles; oil and gas separator; wave force measurement; ocean environment measuring; further design and development of a helicopter escape survival simulator; the impact of a North Sea gas pipeline network on platform energy utilization, as well as many other subjects. RGIT offers a post-graduate diploma in offshore engineering which it started in 1973 after extensive consultation with the offshore engineering and petroleum industry—a full-time one-year course which covers drilling technology, production technology, geology and reservoir engineering, operations planning and control, offshore materials technology, offshore structures, project activity, offshore diving and underwater operations. The RGIT's involvement in oil-related courses has all been built up during the 1970s, and situated in the centre of Aberdeen the Institute is ideally placed to maintain its contact with the oil world and provide relevant training for it.

The Oil Development Council which advises government on all aspects of oil affecting Scotland has reviewed Scotland's training provisions. There are three group training associations: the Offshore Petroleum Training Association (OPTA); the Petroleum Industry Training Board (PITB); and the International Association of Drilling Contractors. Apart from Aberdeen University and RGIT there is the Drilling Technology Centre at Livingston and the Underwater Training Centre (UTC) at Loch Linnhe.

In addition the following bodies are concerned with various aspects of onshore training related to the oil business: the Construction Industry Training Board; the Engineering Industry Training Board (EITB); the Shipbuilding Industry Training Board; the Petroleum Industry Training Association, Scotland (PITAS); and the Engineering Construction and Related Industries Manpower (ECRIM) Scottish Committee. Altogether there is now a wide range of bodies concerned with the training and job aspect of North Sea oil and its support industries.

12

Scotland: Aberdeen and the Islands

The most obvious onshore impact from oil has been in Scotland and the islands—Orkney and Shetland—and despite protestations about ill-effects, the overwhelming reaction is one of pleasure: oil means jobs and development. The objectors have usually been conservationists or farmers and sometimes those who have not managed to sell their land or otherwise profit from some of the speculations that have taken place. These latter have subsequently turned into ardent conservationists.

For many years Scotland's rate of growth had been insufficient to absorb the available labour supply with the result that labour constantly migrated southwards. The public sector in Scotland—shipbuilding, aerospace and those contracts in receipt of Scottish Development Agency subsidies—is a substantial one but there had nonetheless long been a need to create new industrial divisions. After Ulster Scotland has been the most depressed region of Britain ever since the First World War with incomes averaging 8 per cent less than the national average.

Closer to the oil era, the late 1960s were a difficult time for Scotland with regional policies failing to stimulate growth. Britain's entry into the EEC was against Scottish interests, especially fishing; then came a collapse of shipbuilding. One result of these pressures was a doubling of the SNP vote in the 1974 election when the National Party gained 30 per cent of the poll. As one observer put it: 'North Sea oil represents a way out of generations of neglect, decay, demoralization and exploitation.'

George Rosie, the author of a lively extended pamphlet entitled 'Cromarty: the Scramble for Oil', sums up many of the attitudes to oil and its effects upon Scotland when he says:

Of course we've got problems but at least they're the problems of life. And that makes a change, believe me. It's all very well worrying about the effects on the simple life, the effects on the grass and the dunes on Nigg Bay, the effects on the ducks and all the rest of it. But for generations we've watched our youngsters pack up and drift south looking for work; and the fact education around here has always been pretty good just aggravated it. Just what is there for an educated youngster to *do* in Easter Ross?

Oil in Scotland has provided a field day for sociologists examining its effects. Oil has brought employment and prosperity, although some of this will not last. On the other hand, the production employment on the platforms will go on indefinitely and is likely to be higher than originally estimated. But there are disadvantages too. What happens in the areas where the construction facilities have been created after the construction phase is over—Nigg, Kisshorn and such places? And how do small communities such as Shetland deal with the problems of social upheaval? And what of soaring costs?—housing in Aberdeen is now as expensive as in London.

According to Professor Gaskin, the proportion of oil money that has gone to Scottish industry is 15 per cent. In 1977 the Fraser of Allander Institute of Strathclyde University predicted that North Sea oil production would boost Scottish economic growth for the year by 9·8 per cent compared with its contribution in 1976. This figure compares with one of only 2·7 per cent for growth of non-oil output.

Oil has been associated with Scotland longer than with other parts of the United Kingdom and so it is fitting that the major offshore discoveries have all been in Scottish waters. The discovery of seams of oil shale in Scotland last century did not lead to the sort of excitement that early oil field discoveries produced in the USA—but there was some excitement. The potential was never to be fully realized although a substantial industry developed. The total quantity of crude oil produced in Scotland during the three years 1892-94, for example, was as follows:

1892	44,238,280	gallons
1893	45,725,841	,,
1894	47,693,458	,,

and in 1894 fourteen companies in Scotland were listed as engaged in the oil business.

A large area of shale oil was discovered in central Scotland stretching southwest from St Andrews and Dunbar to Ardrossan in a belt thirty to forty miles wide. The shale industry existed from these discoveries to the beginning of the 1960s. In 1962, however, the government withdrew the 1/3d preference on hydrocarbon oils which at that time allowed the shale industry to exist, so it closed down. Not many years later the new offshore industry opened up and brought a new measure of prosperity to Scotland.

Oil has had three geographical impacts upon Scotland: at the supply bases and ports; in the various, usually remote, fabrication yards; and at the landfall terminals. In each case it has made a substantial contribution to employment and prosperity as well as to lifestyles. A Department of Energy estimate of direct employment in North Sea activities for Scotland in 1977 was as follows:

Highland	7,400
Shetland, Orkney and Western Isles	700
Grampian	11,500
Tayside	1,600
Fife, Central and Lothian	2,700
Strathclyde	3,100
Total	27,000

By 1977 Scotland had become oil-dominated; it might be argued, unhealthily so. A month's issues of the *Scotsman* contained few numbers without oil or oil-related stories and there was always a hint of expectation, as indeed in the national press, that the long-term hopes raised by the discovery of oil would be realized. Lord Clydesmuir, Governor of the Bank of Scotland, has claimed:

> North Sea oil is making Scotland into a new and intensely active international Oil Centre. The continuing discoveries of offshore oil resources are generating a whole new range of industrial and commercial opportunities in Scotland.

Much of lowland Scotland is industrial, yet most of the North Sea discoveries have been made off the more remote and rural areas so that the greater part of the most obvious impact has been upon these districts. There has been a great deal of debate over the extent to which oil is damaging traditional life in Scotland. It should be remembered that all too often the people who lament such a change in traditional life are outsiders or wealthy landlords who have bought property in remote areas rather than the ordinary people upon whom the impact most impinges. In their cases, if oil means better jobs and greater prosperity, they are only too happy. The impact upon certain towns and most notably Aberdeen has been of major importance, less by changing the pattern of life than by widening the base structure and providing wider long-term opportunities.

The impact of the huge fabrication yards is worth underlining, for they can be exceptionally important in what had previously been a sparsely populated rural district with little or no industrial activity. To quote George Rosie again—and he enjoys a certain style of rhetoric:

The combination of a largely unskilled labour force working at
great speed, on a remote site in difficult working conditions, in a
new industry, on the frontiers of technology, under foreign supervision [he has the Americans in mind], creates problems to say
the least.

Housing, education and extra work for the police have all been a
part of such impacts, yet despite real difficulties such problems have
been overcome. In Cromarty Firth, for example, Highland Fabricators wanted to build labour camps, but the County Council turned
them down because it wanted the labour to be integrated in the
district. Part of the trouble is that such huge yards attract temporary
workers who move from place to place. Many caravan sites have
sprung up beside these yards; once the project is completed the men
and their families move on.

According to Rosie, the impact of the Nigg yard upon local occupations was as follows: 10 per cent of the labour force was drawn
from farming, fishing and forestry, 7 per cent from the local electronic
and electrical industry, 15 per cent from local engineering, 2 per cent
from local woodworkers, 4½ per cent from the local transport business and 11 per cent from the local construction force. Clearly
ordinary building such as houses or repair work was hit. These
figures, however, for an area that was depressed are at about the right
level—a considerable boost without totally upsetting the traditional
pattern.

Most of the yards employed a high proportion of their men from
farther and farther afield; there were simply not available locally
either the numbers or many of the skills which they required. In a
good many cases, too, the wages paid in the more remote yards did
not compare with those a man could earn for similar work farther
south.

The Industry Act of 1972 made Scotland a development area; it is
ironical that this Act, which was designed to attract new industries,
in fact enabled oil-related companies such as Highland Fabricators
at Nigg (who would have come anyway because of the oil) to qualify
for 20 per cent of the cost of clearing the site, 20 per cent of the cost
of buildings and 20 per cent of the cost of their capital equipment. In
addition 44 per cent of building costs were written off in the first
year and 100 per cent of plant and equipment costs. The way the
Act has worked raises important questions about whether it helps
Scotland at all. In the Nigg case it certainly helped an American
company.

Though many people have obtained jobs in Scotland as a result
of oil, the overall impact has by no means been universally beneficial.

In 1976, for example, 200 women fish gutters at Fraserburgh were lost to the industry to become clerks and secretaries in oil-related business: the change represented a step up for them both economically and socially. Many local companies have lost staff and often their best people to oil. Moreover, in the early 1970s the oil industry enjoyed a great advantage as it moved into such areas as the Grampians and Aberdeen since as 'new' business these companies could break the pay pause and offer higher wages than local industry was legally permitted to do, thus stealing the latter's personnel. Had there been no pay pause, the local industries could have increased their wages and not lost so many of their best people.

According to a study by the Church of Scotland, oil has shifted the centre of gravity of the Scottish working population northwards, though not by much. Another judgement upon the impact of oil claims:

> In Scotland oil developments have created extra jobs and bid up wages to the competitive disadvantage of almost all other Scottish industries. Some time, probably soon, the short-term benefits of the former will be overtaken by the lingering damage to the latter.

That quote comes from a paper produced by BP. The multinationals have more experience than most of the effects of a major new industry moving into an area.

Impact effects vary widely from area to area and town to town. The principal onshore bases, for example, are all to be found on the Scottish east coast from Dundee to Peterhead, and then in the islands. The Grampian region as a whole has gained some 12,000 jobs (1977) directly attributable to oil, while unemployment in the region has fallen to half the national average. Aberdeen, moreover, has enjoyed the growth and development of some industries that will be lasting. They include supply, services, maintenance, helicopters and headquarters for the companies and though exploration may now be beginning to drop, production is going up. Glasgow has done quite well out of oil: apart from both OSO and BNOC locating their headquarters there, parts of the shipbuilding-fabricating business have come there as well, and in and around Glasgow there is offshore work for companies such as Foster Wheeler making platform modules.

A quite different problem for Scotland concerns conservation. When all the oil has gone, the other industries and the fisheries as well as the scenery will remain; it is important to take measures to safeguard their long-term future now. There have been a good many conservation arguments in Scotland since the oil came: about the huge yards and their effect upon the countryside; about the pipelines and the disruption to agricultural land these cause when they are laid—four different sets of pipelines at four separate times have been laid from the Cruden Bay area down to the Forth Estuary. And in some cases—Drumbuie near Kisshorn made a good deal of news—small and beautiful areas became centres of debate as to whether or not they should be used for yards or other oil-related developments.

In the case of Drumbuie a furious conservation row in the end meant that the site was not used. By early 1978 Shell's plans for the first ever pipeline in Britain to carry natural gas liquids, which is to come down from the north of Scotland to the Firth of Forth, was running into increasing opposition from communities through whose districts it would have to pass. Commenting upon the coming battle between objectors and Shell, the *Sunday Times* of 15 January 1978 said:

> Five local authorities in the north-east of Scotland have lodged objections to the project on safety grounds, and farmers in the area have formed a group to fight the proposed pipeline. Unless Shell can reconcile the objectors to the NGL pipeline, the company will be faced with *an expensive and time-consuming public inquiry*.

Perhaps the *Sunday Times* did not mean it, but the emphasis in the above passage implies that the objectors are a nuisance and expensive and could hold up progress. This, indeed, is part of the North Sea story. The oil companies are represented as being in the 'van', saving the economy and producing jobs while objectors are holding up progress.

The questions that have to be asked are too often passed over and ignored: who will benefit? who will get what kind of job? where do the profits go? and, above all, will all the affected people—including those who object to a particular development—be better off if they win or lose?

Shell's project manager, Ron Stark, claimed that although NGL has so far not been transported by pipeline in Britain the business is 'old hat' in the USA: 'The only danger is if we get a leak. But we'll be building a tight, first-class pipeline. A 100% of the weld will be X-rayed and it will be buried to a depth of 4 feet.' He failed at that point to reassure the local authorities, and a number of district councils as well as Grampian Regional Council lodged objections to the pipeline at the end of 1977 on the grounds that 'not enough is known about the potential hazards'. Moreover, local farmers and villagers in Kincardine came up with a list of incidents, some serious, to pipelines abroad. Farmers object further on the grounds of disruption, since it would be the fifth pipeline to pass through an area which has already had two gas and two oil pipelines laid through it.

The objectors want Shell to re-route either through the Grampian hills or under the sea to the Firth of Forth. Shell calculate that such a re-routing would double the cost, meaning an extra £40 million. In view of the huge sums being spent anyway, one could well argue that another £40 million was a small price to pay to obviate further local disruption as well as safeguarding against the possibility of a disaster to some isolated rural area.

Prosperity has certainly touched a different commercial sector—that of hotels, boarding houses, garages and pubs near fabrication sites or service centres. One garage, for example, obtained a contract for transporting workers near a platform site that was worth £8,000 a week. Hotels and pubs may do well taking the money from the big spenders at the construction sites, yet their old customers suffer: prices go up, the standard of amenities often goes down and the local people cannot compete and feel excluded.

None the less, though it is always possible to produce disturbing stories of the bad effects of such an industrial influx of activity, there is in fact a substantial future for Scotland in permanent investment if industry makes a determined bid to capture the offshore business properly. Over the next decade, for example, some 40,000 miles of underwater pipeline will be required worldwide and there is no reason why a proportion of this business, as of many of the others, should not be won by Scottish firms.

There has been a major influx of job seekers either from other parts of Scotland such as Glasgow, or from south of the border to work in the various yards. Thus on the big construction sites perhaps as many as 60 per cent of the men will come from Liverpool or Glasgow. Such workers are rarely savers; they spend their money freely, drink, cause problems for the local communities and then are gone. None of this is either surprising or unusual for any kind of boom situation; the problems caused, however, are part of the price that various Scottish communities have to pay for the oil boom. On the other hand, possibly 40 per cent of the construction workers will be recruited locally and they are likely to be canny with their money and save it. One major effect, most especially upon small communities, has been pressure upon housing and the consequent increase in the local building programme.

One occupation that claims to be adversely affected by oil is fishing: the Scottish Fishermen's Association (the inshore fishermen) complain that oil installations are liable to affect their catches.

As usual in any boom situation a good measure of greed has been involved. Thus, as opposed to the conservationists, there are people with land only too eager for the oil companies or the fabricators to come along and buy it. Some landowners have sold their land at high profits and in the process dispossessed farmer tenants, who in their turn have become bitter since they found little chance of securing a new farm of comparable value at the present high land prices.

Aberdeen has become known as the oil capital of Europe—justifiably in terms of the position it has assumed in relation to the North Sea. Aberdeen has been a pioneer as a new oil centre and in consequence has made mistakes as well as prospering from the oil. The speed of developments has left little time to plan how to absorb and best use some of the spin-offs from oil; the boom had already taken Aberdeen by storm in the early 1970s. Aberdeen takes a certain pride in its title of oil capital. The city is a distribution centre rather than a manufacturing one though it could well now become a specialist manufacturing centre. It enjoys far more of the oil 'action' than does Norway's Stavanger: all the majors use it as an operational base.

As soon as it was clear that Aberdeen had become the oil capital with the advantages that therefore accrued to it, a parsimonious government downgraded the city from being a development area to being an intermediate area—its first 'loss' resulting from the oil impact. The downgrading was resented by Aberdeen for the oil industry does not qualify for incentives and the indigenous non-oil industries have been put at a disadvantage: they need support so they can adjust to the changed labour market.

Aberdeen's rise to offshore prominence took place at great speed. It was chosen by the oil industry because of its harbour and road, rail and air links. In February 1977 NESDA (North East Scotland Development Authority) published an oil directory which listed 370 firms in the Grampian region—the great majority in Aberdeen and Peterhead—with 11,300 jobs directly related to oil, 3,500 on the construction of pipelines and 7,000 working for oil-related firms. It was this record of low unemployment which led government to deprive Aberdeen of its status as a development area. The figure of 370 firms had risen to 420 by mid-summer. The numbers in jobs directly related to oil had also risen to 13,000. In September 1977 the *Scotsman* reckoned that new oil-related firms were still moving into Aberdeen at the rate of one a week.

This constant increasing activity is a new phenomenon for a Scotland whose most vivid industrial memories are of recession. The steadiness of the work is reinforced by the fact that Aberdeen is not dependent upon platform orders with their huge ups and downs in labour demand; rather, it is responsible for virtually everything else, all aspects of support and maintenance.

The best indication of the demands being made upon Aberdeen by oil can be seen in the harbour where £15 million has been invested in new facilities to cope with the expanded traffic. There has been a comparable expansion of airport facilities (£5 million) to handle the growth of traffic. Aberdeen's harbour and airport together provide the basis of its assets as the centre of the service industries for oil. It also has available training facilities at the university and RGIT.

A great deal of development has gone on in Aberdeen during the 1970s as the city responded to the demands upon it: work has been done on roads and sewers, property has been refurbished, shops revamped. Thus, for example, Littlewoods store has been doubled in size to cope with new customers. The city boundaries extend eighteen miles out and some suburbs, Ellon for example, have doubled in size. Much of the oil-related housing is in ghettoes in West Aberdeen for French, American, Dutch or Canadian groups.

On the whole there has been an easy adaptation to change by Aberdonians and professional men, lawyers, doctors and accountants for example, have enjoyed a boom. On the other hand, in social terms there has been comparatively little to notice: a generally easy absorption of the newcomers though to some extent this depends upon the person to whom one is talking. Aberdeen had the advantage of size and possessed all the facilities of a substantial city to enable it to absorb new people. One of the main advantages to Aberdeen as a whole is the support to the rates that has come from the new business. Before oil came, industry was not important in Aberdeen: rather it was education, fishing and administration. Oil, however, has brought a wide variety of skilled trades into the city.

In 1970, before the boom got underway, businesses were overstaffed because of the general situation of underemployment and so at quite ordinary levels it was easy to obtain the services of painters or window cleaners; by 1977 such services were far harder to command. Similarly apprenticeships were no longer being followed since young people were going into oil activities instead. Housing prices had reportedly increased fourfold (1977) as a result of demand.

On the other hand, the city was offering a wider range of goods: British Home Stores had brought down the cost of food and the enlarged market and larger incomes meant more retail outlets. Growth in the harbour, which had taken on the handling of offshore supply vessels up to 10,000 tons and increased traffic for Orkney and Shetland, regular cargo ships to Norway, Rotterdam, the USA and the Gulf ports, was paralleled by a similar expansion of traffic handled by the airport whose passengers had increased sixfold to 700,000 a year, while the heliport had become the busiest in the world and in 1976 handled 35,000 flights. There had also been a substantial amount of capital expenditure upon offices and housing. Industrial estates have been developed and while some industry has moved out to these from the centre of the city, other new industries, especially engineering, have appeared on the scene for the first time.

In the beginning most of the incoming firms specialized in drilling and seismological services, catering and warehousing. By 1970, however, most types of oil-related enterprise were present in Aberdeen including equipment suppliers, manufacturers, steel stockholders, maintenance engineers, diving companies, telecommunications services, management consultants, translation services, geologist cartographic services and personnel recruitment agencies. By 1975 Aberdeen had more than 200 new companies covering this range of activities as well as the established local companies that had turned to some aspect of oil work.

There were 53 service companies in Aberdeen in 1976, yet of these 47 had already been there in 1972: thus, once the 'decision' to make Aberdeen the oil capital had been taken firms moved there fast. In 1970, for example, there were only 67 welders in Aberdeen: the city did not already possess an abundance of the kinds of skills it was going to need for its oil support role.

According to Mrs Deirdre Hunt of RGIT, who has done a considerable amount of research on the impact of oil upon Aberdeen, too much published information is one-sided. Economic information, for example, comes largely from the investigation of 90 companies whereas in 1977 there were 804 engineering units in Aberdeen ranging in numbers from 1 to 300 employees.

The American support companies which have moved into Aberdeen often operate in such a way as to ensure that orders go back to parent companies in the USA and unlisted firms will refer orders back to Houston or elsewhere so that the technology is kept in the USA. In a paper in *The Scottish Journal of Sociology* entitled 'The Sociology of Development: Its Relevance to Aberdeen', Mrs Hunt says:

> Movement from outside the U.K. has been dominated by movement from North America. Taking drilling services and engineering companies operating in Aberdeen in both 1972 and 1976, ten such companies had registered offices in the States, five being located in California. These companies already engaged in oil exploration elsewhere brought with them highly developed skills and already established less obvious but equally salient customer contacts. More numerous have been the movement in of U.K. companies.

In the case of such companies the work all too often goes outside Scotland back to parent firms in the USA or elsewhere in Britain.

The employment pattern of Aberdeen has significantly altered as a result of its new role. In 1970 unemployment was at 4 per cent; by

1977 it had dropped to 2 per cent, the same level as London and the southeast. There has been a long history of emigration from Aberdeen: emigrants have included numbers with higher education. In the pre-oil period an average of 2,000 a year left the Grampian region to seek work elsewhere.

The main groups recruited by new firms have been secretaries, clerical workers, engineers, junior management, technicians and, following the slump of 1973, fish workers, fish porters, drivers and fishermen. Apprenticeships which were attractive in pre-oil days subsequently had difficulty in finding recruits.

A great number of people have moved into Aberdeen according to the various phases of oil development. There were 7,000 during the exploration stage and in 1977 about 10,000, though by that year the background of these people was changing. Perhaps only 10 per cent of the 7,000 originals were qualified people. By 1977 it was possible to pinpoint social and other patterns in relation to the newcomers. A Church of Scotland minister claimed that a sort of cultural apartheid had grown up on the part of local people towards the newcomers. He blamed this upon traditional reticence, the habits of a settled community and plain snobbery. He also said that a number of myths surrounded oil people; they were not all Americans but contained a surprising number of Frenchmen, Dutch, Italians, Orientals, Spaniards and Arabs as well, the minister added, as a 'surprising number' of widely travelled Scots and English. Despite these problems Aberdeen has settled down remarkably well to live with its oil boom and the people who have come to the city as a result.

As in any such situation there have been people to argue that the quality of life has deteriorated. Almost always, however, when people make such a claim, what they really mean is that the quality of their particular life has gone down rather than that for others; in fact the quality of life for others—those who no doubt were less well off or socially placed originally than the critics—has gone up.

Aberdeen has experienced a major property boom including at least six office blocks each costing £1 million, hotel building, the expansion of the housing sector over a fifteen- to twenty-mile radius from the city. Between 10,000 and 15,000 extra people have been housed in about 4,000 houses which cost approximately £10,000 each to build. As the pressure for houses remains the waiting list has become a record for Britain.

The range of new activity oil has brought to the city can be illustrated by the announcement in October 1977 that a medical support company (Offshore Medical Support) was being set up jointly by Aberdeen University and three oil companies, BP, Esso and Shell, who were providing £100,000 for the company's headquarters. It will provide services for men working offshore and incorporate an existing diving service. Profits from the company will be used by Aberdeen University's Institute of Environmental and Offshore Medicine to develop their training and medical divisions.

A key problem for Aberdeen in the future is the question of company control. Though many companies have moved into the city, their parent companies or headquarters remain elsewhere and research is normally done at headquarters, so that little of this has moved to Aberdeen which is a bad omen for the future. Further, while in the early days of oil boom many local companies became involved, by 1972 control of a majority of them had passed to larger organizations from Glasgow, London or the USA. This is not a process which is likely to be reversed; it represents the standard economic practice of the big companies and corporations.

In 1970, average company size for manufacturing was 10 to 15 employees who received wages below the national average. Aberdeen has certainly done well out of oil; but it has not done as well as it ought to have done in the sense that a great deal of the prosperity is of a secondary nature and much of the real value of the oil boom continues to be syphoned off elsewhere.

In a paper in which she asks a number of crucial questions about the effects of oil upon Aberdeen ('Organisational Strategies and Technology Diffusion: the Case of the Oil Involved Engineering Companies in the City of Aberdeen 1977'), Deirdre Hunt points up some of the differences between a superficial incoming of technology and business and what might have been in other circumstances. Part of her argument is simply that if there had not been such a rush, inspired by a government anxious above all to solve the balance of payments problem, Aberdeen firms would have had more time to re-train so that they could cope with at least some of the new business. Instead, there came in many outside companies which relied upon infrastructure already established and operating elsewhere. Moreover, as technical newcomers they had an advantage over the Aberdeen firms because they could offer higher pay. Some local firms that did put up wages so as to compete were later fined for doing so. As Mrs Hunt says:

> The initial contribution of local companies was to offer space and provide time-served engineers. Successful Aberdeen companies therefore went into warehousing, office accommodation and haulage. Less successful companies lost key workers and became increasingly vulnerable to closure or take-over.

In time to come the Aberdeen story might be seen as a classic example of how the interests of central government have over-ridden—again and again—the interests of a particular region. Such a pattern is the kernel of much of the SNP case for independence. Thus to quote Mrs Hunt once more, she is scathing over the role of NESDA:

> But with an already existing development authority, NESDA, suddenly presiding over explosive development, the local brokers were, to their increasing anger, pre-empted. The development authority officials, with no previous experience of multi-national entrance, happily supplied all the information required by in-comers, whether about industrial sites, sources of employees, investment grants or housing availability. Local companies, faced with what they increasingly saw as a competitive invasion, felt betrayed by the very officials who as ratepayers they were supporting.

The result of NESDA appearing only to work in the interests of the incoming oil companies as though that would solve all Aberdeen's problems led to a revival of the Chamber of Commerce, which in 1974 sent a standard letter to companies that had contacted it with a view to entering the area:

> It would be extremely inadvisable for your company to consider coming to the city of Aberdeen. Industrial sites in the town are already full and labour is unavailable.

A development with far-reaching implications for the future concerns American, or other foreign, companies which have estab-lished consultants and engineers in Aberdeen whose presence has made companies feel their problems could be tackled and overcome quickly and expertly: in fact these representatives always refer such problems or sales requirements back to the parent company. This is one of the reasons why there are probably as many as 200,000 American spin-off jobs from North Sea oil compared with about 55,000 in Scotland. The strategy is designed to maintain the dominance of the parent company; it also prevents local research or development breaking the monopoly of the parent company.

Part of the oil development picture in Scotland, as Mrs Hunt points out, concerns the extent to which new companies

> . . . retained manufacturing and research and development outside the area, generated only low-level employment, imported technical and managerial staff, meanwhile making, due to their rapid build-up, greatly accelerated demands on local physical infrastructures: transport, roads, harbours, airports, communications, telephones, telexes, warehouse space. . . .

It is a picture that is all too familiar throughout the so-called developing world. The fact is that though at first Aberdeen may appear to have done very well out of oil, other areas in the USA, England or Europe have done better. Moreover, outside companies have bought up the local firms which might otherwise have competed, so that a number of companies which were formerly Aberdeen-owned have become part of wider conglomerates and are controlled from outside the area.

The population of Shetland according to the 1971 census was 17,327; by December 1975 it had risen to an estimated 19,069; and in 1976 was added a further 457 so that in January 1977 the total stood at 19,526. For a tiny community these increases are huge; they are largely oil-related.

In his book, *Shetland and Oil*, James Nicolson says:

> A symptom of Shetland's decline was the stress placed on education; for education was not designed to equip school-leavers to live and work successfully within the islands: it was regarded as a passport to a good job on the British mainland.

The islands in fact received a major boost in 1965 when the Highlands and Islands Development Board was established so that the fishing industry was helped with grants and loans. By 1971 Shetland's white fish catch was worth four times what it had been ten years earlier. During the 1960s the knitwear industry went through a period of great growth, crofting underwent a revolution and subsistence crofting changed to rearing sheep and cattle for sale. By 1970 the islands had come to support 7,000 cattle and more than 260,000 sheep. At the same time a number of smaller ventures outside the traditional areas of fishing, knitwear and crofting were started. Thus when the oil era arrived Shetland was prosperous; as a result it was in a strong position to bargain with the oil companies.

The impact of oil upon Shetland has been profound; one result was the Zetland County Council Act of 1974 which gave to the council the power to acquire land, to set up a reserve fund in which to bank oil venture profits and to run the marine facilities at Sullom Voe. These powers enabled the council to outflank land speculators. Shetland argued that it was making sacrifices for the national interest in allowing the huge terminal at Sullom Voe; therefore it should be compensated. By the end of the century the council will have received more than £50 million in disturbance payments from the oil companies in return for the right to land their oil at the terminal. When devolution became an issue Shetland looked warily at what might come out of Edinburgh. She is not enthusiastic for any form of devolution.

Meanwhile the oil companies are determined to show how well they are handling a small community and what benefits their presence will bring to it. They will in fact make huge profits. Shetland also is determined to make as much as possible from the oil and on the whole drove a hard bargain with the companies. At the time of the negotiations the Council was led by Ian Clark, who is now deputy to Lord Kearton in BNOC and not exactly loved by the oil companies.

Certainly an added prosperity has come to Shetland: the shops have increased their turnover, the restaurants are full and the hotels are doing an all-year business and charging top prices. The hospital had to extend its services to be able to deal with injured men from the site. There were other unexpected changes such as a huge increase in the demand for water at Lerwick. Except for lamb and fish just about everything else has to be freighted into Shetland; but since so much is being freighted in for the oil terminal development, local non-terminal freight is subject to long delays at Aberdeen. One good result of these delays is the development of a new route via Scrabster. Delays of up to six weeks have also developed for freight coming from Grangemouth. These setbacks are bad for local business and have caused local dissatisfaction as a result. On another level, wholesalers have been bought out while both hotel and bed and breakfast establishments' prices have risen so much as to make it too expensive for many tourists.

When Shetland was proposed as a convenient landfall for North Sea oil, the islanders were interested. As Nicolson says:

> The prospect of Shetland being used as a kind of super service base was well received by the islanders in general. They welcomed the prospect of harbours long idle being revitalized and new quays, constructed at the expense of oil companies, being utilized by local fishing fleets long after oil-related activities had ceased.

In April 1972 the Shetland Island Council accepted the recommendations of its Policy Committee, 'that land required for the oil industry should be acquired by the County Council, by compulsory purchase if necessary, to ensure controlled development'. The Council appointed its own Oil Consultant, a Shetlander who had senior executive experience in the oil industry. Also that year a Shetland company, Nautical Services (Shetland) Limited, set up at Scalloway offering a complete range of services to oil companies operating in Shetland waters. Then, as the scale of the proposed Sullom Voe terminal became apparent, fears grew concerning the number of people who would come to the island and their effect upon its life. These fears were increased when the size of Brent became known; conservationists saw the islands being engulfed in oil and the possibility of 10,000 'incomers' was mooted. In August 1972 the *Shetland Times* said:

It is almost pathetic that the Government, pinning its hopes on oil for the economic salvation of Scotland, seems to have left it to a relatively impoverished local authority to wrestle with the enormous infrastructural problems the oil boom has created.

Perhaps the strictures of the *Shetland Times* were justified; there is no evidence to suggest that Shetland, then and later, did not in fact relish its role.

Obviously the first question for Shetlanders was what they stood to gain from the oil boom. There was the justifiable fear that after a boom of a decade or so the whole business would collapse, leaving behind many problems and an emigrating community. An informal referendum in the island showed, however, that three-quarters of the people favoured some form of oil-related development.

When in March 1973 Shetland was discussed in the House of Commons, Willie Hamilton who combines a nice turn of phrase with some often peculiar flights of fancy managed to paint a picture of an almost idyllic people faced by ruthless villains from outside. He spoke of 'the simple gentle people' of the Highlands and Islands being outwitted by the 'land-grabbing Mafia of Edinburgh and Texas'. A good many of the oilmen who had to deal with Shetland's Ian Clark found he was anything but simple, and that when it came to negotiations he was as tough as anyone in the oil world. No doubt, as they eyed the small rural Shetland community, the oilmen from the huge multinationals thought they could obtain what they wanted easily enough. However, the simple gentle people turned out to be shrewd tough operators. What is most appealing about the Shetland story is the fact that a small community really did exceptionally well in bargaining with the oil companies, and Shetlanders obviously take a certain pride in their 'Jack the Giant-killer' stance. At the same time, of course, they wanted the business and the extra wealth that oil would bring.

It is generally a fallacy to believe that remote rural areas only want to remain remote and rural. The people who believe that are either outsiders who visit such places for holidays or local landowners or retired people who do not want to be disturbed. If and when the possibility of major developments occur for such regions, the average person—despite any problems that may also come with the developments—is only too anxious for these to take place, since they are likely to mean greater prosperity, better jobs and more opportunities for his children. Such considerations undoubtedly held good in Shetland.

As oil came nearer, the Island entrepreneurs began to reorganize their businesses so as to take advantage of the coming boom. In October 1972, the County Council's Interim Development Plan was approved. Special consideration was given to the Island's three main industries—fishing, agriculture and knitwear. Sullom Voe was identified as the area most suitable for major oil development. The Shetland Planning Authority was to take four steps: designate areas for major oil development; carry out an independent survey to confirm or otherwise the choice of sites; obtain private legislation to give port and harbour powers to the County Council; and purchase land to ensure controlled development.

There was opposition in Shetland to the powers being sought over land; the Crofters Union as well as fishermen at first objected. Then in 1973 a Select Committee visited Shetland and its Chairman and two Tory members opposed compulsory purchase powers; the Council would not accept defeat, especially as it was becoming clear that the oil was much greater than had at first been thought, so that any landfall in Shetland would have major repercussions upon the life of the Island. At a Shetland Council meeting of September 1973 it was resolved:

> This County Council, recognizing that it may be in the national interest that Shetland be used for oil installations, and having sought to devise policies and to provide machinery which recognizes the national interest while protecting those of the Shetland Community, will continue to have regard for the national interest but will give no encouragement to developments and will oppose proposals where these developments or proposals put Shetland at unnecessary risk or fail to provide available safeguards and will at no time put commercial or industrial interests before those of the Shetland Community.

It is rare indeed to find a resolution of a County Council paying such attention to the national interest. In fact the Shetland Council was serving notice on the oil companies that a landfall in Shetland would cost them dear. The Council went to great lengths to ensure that it got maximum advantages for Shetland out of the oil and that the onus for action was placed squarely upon the oil companies.

A year later agreement was reached in Lerwick between the Shetland County Council and the major oil companies and their associates, which guaranteed to the County Council payments of at least £25 million up to 2000 as financial compensation for disturbance. This agreement cleared the way for the Sullom Voe terminal to be constructed: it was to be capable of handling 200 million tons of crude oil a year. By then it was clearly recognized in Shetland that the impact of oil would produce a number of benefits: better roads and harbours, more hotels (if also more expensive) as well as better living standards for the people.

The oil companies were inefficient in their bargaining in Shetland: there were at first some fifty-seven companies with various stakes in the two pipeline systems that were to use Sullom Voe, that from Brent (Shell-Esso) and that from the Ninian system (BP), and they found it very difficult to form a common front. For the Council Clark lifted the stakes at one stage, forcing the companies to start negotiations again. Moreover, they were challenged over points of expertise. When Shell wanted to bring in the Brent pipeline at a certain point, the fishermen advised an alternative, arguing that the pipeline would surface because of currents. The oilmen said, 'Leave us to deal with oil matters, you fish.' The pipeline did subsequently surface.

There was a RAF base at Sullom Voe during the Second World War, housing 15,000 men, so the area is not totally without experience of large ventures. When completed the terminal will handle about three tankers a day, which is a large amount of shipping by any standards. Sullom Voe business divides into two: the construction phase (now behind schedule) which was supposed to be completed by 1980; and the permanent running of the terminal. By mid 1977 the construction phase had brought some 3,000 temporary workers to the island; the second phase will account for about 600 to 750 permanent jobs.

Sullom Voe is to be developed as an oil service and storage centre whose facilities will be leased to the various oil companies. The site was chosen because it fulfilled two vital requirements: there was a large flat area for the terminal near the deep water of the Voe and it was situated as far as possible from the Island's centres of population. Sullom Voe can handle vessels of up to 100,000 dwt at all states of the tide. Estimates suggest that as much as 200,000 tons of crude oil a day could be pumped ashore at Sullom Voe by 1980. Because of the need to stop tanker operations in bad weather, there will be storage capacity at the terminal for 5 million tons. The possibilities go farther: Sullom Voe might take on a role as a trans-shipment port for oil from the Gulf to northern Europe.

The cost of the terminal has been upgraded several times; it is now expected to cost in excess of £670 million. Oil from the Ninian pipeline is due during May 1978 and the amount coming ashore from the Ninian and Brent pipelines will build up to more than 1 million b/d by 1980. The terminal is being built so that it can expand to handle as much as 3 million b/d.

Alongside the terminal new residential and social facilities are being created. The Council decided against allowing a company town and instead four villages near Sullom Voe—Brae, Voe, Mossbank and Toft—were chosen for settlement and expansion. When all the temporary construction workers have left, there will still be a substantial influx of people to accommodate permanently and their presence will have its effect upon education, health, shopping and recreational facilities.

It is a huge development and in a small community potentially enormously disruptive. Shetland appears to have coped remarkably well. None the less the oil business has had a number of bad effects upon the life of the Island. Milk is no longer delivered and the one small overstrained laundry was trying to sell out in 1977 because it could no longer find labour at a reasonable cost. The hotels had to import staff from Glasgow and elsewhere because former employees had gone into oil, and fish processing had suffered for the same reason. The knitwear industry has also been badly hit: there is a high demand for its products but only 50 per cent of this is now being met. The fishing industry was regarded as the most valuable in the Island; now there are fears that the men will go over to oil work, for example as crews on standby vessels. There are also fears that the pipelines will destroy valuable fishing grounds which they cross and that spillages—sooner or later—will damage the Island.

Sumburgh airport has developed from a small sleepy strip into a hive of activity. Both British Airways and Bristow Helicopters have established bases there and by 1974 it had developed from handling one daily flight from Aberdeen to handling as many as ninety-seven flights in one day. In 1970 the Sumburgh area (the airport in effect) had six employees; by 1980 it is expected to have 400. The airport has become one of the busiest in Britain with helicopter flights to the fields and charter flights taking oil personnel to and from the mainland. The service to Aberdeen has also suddenly become profitable; in 1975 the return fare was £30, but by 1977 this had increased to £54 which was very expensive for the ordinary Shetlander. Another effect, comparable on a small scale to what has been happening in Aberdeen, is the purchase of Shetland companies by larger concerns from outside, with the result that profits are not reinvested in Shetland but drained southwards. All major Shetland companies, including the hotels, have been bought out. In the light of the impact of oil upon the Island's traditional occupations Shetland certainly needs the cash compensation that it is to receive from the oil companies.

On devolution Shetland is less than enthusiastic. And taking this fact into account, the government in November 1977 arranged that voting for the Scottish devolution referendum should be counted by region so that Shetland's stand could be clearly seen. During the devolution debate Jo Grimond, MP for Orkney and Shetland, steered into the bill an amendment that would allow Orkney and Shetland to exclude themselves from the Devolution Bill if a majority of the islanders were to vote against devolution in a referendum. In such a case a commission would have to be set up to study the relationship of the islands to any Scottish assembly.

On the whole Shetland is happy as it is and sees little advantage to itself in devolution; nor does it contemplate with equanimity control from Edinburgh rather than Westminster. This is neither a helpful nor welcome stance from the viewpoint of the SNP. Shetland obviously wants to hold on to the very considerable power which the Council already has rather than opt for minuscule independence or some other alternative—always depending upon what ultimately emerges from the devolution debate at Westminster. As the Chairman of the Shetland Island Council said in April 1978:

> We have been given ministerial assurances that nothing will be changed, but one government cannot speak for the next, and it seems that an early task of the Scottish Assembly will be to reorganize local government. That means us. All we seek is to have Shetland's autonomy safeguarded by law. I mean, we really are the most reasonable unreasonable people you are likely to meet.

The other island in the group, Orkney, has also been affected by oil but on a more modest scale. When the Occidental Consortium had confirmed the Piper field, they had to find a suitable landfall terminal and after considering nine sites finally decided upon Flotta in Orkney. Flotta Island is in Scapa Flow; it has a sheltered anchorage and deep water and both local and central government felt it was a suitable site. The terminal is designed to provide storage of up to 250,000 b/d for Piper and various processing facilities. When Claymore was discovered arrangements were made to expand the terminal to handle that production as well.

A great deal of thought about the impact upon the environment went into the planning of the Flotta terminal. Two main problems had to be considered: the general effects and scale of the project, and its impact upon plant and animal life. Social effects also had to be considered, though mainly only for the construction phase when large numbers of people would be temporarily involved. At the Offshore Technology Conference it was claimed:

> The design and construction of the Flotta Terminal and its successful integration into a small and primarily agrarian community has been largely due to the effective synthesis of engineering and environmental skills which has existed since the inception of the project.

1 *(facing page)* Production platform FB (Graythorp II) in BP's Forties oil field with platform FD (Highland Two) in the background

2a Graythorp II jacket section of production platform for the Forties
oil field on tow to site. 2b Graythorp II on tow to the Forties field.

3a   Aerial view of the Sullom Voe terminal under construction.
3b   Pipeline across Scotland before 'burying'.

4 (facing page)　The world's largest movable object, the 600,000 tonnes Ninian Central oil platform, in the Inner Sound of Raasay.　5a　The signing of the participation agreement between the Government, Shell and Esso, November 1977. Left to right: Dr Austin Pearce, Chairman of Esso Petroleum Company Ltd, Mr Tony Benn, Secretary of State for Energy, Mr Peter Baxendell, Chairman of Shell UK Ltd.　5b　The Prime Minister, the Rt Hon James Callaghan, on the occasion of his visit to BP's Forties field in September 1977.

6   Graythorp I in BP's Forties field, with supply vessel in the foreground.

7a The sea beneath a platform. 7b A robot submersible plumbs the North Sea.

The Occidental Group went to great trouble to satisfy the environmentalists in Orkney that they had the good of the community at heart and they spared no expense in their investigations. In an impressive operation on behalf of the group, W. J. Cairns and Associates (Urban and Regional Planning Consultants and Consulting Landscape Architects of Edinburgh) produced impressive reports on Flotta: 'An Environmental Assessment', 'Visual Impact Analysis Landscape Proposals' and 'Marine Environment Protection'. These reports were quickly followed by approval and the go-ahead for the terminal.

Like Shetland, Orkney has a population of some 17,000 and is a prosperous community dominated by agriculture, whisky distilling and tourism. The oil terminal will produce rates; but at the beginning of 1978 it was far from clear how much would come from this source because the Occidental Group was in the process of claiming industrial derating and the Island was appealing about it. Even so, there will be substantial income from this source, though hardly on the Shetland scale.

Outsiders may think that the islands are doing remarkably well out of oil which they neither discovered nor are developing; but to people who for years have been in backwaters, neglected or ignored by Westminster, oil wealth means they can do something to safeguard the future of communities which otherwise would almost certainly continue to be bypassed. Moreover, the ups-and-downs of the oil business should not be ignored. The fortunes of the remote islands off Scotland have rarely been easy. In April 1978, as a reminder of this, 300 employees of Lewis Offshore, the oil rig construction base at Arnish Point, Stornoway, were given redundancy notices because of the lack of orders. The news of these dismissals came in the wake of redundancies at a knitwear factory and a fish-processing plant. The islands are prudent to grasp anything they can from the oil boom.

9

8 *(facing page)* Drilling platform FC (Highland One) in BP's Forties field with crane barge *Thor* alongside

13

Other Energy Sources

Britain's energy policy was founded upon coal for generations while for a short time in the 1950s the country led the world in the production of nuclear energy for peaceful purposes. It is one of the ironies of the North Sea story that the NCB applied for the block containing the Forties Field, which was of course awarded to BP. In 1978 the field should make £800 million profit. Had the award been made to the NCB instead, the Corporation would be in a far more commanding and glamorous position than is now the case.

Since energy experts predict that as world oil supplies seriously decline, so coal will come back into its own, the coal industry is planning to produce substantially more coal by the 1990s. Exhaustion of mines leads to the loss of between 2 and 3 million tons capacity a year, so there has to be constant reinvestment for replacement. At present the industry is producing approximately 110 million tons a year; for this capacity to be raised to one of 150 million tons by 2000, the development of not less than 100 million tons new capacity must be achieved. In fact the plan is to produce 170 million tons by the end of the century.

At present the NCB's major coal markets are as follows: electricity takes 65 per cent of production; carbonization for the steel industry 12 per cent; the general industrial market 10 per cent; the domestic market 11 per cent; exports, currently worth about £75 million, about 2 per cent. The biggest growth area lies with the generation of electricity, especially if oil is to be increasingly channelled into its premium uses only, so that electricity production has to depend upon coal and nuclear power. In Britain coal supplies a higher proportion of energy requirements than in any other OECD country except Luxembourg.

Coal is not a preferred fuel, although resources are enormous. At current prices economically recoverable coal in Britain is in the region of 6,000 million tons; but technologically recoverable coal is at a staggering 45,000 million tons. The 6,000 million tons at present rates of consumption will last another 50 years; the 45,000 million tons more than 300 years. According to Michael Clarke, chief geologist of the NCB, reserves are even greater; it is a matter of developing the technology to mine them. Although there are perhaps 160,000 million tons of coal in all the known reserves, there could be ten times that amount either below a depth of 4,000 feet or under the North Sea.

This may be an encouraging long-term prospect; but it does not solve immediate problems for the NCB, although it provides an indefinite base for a coal energy policy. A recent OECD report suggested that coal consumption in Europe could rise quite substantially by 1985 and that coal would compete with imported oil, especially for electricity generation. At present, despite North Sea oil, Britain is the only important European coal producer to plan a significant increase in its production capacity over the next ten years; Britain is also the leader in coal extraction technology.

The NCB programme envisages an expansion to 135 million tons a year output by 1985, of which 120 million tons will come from deep pits. The NCB is now sinking new deep pits, the largest being the giant complex at Selby in Yorkshire. In the very long term with oil running out, Britain with twice the reserves of West Germany in the EEC could well become the Community's major coal supplier. Speaking in 1977 Sir Derek Ezra, Chairman of the NCB, said:

> We are planning a new coal industry. By the year 2000 we want two thirds of the industry's capacity to be new or reconstructed, producing coal by new methods at new levels of efficiency and used in new ways, particularly as a source of oil gas and chemicals. We will need to invest between £350m and £400m every year between now and the end of the century. For all these reasons decisions on our Plan 2000, in the context of an energy strategy for Britain, must not long be delayed.

The future of the coal industry, however, depends upon price and coal is neither the cheapest available fuel nor the cleanest or easiest to handle. In a report entitled 'Coal for the Future: Progress with Plan for Coal and Prospects to the Year 2000' the industry contends it will add another 42 million tons of new colliery capacity up to 1985, and that over the longer term it should aim to increase capacity to an annual production of 170 million tons. That programme will require the commissioning of an average of 4 million tons new capacity every year from the mid 1980s to the end of the century.

Despite major expansion plans for the future, the coal industry has to face some substantial problems in the present. 1977 showed a profit for the NCB of £27·2 million and the trend is continuing, but these financial improvements were made against a background of declining output and productivity. Coal has experienced a steady decline since the advent of cheap oil and gas after the Second World War. Throughout these years it has been unpopular to plough development money back into coal, and probably only the political strength of the National Union of Mineworkers (NUM) ensured that the industry received as much attention as it did. If coal is to be revitalised, it will require large capital expenditures over the next twenty-five years. Moreover, much of this expenditure will be made upon a base that, technologically speaking, has been allowed to fall behind some of its competitor fuels. Coal is seriously hampered by the lack of modern technology for burning the fuel in a more efficient and environmentally less objectionable manner than, for example, is the case with power stations.

A turning point for coal came in 1973. For years the industry had been run down by successive governments as a matter of policy, on the assumption advanced in the 1967 White Paper on Energy Policy that 'regular supplies of oil at competitive prices will continue to be available'. The fivefold increase in the price of oil and the Arab boycott that followed the Yom Kippur war meant a re-appraisal of the role of coal; in the new circumstances it was obvious that coal would become more competitive again. Writing in *The Observer* on the long-term future of coal in September 1976, Sir Derek Ezra made a point that applies to Britain's entire energy policy:

> Energy is at its most costly when there isn't enough of it. We are now learning this painfully over water supplies. So, if we are to err in our energy planning, let us make sure it is in the direction of over-sufficiency rather than under-sufficiency. Above all, let us keep all our indigenous options open.

The NUM is one of the most powerful unions in Britain. Their power is clearly a factor of immense importance in ensuring the continuation of the coal industry at its present level; it could well have been run down a good deal more during the period of cheap oil but for union pressures, and also the fact that coal had been nationalized in 1947 and coal-producing areas are major industrial areas of great political sensitivity. The line taken by the NUM usually becomes a pace-setter for other union wage demands. The fact that coal production despite modern technology remains a labour-intensive industry and one that is dirty, hard and dangerous, means that the miners can rely upon greater public sympathy in their demands than is accorded to other industrial groups. The NCB has worked hard to introduce an incentive scheme to tie productivity to wages. Dominating any coal developments is the relative position of coal and oil; at present coal has a modest price advantage, but this could be eliminated by a coal price rise of 10 per cent over oil, which could lead to a loss of coal sales of five million tons a year, mainly to electricity.

Currently, coal supplied for the giant modern power stations is between £3 and £5 a ton cheaper than oil; for smaller stations it is commensurately less cheap. In the controversy that surrounded the commissioning of the Drax B power station in Yorkshire, the NCB was urgently for its being ordered early since it will burn coal. The power stations remain the key to the health of the coal industry.

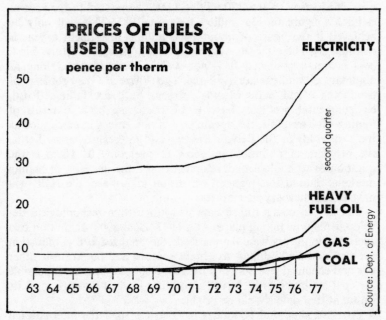

PRICES OF FUELS USED BY INDUSTRY
pence per therm
Source: Dept. of Energy

All energy forecasts for Britain as a whole now place increasing emphasis upon maintaining a healthy coal industry. Since 1974 there has been peace in the pits, and as a result business is more prepared to consider coal rather than oil as a fuel, although industrial unrest could easily reverse this trend. The government promotes coal sales by its policy of insisting upon coal-burning power stations for the CEGB, as well as subsidizing the South of Scotland Electricity Board to burn coal. On present evidence, were coal left to free market forces without government help, the industry would contract further. Its expansion for the future, therefore, depends upon a coherent and stable long-term energy policy that will not change with every new government. This is perhaps to ask a great deal, but coal ought to remain at the centre of Britain's energy industry.

At the heart of many coal problems is the question of labour.

Thus by 1980 in the Coal Board's own words the proposed new retirement age is going to 'force the industry to contract at a time when it planned to expand'.

In March 1974 a Tripartite Group was set up consisting of government, the NCB and unions to look at coal industry problems and prospects. The group produced 'Coal for the Future'. At present, exploration is adding 500 million tons a year to the reserves. The target of an added 30 million tons capacity by the year 2000 will raise production to 165–170 million tons, as opposed to the present estimated figure of 135 million tons for 1985. This will only be achieved if the figure of about £400 million investment a year is maintained. These targets depend upon a number of factors. First, coal is not a preferred fuel, nor will it become one as long as abundant oil and gas are available. Then there are the problems of productivity and manpower: at present both are falling. Third, environmental problems have to be overcome both in terms of mining—for example, the opening up of new mines in areas such as the Cotswolds or the Belvoir Valley—and in terms of use—that is, the problem of pollution and how to overcome it. There is the question of technological developments and the question of finding markets. Should this planned expansion take place, the NCB will have to find new export markets.

The key to coal's future may lie with certain technological developments now taking place. At a 1977 'Coal 2000' exhibition two such developments were emphasized: the fluidized bed combustion process, and coal refining to obtain gaseous and liquid fuels, other oils and chemical feedstocks. If by 2000 technology makes it possible for coal at source to be turned into other forms of energy, then its future at that date should be bright.

Provided that coal continues to cost less than the international oil price, it should be in demand and the demand for it should rise. There is at present a natural hierarchy of coal use: efficient (bulk) power stations; less efficient (smaller) power stations; bulk use in large industry; bulk use in small industry; SNG conversion. As coal moves down this scale, so it requires larger differentials in price to maintain its attraction.

For efficient major power stations, a gross price advantage of 1p a therm is enough; by the time coal is being converted to gas for home use it requires a price advantage of 10p a therm. Thus at present coal is competitive with other fuels for power stations, barely so for industry but not competitive for other uses. It will be a long time before it is competitive for home use. Coal's most obvious market remains bulk combustion; it should, therefore, aim to displace both oil and natural gas in industry.

Since the major market for coal is the power stations, the industry has a vested interest in the way these are developed. In the long run coal's other main competitor will be nuclear power. At present two provisos govern the future expansion of coal: the first, that there is no major nuclear expansion programme which pre-empts coal's electricity power station markets; second, that gas supplies do substantially drop.

According to the NCB, coal plans are not much affected by North Sea oil discoveries. Rather, the NCB believes that as long as coal is cheaper than the international price of oil, the production of coal will make possible an exportable surplus of oil. At present coal meets 40 per cent of the country's energy requirements; if this percentage is reduced, it will mean a cutback in the surplus of oil for export. The option of a controlled depletion of oil must depend on coal resources; there is a case for coal that is not affected by either cost or the quantity of oil.

A huge British nuclear programme would of course lead to a cutback in coal production, especially as the major market in each case is bulk supplies for electricity. At present the aim is to quadruple nuclear supplies of power by the year 2000.

On the question of price, the NCB reckon that every increase in the price of coal by 10 per cent means a loss of orders for 7 million tons of coal. Such a price increase would be likely to follow a 20 per cent wage increase. The miners usually command a great deal of press publicity in Britain, especially when they are militant in pursuit of wage claims; in fact by 1977 they were only just above the industrial wage average. They had not, therefore, improved their relative earnings at all, despite the massive strikes of 1972 and 1974. Indeed they are less prosperous in relation to other industrial workers than in the 1950s. It is essential that the miners should be both prosperous and competitive if the industry is to do well and attract new labour, though whether this situation will be achieved by the Scargill type of union confrontation is another matter. Back in the early 1950s when the country was totally dependent upon coal, the NCB could recruit easily when it was offering a wage 25 per cent above the industrial average. The NCB still feels it should offer a premium of up to 25 per cent over the national wage average if it is to get the men it needs.

New discoveries of coal are made all the time. A typical recent example was a new field under the Firth of Forth with 50 million tons of reserves in an area of about four square miles off Musselburgh near Edinburgh: according to the NCB, this field which should cost £20 million to exploit could provide employment for 500 men for 100 years. The new mines to be developed in the Vale of

Belvoir over the next twelve years at a cost of £500 million are estimated to have reserves worth £10,000 million. The central mine of the three near the village of Hose will produce 3 million tons of coal a year, the approximate equivalent of an oil field producing between 30,000 and 40,000 barrels of oil a day. The other two fields in the Vale will produce about 2 million tons each. Eventually the three mines should employ 3,800 men, half of whom would be skilled craftsmen. When coal is analysed in this fashion as an equivalent to oil, its huge and continuing importance to the economy can be better understood.

The vital need for an overall national energy policy was highlighted in relation to the NCB's plan for the Belvoir Valley by the President of the NFU, in a letter to *The Times* of August 1977. He said:

> It is not denied that coal forms a vital part of the nation's energy resources, but it is also a fact that at the present time 73 per cent of the coal mined in this country is burnt, somewhat inefficiently, in generating electricity, and that it is the present intention of the Coal Board to use the Belvoir coal for its power station customers. It can be strongly argued that in the long term, the remaining stocks of coal are too precious to be consumed in this way.
>
> However, what is much more important is that by the end of the century, the world's food situation could be more critical than the fuel situation, and as the world's main importer of food, the United Kingdom will be particularly vulnerable. This is why a comprehensive energy policy that takes full account of the relative demands on the land is so necessary.

It has recently become part of the conventional wisdom for energy experts, including oil men, to talk of coal as the long-term key to Britain's energy, especially as technology will eventually enable it to be transformed into other fuels. Over the short term, however, the security of that future will depend upon prices. In 1976, for example, BP's P. G. Milne, a managing director and chief executive, argued that oil should relinquish to coal some of its traditional markets. Coal, he said, is the most plentiful fossil fuel and should be at the centre of a long-term world energy policy until the nuclear age arrives. A number of oil companies are taking stakes in coal finds round the world and beginning to describe themselves as energy rather than simply oil companies.

The Norwegian Parliamentary Report (No 25) which examines the Petroleum Industry in Norwegian Society makes the point:

> When for example it is technically possible to convert coal to gas in the mines, coal could then become as valuable as oil is

today. This could revolutionize the situation for the British industry.

In technological terms, that day is not very far distant.

Meanwhile the industry has to contend with plenty of problems. For example, open-cast mining, which has always been profitable for the NCB, is in fact limited by agreement with the unions, so that it only supplements output from the deep mines when these fail to meet demand. Such a limitation is union-political and not technological, and the NCB will face many difficulties in persuading the unions to accept all aspects of technological advance.

In answer to an invitation from Sir Derek Ezra in 1977, various companies from outside the industry presented ideas for mining in the future. One possibility advanced for exploiting the huge coal deposits which the oil companies have located more than two miles beneath the bed of the North Sea is to use nuclear explosions to mine the coal. Another idea is microbe mining, the use of bacteria to break up coal underground. Of all the ideas under examination, the most important and far advanced is to gasify coal underground, a process already under experiment in the USA, Belgium and West Germany. Many ideas about the technology to be applied to coal are now being examined. Joint NCB studies with BP into the possibilities of converting coal into liquid fuels—high grade chemical feedstocks and petrol—are being conducted.

Sir Derek Ezra regards coal and oil as complementary fuels, not alternatives, and thinks that because of its limited reserves, oil should be used in more valuable ways than for bulk heating in power stations; coal should continue to be the major fuel for power generation, as it is now. He argues this ought to be a simple rule to apply, particularly the need to commission new coal-fired power station capacity. The trouble is that in the short term the ready availability of oil and the temporary lack of any price incentive to change to coal seem to make such a rule difficult to apply.

The immediate future of coal must be greatly affected by oil. Sir Derek Ezra says that while there is no point in flooding the market with oil, the government must also take account of the advantages to the balance of payments of building up production of indigenous oil. So, instead of being solved, the real problem for the nation remains: offshore oil will be over-produced rather than conserved.

The price of oil is the dominant energy price and will remain so into the 1990s. He stresses that no one seriously doubts that oil prices will be sent escalating again by OPEC, enabling coal progressively to regain some of the business lost in the past. Coal will come into its own when the oil shortage begins to become acute, and the time for

9*

industry to turn to alternative fuels will come when the oil price rises steeply after supplies have passed their peak in the 1990s. He naturally welcomes the government's assurance, given in tripartite talks also involving the NCB and the mining trade unions, that short-term market fluctuations should not jeopardize the industry's longer-term plans to increase coal supplies.

The mineworkers' productivity incentive scheme could herald a new era of union-NCB relations. Whether they work out this way remains to be seen. Speaking of the incentive scheme to *Business News* Sir Derek said:

The move on to an incentive scheme honours the undertaking that the board and the unions gave to the Government in 1974, when the tripartite report on the future of the coal industry leading to the current investment programme was agreed. The country will now get a better return on that investment.

One of the effects of the widespread debate in the industry that preceded the introduction of the scheme has been that everyone is talking and thinking about output and productivity in a way we have not known for several years. This must be good.

He regards the incentive scheme as the best possible way to reward mine workers for the extra effort of using machines to mine more coal, in this way increasing the industry's efficiency and ensuring its continuing ability to compete on price with rival fuels. The NCB is determined to put every effort into its search for overseas markets. The long-term future of coal depends upon new investment and development plans, coupled with intensive research to perfect new ways of using coal, particularly for conversion into transport fuels and chemical feedstocks.

If the future of coal is problematic so, too, is that of nuclear energy. Here politics are even more of an acute problem. Possibly one of the greatest advantages to accrue from the discovery of oil under the British continental shelf will be the breathing space it provides for the country to plan the best possible nuclear energy policy. As Mr Cunningham, the Under-Secretary of State for Energy, told the Royal Institution in 1977, it was not a matter of retaining the option of nuclear power but simply one of the scale on which nuclear power should eventually be used. This view is generally supported by people working in energy, all of whom see the finite resources of fossil fuel coming to an end or at least so dwindling that the price must become ever higher.

On the other hand, Lord Avebury, President of the Conservation Society, holds the view that a comfortable life will be possible in the future without enormous recourse to nuclear power. The debate is far from easy. Nuclear power projects designed to come on stream in the later 1980s or early 1990s must be planned and commissioned now. Esso forecasters, however, argue that less nuclear power would be needed at that time if we can be certain of coal—by which they mean price. A nuclear programme must in any case be dependent upon the world demand for uranium; to save uranium, therefore, the pressure for fast breeder reactors will grow stronger.

There are a number of possibilities open to Britain for her long-term nuclear programme, but the choices need to be made now. If, as expected, Britain goes ahead with the reprocessing of waste fuels at Windscale in order to extract re-usable uranium, then in a sense this decision pre-empts the other available options and means that Britain also goes for the fast breeder reactor which uses such fuels. It is argued by some politicians that there is no need for too hasty a decision over this matter (and Benn himself, the responsible minister during the height of the nuclear debate in 1977, was clearly reluctant to make a quick decision), since at present Britain's electrical generating capacity exceeds peak demand by 40 per cent; that fact, however, should not be used as an excuse to put off a nuclear programme decision.

At present, nuclear power produces about 12 per cent of total energy needs. The importance of nuclear decisions taken now lies in what happens when, at the end of the century, oil and gas resources begin (on present predictions) seriously and rapidly to decline. Then nuclear energy must take up a great proportion of the gap. It will be vital that the country has the right 'mix' of reactors and the programme to build these must, at the latest, be launched early in the 1980s.

There are several possibilities: the Steam Generating Heavy Water Reactor, which government has now abandoned after an expenditure of £145 million, was one possibility. There is the Advanced Gas-cooled Reactor (AGR) which is now coming into operation under the second programme of atomic power station building. And thirdly, there is the American Light Water Reactor which uses reprocessed waste fuels. There is also a Canadian possibility—Candu—which is designed to store waste fuel for forty or fifty years rather than reprocess it.

The technical arguments are endless and the merits of the various types of reactor beyond the scope of this book. The political decision, however, has to be made: or rather, several political decisions. The first is the size and scope of the British nuclear programme: what percentage of total energy needs ought to be provided by nuclear power in the twenty-first century. This decision in turn will depend upon the amount of investment put into the research and development of the coal industry, and the extent to which coal, in its turn, is intended to expand to take up the slack. Both nuclear and coal decisions will, in their turn, be affected to some extent by work that is done upon renewable sources of energy—solar, wave and wind power.

After a firm decision has been taken as to the scope of the nuclear programme will come the need for the secondary political decisions as to which reactors to adopt. Early in 1978, however, it seemed the government was hedging its bets, taking only partial decisions that left open the possibility of rapid policy switches in the future.

The importance of nuclear energy for the future may be more immediate elsewhere in Europe, where there are at present no prospects of oil, than in Britain. The two-year argument in the EEC as to whether the Community's thermo-nuclear fusion experimental project for Joint European Torus (JET) should be based at Culham in Oxfordshire or Garching in West Germany simply underlined this concern—apart from nationalist reasons of prestige. Mr Benn said of the project, once it was decided to site it in Britain, that it 'opens up a new and virtually inexhaustible source of energy for the twenty-first century.'

After the go-ahead was given for Culham, up to five years were needed simply to construct the JET which is a giant test rig designed to simulate the reactor conditions required for thermo-nuclear fusion. Thereafter, ten years of experiments will probably be needed, and if these are successful, a pilot reactor will then be built from which a range of commercial reactors will eventually be developed for the generation of electric power. This timescale illustrates why nuclear decisions need be taken now for programmes that are to exist by the turn of the century.

The programme will not be decided simply on technical grounds, for there are too many vested interests involved. The choice has to be made between British and American technology and Benn has led a determined fight to continue relying upon British technology, the AGR, and to defer a decision on the American pressurized water reactor (PWR), despite massive opposition from within his own department and much of the nuclear industry. Because of the breathing space allowed by oil, Benn thinks he can afford to defer the decision till the early 1980s. According to the WAES study, high nuclear expansion can only be maintained if fast breeder reactors that both burn and produce nuclear fuels become commercial from 1990 onwards.

By the end of 1977 it looked, as usual, as though a compromise solution would be the answer. The Central Electricity Board, the main customer for nuclear generated power, recommended to the government that the Nuclear Power Company should build another AGR and that this should be followed by a PWR. Mr Benn dislikes the idea of adopting US technology and favours only the AGR, but the compromise does take account of both sides of the argument.

Finally, in January 1978, the government authorized immediate orders for two British-built AGRs for power stations to be ready by the late 1980s while the option was 'retained' (whatever that meant) for ordering the American PWR later. The AGRs are expected to cost about £650 million each; between £30 million and £40 million will be spent upon design studies for a PWR by 1982. Mr Benn had won and British technology was given another chance. The Tory opposition warmly commended this nationalist decision; Mr Benn had rebutted some of the severest pressures ever by the nuclear lobby. As he told the Commons, the decision still gave the country until 1982 to make wider choices once the PWR designs had been submitted.

After one of the longest inquiries for years in Britain, Mr Justice Parker in his report on Windscale argued that a new plant for reprocessing atomic waste should be built there without delay. Stocks of spent fuel from AGRs, unless reprocessed, would pile up and have to be stored somewhere. As he said:

It is necessary to keep the nuclear industry alive and able to expand, should expansion be required. Such expansion might be required either to meet additional energy demands or to preserve a 'mix' and to avoid over-dependence on a particular energy source.

Keeping the industry alive involves building further reactors; these, in turn, involve further sources of spent fuel which would also have to be stored unless reprocessed. Mr Justice Parker made out a powerful case for reprocessing simply by quantifying Britain's own spent fuel; if the possibility of reprocessing other spent fuels is added to this, it makes sense for the plant to go ahead.

The judge based his conclusions on three considerations: that we should not throw away indigenous energy sources and become wholly dependent upon foreign supplies; that disposal without reprocessing implies avoidable risks, especially that of too much plutonium 'escaping'; and that if there is to be reprocessing eventually anyway, it is better to start at once and so gain the necessary experience.

The Americans are opposed to reprocessing on the grounds that it makes nuclear proliferation easier. Debates about nuclear energy are coloured by fears about radio-activity, the fact that nuclear power was first presented to the world in the form of the atom bombs dropped on Japan, and the general association of nuclear developments with arguments about the balance of terror. As a Frenchman shrewdly remarked, there would hardly have been all the debate, had nuclear energy merely been developed as an alternative to oil or coal without its war connotations. Then the risks would have been discussed more rationally.

There are dangers: of radiation, of a major accident; and dangers arising from the disposal of waste and especially from plutonium, which is highly toxic and can be used to make an atom bomb. In an article in *The Times* shortly after publication of the Parker report on Windscale, six eminent engineers and scientists (see appendix 4) argued that, despite risks and fears, world energy demand has risen at the rate of 8 per cent per annum since 1945 and still increases, while the developing nations are now expanding their demand and world population grows by 2 per cent a year; all these pressures upon energy sources have to be taken into account. Since there is little prospect of the renewable forms of energy filling much of the need until well into the next century, it is essential, with proper safeguards, to step up present sources of nuclear energy. They make a vital point often overlooked in nuclear debates:

> We therefore support its expansion based on a carefully controlled development programme. We believe that the risks involved would be far higher if nuclear power were not allowed to grow progressively, but had to be stepped up in a few years time in a crash programme—with inevitable cutting of corners—to meet a world energy famine which by then had become imminent.

The subject of energy and fierce debates about it made news throughout 1977 with the argument about the new power stations. Electricity is often at the centre of energy debates, certainly as far as price is concerned, and in Britain is produced mainly from coal-fired plants, then from nuclear power stations or oil-fired plants. Electricity has lost markets as a result of North Sea gas. Gas now enjoys a 64: 40 lead over electricity in meeting the needs of local authorities, and is also making inroads into all housing estates originally equipped and designed for the use of electricity.

Yet despite the strains it claims to be under, or because of its high prices, the Electricity Authority turned in record profits in 1977 of £206·5 million, more than double its previous best performance in

1968–69. The price of electricity is heavily dependent upon that of coal. Thus Glyn England, chairman of the CEGB, claimed that a NUM wage claim which raised coal prices by 30 per cent would make oil the choice for electricity generation; a 30 per cent increase in coal prices would depress demand for coal at power stations by 10 million tons a year.

The endless argument about the Drax B power station, and the politics of unions and other pressure groups which surrounded it, merely emphasized the scale of interests involved: coal, unions, various engineering firms, local politicians anxious to secure work for depressed areas and so on. The CEGB did not want to place the order with C. A. Parsons. Questions of redundancy in a particular industry and area, as much as immediate energy requirements, influenced the government approach to the problem.

Ironically, after all the debate, the power chiefs quietly dropped their claim that the Drax B order, finally announced in October 1977, was being placed two years earlier than need be. The power station would be needed much sooner; the industry had become freshly optimistic about growth of demand and had adopted a more realistic view of the time the construction period would take.

The field of 'renewables' is becoming speculatively lively, even if it is unlikely that much will be done about tapping such resources for some time to come. One renewable source of energy that has long been used is that of hydro-electric power, and in this respect Britain's resources are limited.

The possibility of a Severn barrage to harness the power of the tidal wave in the river is, however, an exciting, if expensive, hydro-power project. A massive dam across the Severn Estuary from Wales to Somerset would have to be built at a cost of something like £4,000 million. The proposed barrage would be one of the world's largest engineering projects, equal in cost and scale to a major North Sea oil field. Plans for this have been mooted periodically ever since 1910, so it is not a new idea. The river has the biggest tidal rise and fall in Europe; now, with an energy-conscious nation turning more and more to the idea of renewable sources of energy that neither deplete finite resources such as coal or oil nor offer the hazards associated with nuclear energy, such a project as the barrage offers renewed attractions.

But though the idea is generally welcomed by Bristol and Cardiff, and by MPs from the area (both Benn and his opposite number in the Tory Party, Tom King, come from seats nearby), objections have been raised by the conservation lobby: 'It could turn large areas into

septic stagnant pools', objected a representative of the Friends of
the Earth.

After a report by NEDECO (the Netherlands Engineering Consultants Foundation) that it is feasible, comes the more difficult
question of cost: between £3,000 million and £4,000 million would
make it one of the most expensive construction jobs in Europe. It
is therefore unlikely to appeal to governments as long as other
sources of energy are more cheaply available. On the other hand, it
can be argued that, despite these huge costs, the barrage would be
more than worthwhile in terms of the fuel costs it would eventually
save in the 1990s.

Renewable energy sources are still largely for the future and it is
not expected that more than a small amount of energy will be
derived from them this century. Research so far has not been
especially promising. Yet the appeal is undeniably there: what better
form of investment for part of Britain's oil wealth than renewable
forms of energy which, once properly established, should for all
practical purposes be everlasting? The government, both major
parties, unions and many researchers, parts of industry and local
interests or regional groups where such developments would take place
are all in favour of them. The problems at present are largely financial.

Capital investment in energy resources now runs at £3·75 billion
a year, or 16 per cent of total injections of capital into the economy.
This is almost as much as total capital investment in the manufacturing industry; moreover, the scale of investment in the North
Sea over the next few years will continue high. On present form,
North Sea oil, electricity and coal will between them account for
£3·5 billion capital investment every year for the next decade. In
part, therefore, it is simply a question of enough money for research,
a sum that is so often begrudged by governments.

Huge windmills to capture and harness wind power may sound
romantic and exciting: the engineering involved is far more complex
than might be supposed. There are problems of noise and interference with television and microwave transmissions. Such windmills
might work economically or fall over in the first big gale. Millions
of pounds for experimenting will have to be used before such
questions can be answered. Research into such activities comes
under ACORD: the Advisory Committee on Energy Research and
Development of the Department of Energy under the chairmanship
of Sir Hermann Bondi, chief scientist of the department.

Solar energy is another possibility, though the prospects for this
are unlikely to rate high in Britain. On current estimates, for
example, solar power should account for 5 per cent of Europe's
needs by the end of the century.

Perhaps fittingly for Britain, the most work has been put into the development of wave power. Dr Salter at Edinburgh University has been engaged upon this problem since 1973; other research dates back to 1947 under the Ministry of Fuel and Power. Research has also been carried out in Japan since 1945. Experiments by the Mechanical Engineering Department of the School of Engineering Science at Edinburgh have, according to Dr Salter, now reached an 'advanced stage of about 100th scale and work has begun on 10th scale models in sheltered water'. According to Dr Salter, who is in charge of this research:

> Wave power will not be cheap, but we think that the cost will be within a factor of two of the cost of electricity generated by a fast breeder reactor. It is not clear which way round the factor will be!

There is still a long way to go.

The machine to extract the energy from waves, called a 'duck' (sometimes now referred to as Salter's duck), is a rocking cam-shaped device which is designed to give a high efficiency of energy extraction over a wide frequency band. As Dr Salter says:

> In the very long term, wave power is as secure as we could wish. We know that the winds will blow for ever. In the very short term, wave power is at least predictable. We know enough to prepare reliable forecasts for twenty-four hours ahead so that stand-by plant should have plenty of warning.

The advantages of ducks to tap wave power are considerable: there is enough wave energy, they are safe, secure and clean. There are now four techniques for developing them under study in Britain, and at least the cost of determining the costs will be low. A drawback that wave power will have in common with wind and solar power is predictability: it comes at times not necessarily convenient to the user, so that there will be problems of storage and distribution.

The first of these bobbing ducks is expected to be in operation off Caithness by 1982. They would be substantial in size, looking rather like huge elongated buoys, perhaps three miles out to sea. One estimate suggests that 2,400 would be needed round the coasts of Britain to supply twice the country's present electricity consumption. There is certainly something appealing in the picture of a Britain ringed with huge bobbing ducks supplying it with electricity from the waves forever.

PART FIVE
Politics

14

Foreign Impact

Oil will provide Britain with certain advantages in her conduct of foreign affairs over the next 15 years which should render her position in international dealings somewhat stronger than it has been for at least a decade. In so far as North Sea oil eliminates a standing balance of payments deficit, governments will have greater financial room in which to manoeuvre. Since, formerly, Britain's oil came mainly from the Middle East, her self-sufficiency will also mean that, unlike other European countries or the USA courting Saudi Arabia, Britain will be freer in determining her policies towards the Middle East oil-producing states.

In addition to self-sufficiency, as long as Britain also produces a sizeable surplus of oil for export she will enjoy distinct bargaining advantages in relation to her EEC partners and to the USA, both of whom are voracious consumers of oil and will exert considerable pressures upon Britain to produce for export. Oil exports can be used as a bargaining counter in trade agreements with countries like Japan with whom Britain has had an adverse trade balance for years. Oil is the one commodity which all countries want and most especially the advanced economies which are also Britain's chief international trading rivals. For two or more decades oil will be a most useful weapon in Britain's foreign policy armoury.

In addition the oil will provide two other advantages: security of supply, and, resulting from the greater room of manoeuvre derived from both the internal impact of oil and the surplus which may be produced for export, it will give governments a greater sense of self-confidence in international dealings than they have displayed in recent years. These are the potential advantages. However, they should not be regarded as more than of marginal importance, though margins in foreign affairs as in economic matters can often prove decisive. The point is that oil should no more be seen as rescuing Britain from a period of somewhat feeble international relations than it should be expected to act as a panacea for all our economic ills. It can provide the stimulus for a more independent foreign policy—no more.

As North Sea production rises by 1980 to its full level, so British dependence upon imported oil (though not upon imports for her 'mix') will be phased out. In fact, because of the light low-sulphur quality of most North Sea oil, a high proportion of it will continue to be exported, mainly to the European and American markets while Britain continues to import the heavier crudes she requires for her 'mix'. Since the light sulphur oil is more valuable than the heavier crudes, the export for 'mix' will not just be a simple exchange but should provide Britain with a further source of income.

Various estimates of the extent of Britain's oil surplus for export have been made during the 1970s. The surplus must depend upon a variety of factors including new finds and government conservation and depletion policies. It is possible that by 1980 Britain will be exporting 40 million tons or more a year, yet in 1977 the Department of Energy was deliberately damping down the idea that the country would be exporting oil in any quantity.

In a parliamentary answer to Mr Woof, who asked in July 1977 about future market prospects for North Sea crude oil, Mr Benn replied:

It is likely that the world crude oil supply situation will become increasingly more difficult and that there will, as a result, be excellent opportunities for sellers of North Sea crude oil in the 1980s. It is reasonable in these circumstances for the Government to expect oil companies to keep long-term options open and not to commit substantial quantities of North Sea crude for more than two years ahead to markets either at home or abroad.

The government in other words wants to keep all the options open.

By late 1977, Britain was exporting 350,000 b/d, and for balancing her 'mix' she was importing the equivalent and more. The crude was going to countries such as the USA, Finland, Sweden, Holland, West Germany and France, and in selling to those customers for the first time, Britain was establishing a pattern both for herself and for them which she will not find easy to break at a later date, even if she wants to do so. Should Britain later decide to change her oil export policy, these trading partners will be able to argue persuasively that they have become dependent upon such supplies.

In November 1977 Dr Mabon answered another question in Parliament about the value of oil exported. He said:

In the twelve month period ending on September 30 this year, nearly 13 million tonnes of North Sea crude was exported, representing nearly 40 per cent of production in the period. The total value was approximately £750m.

After further questioning from Mr McNair Wilson of the Tory benches who expressed surprise at this level of exports, Dr Mabon was obliged to admit that the level of exports was too high. He went on:

It is no intention of Government to allow oil companies to market at will. But we have to respect and observe international agreements and we have to respect the concern of our friends in Western Europe, North America and Scandinavia to whom most of these exports have gone.

What Dr Mabon did not explain was what international agreements had already been entered into by the oil companies to dispose of British North Sea oil abroad at that early stage in its production.

If government decided only to allow enough North Sea production to meet British needs, then exports would only consist of that proportion of the oil which needs to be exchanged for the heavier crudes required for Britain's 'mix'. This would still be a valuable export transaction because of the difference in price between the two kinds of crude.

It is obvious from the multiplicity of predictions and statements, however, that government itself is far from clear as to what export policy it will follow, once self-sufficiency has been achieved. According to Energy Paper No 12, for example, 'In 1985 there would be a substantial net export of energy from the United Kingdom due to the rapid development of North Sea oil and gas supplies.' Here it appears to take for granted a development that is uncontrolled.

A senior executive of Shell, J. M. Raisman, puts forward a view which is also conformable to company wishes:

Dependent upon any Government decisions on offtake, a production level in the mid 1980s of around 150 million tonnes a year compares with a UK domestic oil demand of around 100 million tonnes. In other words a net surplus on a self-sufficiency basis of some 50 million tonnes.

He continues, concerning the 'mix':

This leads to the proposition that a better use of resources is to find the best mix of indigenous crude and imported cheaper Middle East crudes. The higher quality crudes can then form the basis of exports to countries that are prepared to pay premium prices for them and thereby enhance the UK's balance of payments.

This of course is unexceptionable; but it is no reason why more oil need be exported than is necessary to achieve the balance.

The oil companies, however, would greatly prefer to produce

more than the mere self-sufficiency equivalent for Britain. To quote Raisman once more:

> On this basis the UK demand for North Sea oil would amount to about 40 million tonnes, leaving a potential export in excess of 100 million tonnes derived from the 60 million tonnes 'exchanged' for Middle East crudes and the balance, over self-sufficiency, of 50 million tonnes.

There is in fact no reason why production should not stop at the 100 million tonnes mark.

The arguments are difficult: it could be just as sensible in economic terms to produce a substantial surplus, since North Sea oil sells at a premium of about $1 over heavier crudes and then use the income for other developments—always provided that in such a case it would be treated as income for investment rather than just for general purposes. Such a policy through the 1980s, for instance, would provide Britain with a powerful economic weapon in her dealings with overseas trading partners, most especially the USA and the EEC, and could be as good a way of using the resources, albeit more quickly, than by following a policy of conservation which only permitted extraction of oil to a level of British self-sufficiency.

Ownership of North Sea resources is another factor that will influence export policies.

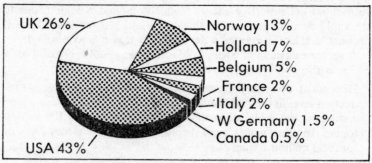

THE UNITED STATES owns nearly half the North Sea (as this chart of ownership of UK and Norwegian oil shows). Britain owns about a quarter of the total. This foreign domination is the reason why the government negotiated participation agreements with companies, so that the state will control the destination of half of production. Profits, interest and dividends taken overseas will peak in 1980, as the table shows.

[*Sunday Times*, 27 November 1977]

How much do foreign companies make out of the North Sea?
Table shows the total of interest, profits and dividends to be paid overseas.
(£ million)

1976	1977	1978	1979	1980	1985
—	500	700	1,300	1,600	1,100

Source: Treasury. In 1976 prices.

There are complications in relation to Britain's particular export markets or allies and these have to be dealt with as they arise. The EEC commercial policy, for example, does not apply to oil, so that sales by oil companies to EEC members would be on a voluntary basis. On the other hand it is illegal for Britain, as a member of the Community, to prevent exports to the EEC. This means in theory, and perhaps at some future date in practice, that the British government guidelines (see appendix 3) and the Treaty of Rome could be in conflict, resulting in a political crisis. Then Britain is a member of the International Energy Agency (IEA) and has accepted certain obligations: if there is a 10 per cent shortfall in supply to members as a group, there is in fact little more than an obligation to make efforts to cut back consumption; if, however, the shortfall goes farther than 10 per cent the question of sharing then arises, providing (a key proviso) that the producers agree. Effectively this gives to a producer such as Britain a way out: she has a veto on sharing. There is also the role of the companies which have international, rather than just national, obligations to all their customers.

The importance of individual customers—actual and potential— will again be a guide to the kind of export policy Britain follows. Sweden, or Scandinavian countries with high environmental standards, wants North Sea sulphur-free oil and is prepared to pay the premium price to get it; in export terms, indeed, Sweden represents the best possible market for British exports—it is very close and wants the most expensive oil on offer. The USA with its voracious energy appetite presents many more complex problems as an oil trade partner. Britain has, of course, no obligation to sell oil to the USA. On the other hand American companies own 43 per cent of the North Sea fields; the USA is an ally and a member of the IEA; and British companies such as BP have huge stakes in North America.

There is a quite different long-term consideration: it might be sensible to continue importing the country's entire requirements from traditional Middle East suppliers, thus maintaining existing export-import relationships with these markets against the day when Britain has to turn to them again anyway, while selling all North Sea output, since this will be more lucrative because of the premium North Sea oil commands. Early in 1977, for example, a sharp rise in American demand for low sulphur crude raised the value of oil from the British and Norwegian sectors of the North Sea by 25 cents a barrel on the open market.

On a different plane, that of conservation, it might well be asked why Britain should supply any oil to the USA when that country consumes so large a proportion of it in fuelling its excessively wasteful fleet of enormous cars.

Another result of North Sea oil will be the expansion of the British petrochemical industry and it will be vital to find new overseas markets for these products as well.

In the context of any export policy, government controls ought to be decisive. The Department of Energy exercises statutory control over the oil loaded offshore: a company must get a waiver if it is not to offload its oil in Britain, otherwise there is an automatic British landing requirement. Government can also specify prices at which oil is exported. Under the Energy Act of 1977 the government can, during a state of emergency, tell such companies as BP, Shell (UK) and Esso (UK) what to do with their oil—that is, all their North Sea oil. Further, companies may not enter into definitive export contracts; rather, these should be 'evergreen', or for only two years at a time. Then, provided there has been no change in circumstances, such contracts can be renewed for another two years. Such export arrangements can be terminated at government insistence. This two-year limit is currently normal practice. There has also been written into all the participation agreements a clause to the effect that there should be a discussion between the companies and the Department of Energy about policies every six months.

Despite these regulatory controls civil servants argue that it is not possible to completely control the oil and its direction since Britain needs imports for mix purposes. Furthermore, the international oil companies may come under pressure from their other customers to use all their other, non-North Sea supplies elsewhere.

In the case of oil landed in Britain by pipeline there are two controls: first, the BNOC option to purchase 51 per cent of it; and then, covering the remainder, the government requirement that up to two thirds of oil landed should be refined here, which effectively means, in terms of world refining capacity, that it is also used here.

Lord Kearton says there is no easy answer to just what makes the right export policy or depletion-conservation policy. We should not want the balance of payments to become too strong or this will lead to other problems. Policy, in other words, should be flexible. On balance, perhaps the best approach is to say that since oil is a precious commodity and will remain so, the longer we have some of our own the better; the consequence of such an assumption ought to be a policy of minimal exports. Even so, no one is prepared to be tied down over future export policy.

As North Sea oil began to flow so British concern with OPEC noticeably receded. In 1976 Mr Benn had talks with Sheik Yamani in which he stressed that another price rise would have adverse effects upon western economies; by early 1978 Lord Kearton was arguing that without another price rise soon the North Sea bonanza would be over, so quickly had events changed the British attitude.

Where North Sea oil could mean Britain losing to her competitors is in the race to obtain the huge development contracts on offer from such countries as Saudi Arabia or Iran. As long as Britain purchased a major part of her oil from those sources, she had to offset the balance of payments involved by capturing at least a proportion of the work on these huge, lucrative development projects. With her own oil, however, although manufacturing exporters will be as eager to obtain the contracts, there is not quite the same sense of government urgency. Moreover, government ministers such as the President of the Board of Trade will not be able to argue that as a major market for Saudi or Iranian oil Britain has some reasonable claim to a fair share of their markets in reverse. The rapid growth of North Sea oil supplies has cut away at OPEC power, at least during the period of recession and oil glut.

OPEC was noticeably quieter during 1977: it patched up its own internal differences between the hawks and doves, and did not raise the oil price. This situation, ironically, worked against British oil interests, since when OPEC puts the price up North Sea oil follows suit, with a resultant increase in income from exports and government tax take.

In the long run the two keys governing oil are American demand and Saudi supply; the rest of the oil world will increasingly depend upon the interaction of these two factors in the future.

President Carter's attempt to introduce a more stringent energy policy in the USA reflects his administration's concern with long-term American dependence upon outside supplies, most especially those from Saudi Arabia, and this continuing dependence as well as the sheer volume of American needs and imports is bound to have some effect upon Washington's attitudes towards possible British depletion-conservation policies, or the limits any British government decides to put upon exports over the next fifteen years. The USA will be looking for every conceivable source of oil it can obtain, not only to meet its needs but also to vary its excessive dependence upon Middle East sources.

Norway will have a larger surplus of oil for export than will Britain. Comparisons are often made between the two European countries which share the North Sea resources. The policies they each adopt will interact upon the other. There has been a turn-round in Norway from optimism to a degree of pessimism. In the early 1970s, the Norwegians were looking to a bright future based upon oil; Norway in any case is one of the most prosperous societies in the world. By 1978, however, a Labour government member could say, anonymously: 'A balance in our payments may never be reached and it won't under any circumstances happen before 1990.'

There have been some setbacks: the Ekofisk blow-out and the delay in opening the gas pipeline to Emden in West Germany, so that the government has been obliged to resort to further borrowing and faced a deficit in 1976 of £2·7 billion. Moreover, although in the early days of North Sea development the British bewailed the extent to which orders for platforms and equipment went abroad, often to Norway, the Norwegian industry has not done anything like as well as it might in supplying its own oil industry. The home contribution to equipping the Ekofisk and Frigg fields is in the range of only 15 to 20 per cent, while even for the giant Statfjord field the local contribution is only 50 per cent. In consequence, many of the expectations that had been built up remain expectations.

Norway's advantage is derived from her tiny population: she owns approximately one third of North Sea oil as opposed to Britain's two thirds with only a tenth the population of Britain, so that her problems and outlook are quite different. As her Parliamentary Report 25, 'The Petroleum Industry in Norwegian Society', stated:

> . . . only a minor part of the areas considered promising today will have been explored by the turn of the century. In the North Sea exploration will continue into the 1980s at least, and production from established finds will continue through the 1990s. The Continental Shelf North of Lat. 62° N is several times larger than the areas in the North Sea, and their exploration will take a very long time, also because of the deeper waters.

In 1976 Norway officially aimed to produce about 75 million tons of oil a year by 1985—it had earlier been talking of 90 million tons. The Parliamentary Report suggested a production by 1981–82 of around 50 million tons, and with Norwegian consumption of only 8 million tons this gave a surplus for export to Europe of 42 million tons. An additional production of between 45,000 and 50,000 million cubic metres of gas was expected. Should Norway reach the highest possible production which has been suggested—that is, about 100 million tons in 1985—and should European consumption at that time be a predicted 1,200 million tons, then Norway's contribution towards meeting total demand will be 8·5 per cent. Just how much Norway does produce is of great concern to the West generally and could have an influence upon export policy followed by Britain.

According to a Shell briefing paper, *Offshore Oil and Gas*, Norway expects to produce approximately 1·8 million b/d oil and gas equivalent through the 1980s; since her consumption works out at only 200,000 b/d, this leaves her with an exportable surplus over the decade of 1·6 million b/d which would put her on a par with an OPEC country like Libya. On the other hand, Nore in his *Six Myths of British Oil Policies* argues that a major aspect of Norway's policy which causes resentment in the West is the ceiling of 90 million tons oil output a year. One might have thought that an exportable surplus which works out at ten times her consumption of a valuable resource is a very generous ceiling indeed.

In his *Oil the World Power* Peter Odell says '. . . Norway, by 1985, could have enough oil production surplus to its own requirements to provide the total needs of Denmark, Sweden, Germany and much of the Benelux countries as well!' Should it do so, pressure might well be mounted upon Britain to supply much of the balance.

Although at first Norway decided to take only what oil she needed and adopt a policy of maximum conservation, this soon came to be modified. The difficulty, as pointed out in her Parliamentary Report, was that although a huge level of production over and above her own needs threatened major problems of adaptation, 'Once discoveries are made, technical, economic and political reasons make it difficult to limit their exploitation. Exploration activities should therefore be regulated by the size of finds already made.' This is easier said than done.

As a result of the delays on Ekofisk as well as escalating costs, early projections of Norwegian production have been revised downwards so that at the end of 1977 a figure of 37 million tons was expected for 1978, rising to between 65 and 70 million tons a year during the early 1980s. From a conservation point of view Norway may come to bless present delays; yet the less she produces during the 1980s the greater will be the pressures mounted upon her and Britain to produce more for export.

The greatest pressures upon Britain will come from her OECD partners: the EEC, the USA and to some extent Japan. According to the OECD's *World Energy Outlook* published in 1977, OECD requirements for imported oil could rise from the 1975 figure of 23·4 million b/d to a 1985 figure of 35 million b/d. If this is added to the increased demand from other non-OECD countries, the total could add up to a greater quantity of oil than OPEC producers are willing to export, so that North Sea, Alaskan and other non-OPEC sources would come under increasing pressures to produce as much as possible to fill the gap.

The OECD countries talk of conservation, but the failure of the Carter proposals in the USA illustrates how difficult it is to do what logically makes sense. People do not want and if possible will not cut back on the use of a resource which makes their lives easier. A crisis has to arise before tough action is taken.

The OECD degree of dependence upon imported oil makes the subject of oil exports a most sensitive one. Warnings about conservation have been delivered constantly since the mid 1970s, but the rate of oil consumption does not diminish; recession rather than effective conservation has enabled the line to be held, though only just. Attitudes change fast.

In the aftermath of the price rises in 1973 and 1974, the OECD countries were for a time mesmerized by a form of economic blackmail on the part of OPEC. The West panicked: it talked collectively of 'recycling' the petrodollars from OPEC; individual countries each sought special deals with Iran or Saudi Arabia; and as a group the West entered into the nearest approach ever—and this with extreme reluctance—to any genuine redistribution of wealth between the rich and the poor in the so-called North-South Paris dialogue. Most of that hectic OPEC-inspired activity of the period 1975–1976 already seems remote; older economic forces re-established themselves, and helped by recession, the West conceded nothing while OPEC power appeared to recede. Even so OECD remains immensely vulnerable.

No doubt there will be a continuing dialogue between North and South though the interest in such talks—never anything more than superficial among the rich economies—has disappeared, and the ability to press for dialogue which was an OPEC function has, at least for the time being, also gone. The idea of a direct link or index between oil prices and manufactured goods has not been heard of for some time, although when the recession ends and the price of oil rises again, such talk could once more become fashionable. The fact that a dialogue took place at all was a measure of the oil dependence of the rich—nothing else.

The West bitterly resented being obliged to take seriously Third World demands for a New International Economic Order. This is why North Sea oil is so important to the rest of the EEC: the greater the surplus that Britain and Norway can be induced to produce, the less the likelihood that another series of humiliating North-South talks will have to take place. The fact that such pressure is inevitably going to take place gives to Britain for at least the 1980s a foreign policy weapon in relation to her EEC partners and, to a lesser extent, the other OECD countries, which is of considerable importance.

Political climates change extraordinarily quickly. The sense of crisis in 1976 at the height of OPEC influence subsequently gave way to the sense of frustration which accompanied the recession. Back at the beginning of 1976, however, President Giscard D'Estaing suddenly went on the first ever state visit of a French President to

Saudi Arabia; ten months later he was on another such visit to Iran. In both cases France was trying to secure contracts for development projects in exchange for oil deals. The other OECD countries were busy doing the same thing and a flurry of state visits to the Middle East took place.

There was the spectacular Iranian purchase of a huge stake in West Germany's Krupp organization. Then at the beginning of 1977, the purchase of 9·6 per cent of Fiat by the Libyan government. It was the era of major Arab purchases in Europe, part of the petrodollar 'recycling' process.

It is important to recall this hectic activity and the apparent reversal of economic roles as the Arab oil producers, rich cousins of the remainder of the Third World though under-developed themselves, suddenly erupted on to the European scene to buy into world-famous names of EEC companies. They were welcomed, moreover, with open arms, so much had oil power upset traditional patterns.

OECD countries disliked the shift in economic power; they set up the IEA in the hope that it would enable them more effectively to counter any future crisis, though subsequently quarrelling about its role and assigning to it little effective influence. Then two things happened: North Sea oil began to flow in rapidly increasing amounts as the extent of resources became known; and Britain and Norway saw themselves almost overnight becoming self-sufficient in oil with substantial surpluses for sale to the EEC and the USA.

Dependence upon others for an essential commodity is always worrying, although it needs to be seen in perspective. For the whole of the twentieth century Britain has been increasingly dependent upon food imports; more than any other European country she knows just how it does feel to be at the mercy of political-economic forces beyond her control.

National Oil Statistics—1975

	Refinery capacity (*) (m tonnes)	Consumption (m tonnes)	Consumption as % of refinery capacity	Production (m tonnes)	Tankers (m long tons deadweight)	% of total energy from: Oil	Natural gas	Oil and natural gas combined
ermany	155	129	83	5·7	—	53	14	67
rance	175	109	62	1·0	13	65	10	75
aly	219	96	44	1·0	—	69	15	84
ritain	147	92	63	1·2	33	45	16	61
otal	696	426	61	8·9	—	56	14	70
estern Europe	1,042	665	64	30·6	123	56	13	69
nited States	764	764	100	473·2	11	44	30	74
orld total	3,592	2,702	75	2,708	291	44	18	62

Source: BP Statistical Review of the World Oil Industry 1975.

At year end.

The BP Statistical Review of the World Oil Industry for 1975 shows the degree of dependence of major western countries, although the pattern is changing fast as far as Britain is concerned.

Europe as a whole seems likely always to be in need of more energy than it can produce from its own resources and so will remain a net importer. North Sea oil may be regarded by Britain and Norway as theirs; it is likely to be regarded by the EEC and the rest of Europe as the sub-continent's. Since Europe has to import approximately 60 per cent of its energy, it is dependent upon decisions from outside: those of OPEC and those of the USA which as the largest importer of all sets the pace for OPEC exports and so for everyone else.

When Britain began to work out her options in the light of coming North Sea revenues at the end of 1977, it was apparent that little thought had been given to the fact that the country is a member of the EEC and that her partners had a vital interest in the options she might choose to adopt. Two of the possibilities—whether Britain decided upon quick repayment of overseas debts or floating the pound—were of considerable concern to her partners. If oil means that Britain is no longer impoverished, then she must expect an end to special considerations in Europe such as the green pound for agriculture or having sterling excluded from the 'snake'. Once oil makes the British economy stronger, her partners will ask Britain to adopt different policies; if she does not oblige they will exert much greater pressures upon her. Economic strength has its disadvantages as well as its advantages.

In his book *North Sea Oil and Gas* Keith Chapman says: 'Estimates of the probable duration of the finite resources of the North Sea obviously have an important bearing upon the long-term planning of European energy policy.' This may be true, but only to a certain extent. The statement presupposes a commitment to European planning—as opposed to individual country planning—which on the whole is markedly absent at present in Europe, though more co-ordination and less selfishness may come in future.

At the end of 1977 efforts were being made to forge an EEC energy policy; the omens hardly appeared encouraging. The reason was that while some members—Britain, the Netherlands, West Germany and Belgium—have abundant supplies of coal or other hydro-carbons, others—France and Italy—do not. In essence a common policy means that those with a great amount, Britain first of all, must be prepared to share. There is little indication that this country—or any of the others—want to do anything of the sort.

The Italians, for example, submitted a memorandum to the Community calling for the establishment of an oil community for

Europe along the lines of the European Coal and Steel Community (ECSC). The Dutch with abundant gas showed less enthusiasm for the idea. Britain kept quiet.

Europe has huge surplus refining capacity yet when in 1977 the Community called for limitations, Britain (which also has surplus capacity) invoked her regional policy to reject all restraints on its plans for industrial development. It is one thing for Europe to argue that it makes no sense for Britain to create more refining capacity when the EEC already has too much. Britain answers that it is her oil and that she wants to use it to regenerate industry and growth. Why should Scotland have unemployment that could be absorbed by a new refinery at Nigg because the EEC insists that the oil has to be refined in Europe? This is the sort of inevitable nationalist argument that will recur.

Nonetheless, ever since the 1973 oil crisis the EEC has come increasingly to regard North Sea oil and gas as a major element in Community policy. This is scarcely surprising; as Lord Kearton said in 1977:

> France, for instance, is sweating blood: it imports 75 per cent of its energy. Germany imports 70 per cent. America imports 45 per cent of its oil energy. In 1980 we (Britain) are going to be the only developed country apart from Russia with an exportable surplus of energy.

What he might have added is that if we do not export that surplus or at least a very substantial proportion of it, our allies and friends will regard us with extreme disfavour and put correspondingly harsh pressures of other kinds upon us.

The EEC consumes between 20 and 25 per cent of all energy currently used in the non-Communist world and in 1974 about 60 per cent of this was imported. Only Britain, Germany and Holland produce significant quantities in relation to their needs and only Britain will be self-sufficient to 2000.

It is possible that even with North Sea oil western European imports will have risen to 19 million b/d by 1980 and 24 million b/d by 1985. On the other hand, Peter Odell argues that by the mid 1980s the North Sea could supply most of Europe's total oil needs, especially if serious restraint is practised. Apart from Britain and Norway, Holland's natural gas is a major source of supply for the EEC. Demand for natural gas is fast increasing.

The political problems of British-European relations can be seen in the dealings of the German company, Deminex, with the Department of Energy. Deminex is state-owned and has been looking for opportunities to 'farm in' to North Sea oilfields. It obtained a share in the Thistle field this way, but early in 1978 the Department of Energy refused it a free hand to export its share of crude production. Having encouraged Deminex to become involved so that it could obtain at least some secure sources of oil, the West German government cannot be happy that the company's most successful venture is being blocked by its EEC partner, Britain, at least to the extent of the free movement of the oil. The Department of Energy is concerned with its ruling that two thirds of North Sea offtake should be refined in Britain. No one should be surprised at such a row erupting; as long as Britain insists upon absolute sovereignty over North Sea crude, some such quarrel is bound to occur. More will do so in the future.

The EEC position is ambivalent. On the one hand the Community accepts Britain's right to control its North Sea oil; on the other hand the Community insists that under its rules oil companies have the right to make what exports they like within the EEC framework. Moreover it is an area where the Department of Energy is also likely to clash with the companies, which in any case are mounting increasing pressure to be allowed to export more oil.

A major conflict arose early in 1978 over the control of refining capacity. The European Commission considered invoking its legal powers under the Treaty of Rome to prohibit member governments from providing aid for the construction and expansion of oil refinery capacity until at least 1980. This was to ensure a reduction of surplus capacity by a further 60 million tons a year by 1981–82. Companies had already closed down about 82 million tons capacity during 1977, and while the EEC was proposing these limitations, BP shut down its largest (24 million tons a year) refinery at Rotterdam.

Britain, however, strongly opposed such a move as she plans a significant increase in capacity—about 14 million tons worth by the mid 1980s in order that two thirds of all her oil is refined in Britain. Government regional development grants are being provided for the new refinery at Nigg as well as for various upgrading operations. The British view, understandably, is that having got the oil—its best piece of luck in many years—it wants the bulk of it to be refined in Britain, since this adds so much more value to the end product. Europe, with huge over-capacity, does not want to see still more refineries constructed in Britain, and wants as much as possible of the oil to be refined on the continent.

Much of Britain's refining capacity has been designed for the heavier crudes imported from the Middle East, so that in order to be able to refine North Sea oil she is investing £1,000 million in re-equipping refineries. Mr Benn has argued against any EEC

Diktat and claimed that Britain is in a special position. The companies tend to take the European view rather than the more limited nationalist one.

As a result of British opposition these EEC proposals were drastically scaled down and the objection to government financial assistance dropped. Even so, the clash is not untypical of the kind that will occur again. For Britain Benn fiercely opposes the EEC's right to impose restrictions on any national policy of refinery expansion. The British insistence that two thirds of North Sea oil should be refined in the country may work as long as output is restricted more or less to domestic needs; if Britain goes for major exports, however, it will not, since her EEC customers, with ample refining capacity of their own, would not want to import refined products.

For the next twenty years Britain will enjoy the great advantage of energy self-sufficiency with the added variable of substantial export capacity as well. What will undoubtedly follow from this will be the determination of British nationalists of right and left to play upon anti-EEC emotions by arguing that they (or the Americans) are trying to get 'our' oil. Such an accusation will provide a political card in home elections or other situations—especially during times of depression—of potentially enormous and sometimes explosive value.

In 1977 Britain did agree to accept an EEC scheme to share oil among member states in the event of a threat to supplies, although the government was not prepared unconditionally to accept mandatory cuts of more than 10 per cent in normal consumption. Britain reserved the right of veto if she thought that cuts in such circumstances jeopardized national interests. It was still a substantial concession to her partners by Britain.

A growing EEC energy consumption for the rest of the century will coincide with a steadily dwindling supply of oil and gas. Since Britain will be the only member of the Community that is self-sufficient in oil and gas over this period, it is almost inevitable that she and her EEC partners will have a succession of policy clashes. There was an example of this during a House of Commons debate in November 1977. A Tory member, Dykes, revealed a cable from Brussels in which it was claimed that BNOC was in breach of the Treaty of Rome: it breached the rules of competition under articles 85, 86, 90 and 92 although Mr Biller (a paid official of the Conservative European Group who had sent the cable) reported that 'the Commission is unlikely to take action which might antagonize a Labour Government'.

Another aspect of potential conflict concerns the question of oil stocks. At the end of 1977 the EEC Commission proposed that Britain should be allowed to reduce the oil stocks she holds from 76 to 54 days supply since, as she has argued, North Sea fields make such large stocks unnecessary for her; in return for this concession Britain was to guarantee to supply oil to her EEC partners in the event of shortages at the same level as the equivalent quarter of the previous year. Britain had long been pressing for the right to reduce stocks as being unnecessary in her case; the price put on her request by the EEC Commission seemed too high. It was, once again, an attempt by her partners to tie her down to binding commitments to supply them. Although Mr Benn has said Britain would endeavour to supply all EEC countries in an emergency without discrimination, she is determined not to enter into long-term guarantees which would bind her and in a crisis limit the amount of oil available to Britain herself. As British officials point out, the EEC was not prepared earlier to agree to impose a minimum guarantee price for North Sea oil in the days when it was imagined that for some unspecified reason OPEC would suddenly slash prices to spite us. The nationalist overtones come out very quickly whenever the EEC talks about British oil. As a Department of Energy spokesman said:

> If this, as it appears, is a wheeze to get hold of part of North Sea oil, we shall have very grave doubts about it. It is, in any case, ridiculous that Britain should be required to finance oil reserves in such an expensive way when we have so much in the ground.

As the USA inexorably consumes more and more energy, especially oil, speculation must grow about the degree of pressure Washington is likely to mount upon Britain during the 1980s to over-produce from the North Sea. According to Sir David Steel, BP's Chairman, for example, on present patterns the USA may be wanting to buy 'no less than half the oil in world trade in the 1990s.' In this light the Carter attempt to introduce an energy policy is of great importance to America's allies and the oil producers, since a coherent energy policy must affect the volume of imports the USA seeks. The level of the USA's imports have risen 87 per cent since the 1973 crisis. Total consumption now stands at 23 million b/d. The President's measures would keep consumption down to no more than 26 million b/d in 1985. In fact, without conservation measures, it is more likely that American consumption at that date will have risen to 35 million b/d.

President Carter wants to increase taxes on the oil companies so as to bring about greater conservation; the oil lobby opposes such measures. On present estimates, according to the US General Accounting Office, American imports by 1985 will come to between

12 million and 13 million b/d, which is twice the amount President Carter has set as a target. The President's policy may make sense but interests—oil, industry, the public—will resist such a policy for as long as it is possible to import all the oil needed to ensure the kind of lifestyle to which Americans have become accustomed.

The USA is profligate in its energy consumption which is now the equivalent of 38 million b/d. Nearly a fifth of this is imported. As its huge domestic production—the same as that of Saudi Arabia—declines, the USA will import more, not less oil, as President Carter hopes. In 1977 its oil import bill stood at a massive $45 billion; one estimate suggests that on present trends this could reach a staggering $550 billion by 1985.

Whatever policy eventually emerges from the Presidential-Congressional battles taking place, for the foreseeable future the USA will be in the world market for all the oil it can buy. Since a large proportion of North Sea oil is owned by American companies and the area represents a 'safe' source of supply, US pressure upon Britain to develop the resources for exports above her own self-sufficiency needs must be substantial—and they will grow.

These then are the main factors likely to affect British foreign policy in so far as North Sea oil is concerned. Britain should not expect too much of oil for her foreign policy any more than for home policies and prospects. Oil's two most important functions, however, will be, first, to give Britain greater self-assurance in her foreign relations because she will be economically stronger; and second, almost certainly, to make her more nationalistic. It will be a question of 'our' oil which others are trying to prise away from us.

15

Political Interests

In the eighteenth century politicians unashamedly represented interest groups; today they claim to stand for the nation or what they conceive to be the national interest. British politicians have managed to project themselves as pursuing a career of a different kind from everybody else: whereas ordinary mortals are making a living, MPs are looking after the interests of the country.

There is regrettably little about the performance of British politicians in recent years to give cause for optimism: their universal planning boundary is the next election and policies are based upon expedients to bring them back to power. The chances of long-term planning, in relation to oil revenues as to most other things, are small. Oil can provide opportunities for Britain; it is much more likely, however, that politicians will see it as providing them with opportunities to stay in power longer.

Political opportunism may well mean that there is little effective depletion control exercised over North Sea resources: to restrict output to below what the companies would like to take is also to postpone economic benefits at the disposal of the government. Judging by government performances in recent years, it is doubtful whether any government will do other than take the available economic benefits oil provides while it is in power, since the alternative to such a course is to leave such benefits to be used by their political opponents. It seems probable, therefore, that governments will deplete faster, rather than conserve, in order to reap maximum PRT income and royalties.

Again, in terms of policy decisions, it is unrealistic to suppose that a government faced with a choice of a long-term plan involving the use of oil revenues or providing jobs for 100,000 unemployed will choose the former course rather than the latter. Bolstering uneconomic and incompetent industries has in any case become something of a national pastime; it used to be called 'feather-bedding'. Should government face a choice of major industrial unrest on the one hand and putting money into failing industries on the other hand and calling it 'regeneration', they will choose the latter activity.

Solving the immediate problems of the interest groups they represent is the prime occupation of politicians in this country. It means, effectively, that little long-term planning is ever carried out; this is certainly true if the requirement for such planning is the withholding of present benefits against possible benefits in twenty years time. It seems that little of the extra revenues from oil is likely to be invested for the future. We shall probably experience twenty years of 'British Disease', which will turn out in every respect to be as virulent as 'Dutch Disease'.

The oil from Britain's continental shelf is amongst the safest in the world in political terms. According to one Labour politician who prefers anonymity on this issue, the Treasury was wrong to go for only 45 per cent PRT; it ought to have insisted upon 55 per cent. Had it done so, the oil companies would still have accepted such a tax and continued to make large profits. As the Mackays say in *Political Economy of North Sea Oil*:

> An outstanding feature of the oil industry is the substantial difference between production costs and selling prices—in other words, the industry generates a very high added value, and much of the political debate concerning the North Sea has concentrated on the distribution of this added value.

It will continue to do so.

Mr Healey's budget of April 1978 could be faulted, no doubt, in many ways; but the £2,500 million he gave in tax relief to the British public was made possible by oil. He and his party had their eyes on the coming election. It is not difficult to be cynical about that budget, but if it was designed to catch votes the behaviour of the Tories and Liberals was equally designed for the same purpose. Both demanded that more be given in tax relief according to the simple principle that if Mr Healey did not give any more, they were the parties who truly had the welfare of the people at heart; if he did make further concessions these would only have been in response to their pressures. They won—in theory—whatever he did.

Politicians represent interest groups and so those groups with the greatest punch and most able to organize, such as unions and certain professions, get the most persistent attention. Some of the most powerful interests are corporate ones, including the oil companies, and in the constant political bargaining that goes on it must be seen that their interests and so-called national interests are not always or necessarily complementary. How the benefits of North Sea oil are going to be passed on to the British people as opposed to individual groups or segments is a difficult question to answer. People are not as naive or foolish as sometimes they are made out to be, and since there has been so much 'ballyhoo' about North Sea oil they do, perhaps, have a right to ask whether any of its benefits will percolate through to them.

The press talks of a competitive auction between the political parties over possible tax reductions and offers various suggestions of its own. One idea put forward by the *Financial Times* in 1977 was for a National North Sea Equity to be allocated to all citizens of the country: all the revenue from royalties, PRT and Corporation Tax coming from the North Sea would go into a special fund whose annual proceeds would be distributed, as of right, to each citizen holding such a bond. Certificates of entitlement would be transferable. The writer worked out the value of such certificates at more than £200 per head per annum. It was an interesting idea whose chief attractions were two: first, that everyone would have his or her share of North Sea wealth as opposed to only interest groups being affected; second, this or any comparable scheme would take oil profits out of the hands of the politicians. This second aspect of the suggestion naturally meant that the idea was a non-starter.

Higher tax and more control of oil were aims broadly agreed by both parties in the aftermath of the Public Accounts Committee Report and this has taken place. There is little real difference between the two major parties over control of oil or the extent of the revenue they would like to take from it, though there will, no doubt, be considerable differences on detail. Argument will be over spending policies.

The Tories in general simply prefer a lowering of individual tax levels. In November 1977, for example, Mr Michael Spicer of South Worcestershire moved:

> That this House will use North Sea oil revenues with other measures to reduce income tax on taxable incomes of up to £5,000 per annum to 20 per cent, on taxable incomes between £5,000 and £10,000 to 25 per cent, on taxable incomes between £10,000 and £15,000 to 35 per cent, on taxable incomes between £15,000 and £20,000 to 40 per cent, on taxable incomes between £20,000 and £25,000 to 45 per cent, and on taxable incomes over £30,000 to 50 per cent.

He was not going to get his way, but that was hardly the point. The auction is on, and when tax is debated reductions linked to oil revenues are going to be called for from right and centre if not from the left. 'Spending the oil money' now looks like providing one of those perennial pastimes with infinite variations, in which all can regularly take a hand.

The British often display a tendency towards complacency that can excuse almost any level of incompetence in themselves while pointing the finger of scorn at others for their shortcomings. We seem set to do this over oil and what we are pleased to call 'Dutch Disease'. A long article in the *Sunday Times* of 4 December 1977 examined aspects of contemporary Holland: 10 per cent of the work force is officially sick at any one time and 'that does not include the disabled, who have also become much more numerous since the nation's gas-based affluence worked its way through the welfare system.' These, however, were not Dutch Disease symptoms proper, though they were related. In answer to its own question, 'What then is Dutch Disease? the article continued as follows:

> Its principal manifestation is a decline in the profitability of industry and services alike, and a parallel decline in investment. Moreover, a rising exchange rate has failed to curb inflation, with the result that Dutch goods have become too costly to compete in international trade. The balance of payments remains in surplus—but only because of a prolific output of natural gas . . .

The description sounds alarmingly like a picture of Britain in the 1980s if we treat oil in the same manner.

It is, of course, easy to enjoy hindsight at the expense of the Dutch and point out where they have gone wrong. The article quoted above is only one of many British references to Dutch Disease. In part we appear to be reassuring ourselves that it can't or won't happen here. In part, however, it seems as though our politicians and economists are studying the form; there is plainly no reason why we cannot also do with our oil and gas what the Dutch have done with their gas.

It is not difficult to be cynical about politicians though they do come under enormous pressures. Yet it is important to realize how easily the public may be misled by current political fictions. One of these is that we are among the most overtaxed people in the world. This is a useful myth, especially for an opposition to use in belabouring a government that most certainly must take responsibility for a high level of spending. Equally, with oil coming on tap, it is tempting to talk of lowering the tax burden. No politician, however, talks of reducing the services available to the public at large, although this is the logical outcome of most tax cuts which are so glibly proposed.

During 1977 the Treasury did an interesting exercise in its September Economic Progress Report to show that total tax paid by British taxpayers as a proportion of their national income has averaged 40 per cent for a decade. Furthermore, only the USA and

Japan (if social security contributions are included) have lower taxes than Britain out of ten major industrial nations.

Comparative Taxation Table

(As percentage of gross national product at factor cost in major industrial countries)

	1974 Including social security contributions	1974 Excluding social security contributions
A		
Denmark	53·4	52·4
Norway	52·9	37·7
Netherlands	50·6	30·4
Sweden	49·1	39·4
France	41·1	24·9
Canada	39·7	35·9
UK	38·7	32·0
USA	32·0	24·3
B		
W. Germany	42·5	29·0
UK	38·0	31·4
Japan	24·6	20·0

The figures in part A of the table are drawn up according to the UN's new (1968) system of accounts. Some countries do not issue figures in this form. Part B used the former UN system of accounts (a comparable UK figure is shown). Capital taxes are excluded in both.

It is the pattern of taxation rather than the level that makes Britain seem so heavily taxed, and this is a problem to be solved by new financial measures rather than North Sea oil money.

Oil will probably continue for longer than people are either told or expect. This opens up a number of political options. The first of these is that the party in power will regard oil revenues as the answer to the most immediate and pressing problems of the day, which is the surest way of bringing about a British equivalent of Dutch Disease. The second option is to treat oil revenues (as opposed to the savings on the balance of payments) as strictly investment income to be put into other energy developments, into industry or social infrastructure, but not simply to be used for tax cutting purposes. This approach raises endless questions for debate as to what makes a good national investment. The third approach—similar to the first—is simply to treat oil income like any other revenue and behave as though there is no 'bonanza'. In the long run this may turn out to be the most sensible approach of all, since it would end the constant speculation that has already created a kind of lottery atmosphere. Fourth, there is a curious though appealing closed shop attitude: oil will now somehow allow us to insulate ourselves from the rest of the world. There is a form of political arrogance around in Britain which rears its head quickly enough given the chance, and there are some nationalists of both right and left who would treat oil as a compensatory instrument in lieu of Empire—'now we can be independent again'. There are, however, many political variables and pressures to be taken into account.

First, there are the oil companies. As Hugh Sandemann wrote in *The Banker* of May 1977: 'After the pessimism that surrounded the long months of official indecision, oilmen are now praising the secure political and economic environment that exists for their operations in the United Kingdom.' This is true for the moment and the most obvious government change—from Labour to Tory—is unlikely to affect that oil confidence. Most oilmen, despite preferences, now see little real policy change towards offshore oil between the two major parties: only changes of emphasis and climate.

Scotland, however, is another matter. It could well hold the key to oil and other policies for some years to come, depending upon the extent of SNP influence and the numbers of parliamentary seats it can capture. Certainly during the 1970s both major British parties began to make promises to Scotland: Labour said it would site BNOC there; the Tories promised an elected Scottish Assembly, an oil development fund and that the Department of Energy oil divisions should be moved there.

Despite the level of royalties and taxation on the North Sea, it is still a highly profitable area for any oil company to operate in; during the first half of 1977—hardly a happy industrial year for Britain—the gross trading profits of the industrial and commercial sectors rose quite sharply, largely as a result of oil profits. According to Central Statistical Office figures, £457 million of profits out of £3,185 million in the second quarter accrued to the 'North Sea sector' and £400 million did so out of £2,607 million in the first quarter. The oil figure for the second quarter of 1976 was only £66 million.

Although the figures can be juggled about, a typical oilman's estimate of company profits runs as follows: from a selling price of $14 a barrel, $6 are costs and $8 represent profits, of which 80 per cent goes to government. The remaining 20 per cent still leaves profits for the companies which almost no other industrial concern in the world can enjoy. Despite company talk of risks, once a field has been found and production is under way, there are virtually no further financial risks until the field dries up. In 1977 the New York brokers, Walter Levy, rated North Sea oil as the most profitable offshore oil for investment purposes in the world. National

Westminister summed up for all those interested in the North Sea saga, when it said:

> Clearly this is no game for the weak or faint-hearted—be they bankers or producers—but the rewards for success are very great and the oil companies are prepared to spend large sums of their own money on exploration.

The oil companies have managed to get the notion accepted that a 20 per cent return on North Sea fields is a necessity if they are to continue. It is a remarkable achievement; the average return for the manufacturing industry is 6 per cent. The companies are doing astonishingly well on their own terms, let alone according to anyone else's; however much they talk of special needs and risks, the fact is that when each quarter's returns are made public, the major oil companies usually go to considerable lengths to demonstrate that their profits are reasonable. On this subject of profits Shell's Mr Pocock says: 'In oil and gas production more than in any other part of the business, the levels of profitability needed to cover the risks involved are vulnerable to emotive attack.' That, of course, is no answer; but the oil companies know how to defend themselves—they have been at it for a long time.

According to the Edinburgh-based investment managers, Ivory and Sime, a 250-million barrel field is not marginal: after all tax returns it still makes profits of 22 per cent. Viking Resources International which was incorporated in 1972 'To provide a medium through which investors may participate in the growth of companies connected with the development of natural resources, particularly those of the North Sea, and other European offshore areas', in 1977 produced a presentation to its shareholders and institutional investment managers that gave a fascinating picture of the profitability of the North Sea. In a series of charts comparing oil profitability or take per barrel round the world, they show that in 1976 Middle East oil selling at $12·70 a barrel yielded a profit of 25 cents; US oil selling at $8·11 a barrel yielded $2·69; and North Sea oil selling at $14 a barrel yielded $3·29. Little wonder, therefore, that all the companies want to get into the North Sea; talk of high taxation from a British Labour Government is nonsense. Arab governments take far more in taxes than does Britain.

Now, in theory it is the business of the politicians to take as large a slice of the oil profits as they can on behalf of the public; in practice they are more likely to do this on behalf of the more narrow interest groups which they represent. The unions are one of the most powerful interest groups in the country, and they of course push for economic growth. In a statement to the Government

Energy Commission in 1977, the TUC said that if North Sea resources are wisely used, the economy should be able to grow at a faster rate over the next twenty years than over the previous twenty. Congress suggested ways the wealth could best be used to boost this growth, and among them included investment in the energy business as a whole. Yet one of the more interesting aspects of the North Sea story is the extent to which the unions have so far been kept out. They have little influence upon North Sea policies offshore and not very much as yet on land. They often do not have a presence on the platforms; many of the men working in North Sea related activities appear uninterested in active union membership; and the companies appear only too happy to keep the unions at arms length. And, curiously, a Labour Government which is often ready enough to press union matters in other respects has kept remarkably quiet about union participation in anything to do with oil. The government needed the oil to flow too urgently to contemplate any union complications and to the end of 1977 had had very few of them.

There is an Inter-Union Offshore Committee (IUOC) which receives the official backing of the TUC; it encourages the unions to sort out their demarcation lines in advance. IUOC can bring pressures to bear upon UKOOA and the Government. It was not until mid 1976 that a Memorandum of Understanding for Access to the Rigs was drawn up, nor until 1977 that regular monitoring of the agreement by the Department of Energy was accepted. UKOOA now recognize the right of unions to have reasonable access to the platforms.

The fact is that the rapid growth of activity in the North Sea left the unions standing; much of the labour was itinerant and non-union by tradition and inclination. Soon, however, as the North Sea moves into the era of fixed production platforms that will go on for years, the unions will have their chance as employment becomes more stable. The oil companies have fair relations with the unions onshore, but do not have such relations—if any at all—in their role as explorers.

One of the problems for the unions is that there are so many different skills represented on a rig, from caterers to crane drivers to electricians. Furthermore, if there is a problem or dispute on a rig or platform, the men have to wait for the end of the shift, which is normally a fortnight, before they can contact a foreman on-shore; in a factory they could do so at once. In the case of the plat-form yards which employ many hundreds of men, the problem for unions has been whether jobs are 'once only' or whether the employ-ment will be ongoing. The men are not sure if they will be working themselves out of a job.

In the early days the first forecasts predicted twenty years of platform building; now there would seem to be a prospect of reasonable continuity to the end of the century—at least about as much as in many other industries.

A further problem for union organization has been the fact of remoteness: the big yards or developments such as Sullom Voe have been in extremely remote sites with a number of consequent problems of social welfare, accommodation, leisure opportunities, etc. On the whole there have not been many inter-union problems at these sites.

The concrete platforms involved four unions, the steel platforms five and two types of union agreements have operated in the yards. One with the Engineering Employers Federation stipulates low hourly wages and high bonus levels, a situation that suits union foremen since it gives them more bargaining power. The other agreement with a breakaway group of some oil construction firms (OCPCA or Oil and Chemical Plant Contractors Association) specifies high hourly rates and low bonus levels.

There is OIL (Offshore Industry Liaison Committee) which was set up to bridge the hiatus in orders at a time when no one appeared to be considering the pattern for platform orders; there was no link between the industries involved, the unions and the Department of Energy. Now the Minister of State takes the chair of this committee. According to some union members, companies deliberately chose to go to the far north to set up sites so as to escape from the union influences they would meet on Tyneside or the Clyde. In its 1977 Economic Review the TUC said:

> The TUC welcomes the Government plans to set up an Energy Commission. The TUC sees the Commission as the instrument through which the long-term plans for investment, output and manpower in the coal, oil, gas, nuclear and electricity industries will be co-ordinated.

Its emphasis is upon jobs. It goes on:

> An immediate priority is the ordering of a second Drax coal-fired power station which will also have beneficial effects on the power generating industry.

In its evidence to the Wilson Committee, 'To Review the Functioning of Financial Institutions', the TUC said that oil is the urgent new factor to be taken into account; apart from government take and the difference oil would make to the balance of payments, offshore oil 'by allowing a faster rate of economic growth, will indirectly increase the total amount of savings in the economy . . .' The most important TUC statement to the Wilson Committee was as follows:

> The investment challenge is based on the fact that the benefits of offshore oil are finite. Therefore the key issue is how to use the surplus funds for investment in the regeneration of the UK economy. The objective would be that by the time the oil flow began to lessen, the UK manufacturing and productive sector would have been built up, so that it could meet and beat any international challenge.

There is nothing remarkable about this statement; it is similar to a good many that have been produced with variations by politicians of left, centre and right. It contains possibly the greatest fallacy of the North Sea oil debate: that the vital question is how to invest the surplus funds for the regeneration of the UK economy. The fallacy lies in the assumption that only with North Sea oil can British industry be regenerated; but if British industry cannot regenerate itself, North Sea oil revenues will not be able to do the job for it. Such statements give rise to a dreary vista of endless 'lame ducks' being supported for the rest of the century with oil-derived funds—the operation being dubbed regeneration.

Union concern is first with jobs and second with the rate of government investment in industry: that is the area where their greatest pressures will be applied. In talks between union officials and Mr Benn in July 1977, the unions criticized the approach of the oil industry to the question of refining in Britain; they made plain their support for the Benn opposition to the EEC Commission's attempts to persuade members to cut back on surplus refining capacity in Europe. The unions, on the contrary, see North Sea oil giving rise to new refining job opportunities in Britain. In a National Oil Unions brief submitted to Mr Benn, the unions said:

> The oil unions stand for maximum downstream development based on North Sea feedstocks. Within this the Government ought to regard the target of two thirds of North Sea crude being refined in the UK as a minimum target.

The clash of interests can clearly be seen over this issue, for at the same time the Petroleum Industry Advisory Committee also submitted a brief to Mr Benn, in which they pointed out:

> Pursuit of fixed targets like two thirds could lead to gross refining diseconomies which would not add to employment but could adversely affect the balance of payments and the UK value added.

The difference arises from the fact that the unions are concerned with jobs for their members in Britain; the oil companies are concerned with the profits they obtain from Europe-wide operations and farther afield.

The slow involvement of unions in the North Sea can be illustrated by the fact that only in February 1978 had the men on the Piper field platform reached the point of voting on whether or not they wanted to be unionized. Up to that time, members of the Inter-Union Offshore Committee had made visits to other production platforms, but on few of them was serious interest shown in unionization. For the Forties field, for example, BP claimed that union membership was not widespread on the platforms, although union representatives had visited the offshore installations. There had been no request for unions to be given negotiating rights, although BP is prepared to recognize unions offshore where this is the wish of a majority of the workers.

On the other hand, the attitude of the companies towards the unions has not been encouraging; rather it has been one of definite non-cooperation. Only at the end of 1974 did some companies allow union representatives on some of the rigs. Company recruitment policies tend to seek out men who are likely to be anti-union anyway. This is relatively easy to do since the nature of the work, which is hard, dangerous and away from home, tends to attract tough individualists who will often only take the jobs on a casual basis. In *Labour Law and Offshore Oil*, Jonathan Kitchen maintains that while BP and Shell will tolerate union membership, it is actively disliked by the other oil companies. All the unions would like to see an increase in unionization in the business. In some cases attempts to organize unions have been opposed by both the management and by the other workers. The resultant absence of collective bargaining means disparities in conditions of employment from one field to another, and this in turn means that contracts are of great importance to individual workers.

There have been some North Sea related strikes which have attracted great attention. The Bristow pilot strike lasted for two months and involved highly paid, skilled men on the one side, and an exceptionally rugged individualist boss on the other. Before the strike ended, it had affected helicopter services to the offshore rigs, caused the closure of Aberdeen airport, led to picketing at Grangemouth refinery and obtained support from the Transport and General Workers' Union, whose members agreed to black all supply vessels bound for oil rigs served by Bristow Helicopters. Although the dispute began over an alleged victimization, it developed into a battle for union recognition by the company.

The strike demonstrated what might happen in the North Sea: a total helicopter strike could bring operations to a standstill. At the subsequent court of inquiry the pilot at the centre of the strike, Captain Royston, was said to have been wrongfully dismissed; he claimed he had been victimized because of his recruiting activities on behalf of BALPA. Lord McDonald criticized Alan Bristow for his handling of his men and said: 'Mr Bristow fails to understand the art of communication,' and he 'must bear much of the blame for allowing the dispute to begin in the first instance.'

The other kind of offshore strike has concerned men on the rigs and platforms. In January 1976, 35 men on Brent B platform were taken off after a dispute when they were asked to work in icy conditions. In September 1977, 120 men were airlifted off Shell-Esso's Dunlin A platform after the refusal of the management of McDermotts Oceanics Drilling Contractors to recognize a workers' committee. Within hours of the stoppage McDermotts had ordered a mass evacuation of the platform. Many of the men were out of sympathy with the attempt to organize a workers' committee. As one man said: 'After one trip everyone knows what the conditions are. If they don't like it, they don't have to stay.' That represents an old-fashioned viewpoint these days. In January 1978, 90 men engaged in a sit-in for better conditions on a semi-submarine exploration rig alongside Brent B.

No doubt as North Sea operations settle into the long-lasting production phase the unions will become more organized, but so far they have hardly done well even on behalf of those men interested in being unionized. The conditions are partly to blame—but only partly. British offshore workers, for example, are the worst paid of all the groups working on North Sea oil installations. The Norwegians are better paid, enjoy considerably better conditions and their operations are almost entirely unionized. The Germans, French, Dutch and Irish offshore workers are also all better off than their British counterparts and much of this difference is clearly because the British unions have failed to penetrate the rigs to the same extent, whatever the reasons for this failure may be.

By the end of 1977 union recognition had been achieved on six out of twenty-eight rigs in the North Sea; this was in major contrast to the Norwegian sector where contracts of employment are dependent upon union membership. The unions believe that the Labour government has not exactly exerted itself on their behalf and though the Memorandum of Agreement of 1976 did give union representatives access to the rigs, not much more has been achieved. It is a fascinating example of divergent interests. The unions, which are in any case in a difficult position, tend to blame the government for not exerting greater pressure upon the oil companies. The government, whatever the Labour Party's ties with the trade union movement may be, has been more interested in getting the oil flowing fast and so has not wanted to promote more clashes with the companies than necessary.

A different aspect of union activity concerns the construction unions, largely onshore. There is also the Hook-up Agreement relating to engineering construction hook-up work on oil and gas production platform sites, although many firms which are active in the North Sea, for example from the EEC, have not been unionized. The main sites such as Methil, Nigg, Ardesier, Sullom Voe, Flotta or Kisshorn are all affected by the construction unions. As one union official admitted, the American involvement in much of the construction business has been like a breath of fresh air and at places such as Nigg, for example, they trained unskilled people with great rapidity. A devastating picture of British construction practices was revealed in the 1976 NEDO report 'Engineering Construction Performance'; this compares British performance with that of EEC, Canadian and US companies—and the British come last. The reasons were numerous: inadequate management, bad time-keeping, overrunning on estimates, overmanning, bad industrial relations. The result, when British companies do not perform properly, is that the oil companies go elsewhere and the business is lost. One problem in the British construction industry is that contractors do not have to share the risks, since there are no penalty clauses.

According to Mr J. Baldwin, the Secretary-General of the Constructional Section of the AUEW, the union should go for higher pay so that there is not so much emphasis on overtime. On the industry as a whole, Mr Baldwin says the biggest problems are lack of motivation and poor management. Listing the many obstacles to efficiency in an industry clearly requiring a great deal of change he suggests: management, performance, motivation, completion dates, industrial relations. Further, he argues that overmanning does not achieve any of its objects.

The majority of work for North Sea construction jobs has gone to non-British firms and, interestingly, again because of balance of payments considerations, government has not insisted that work goes to British firms if it knows they will under-perform and so delay the oil flow. It seemed likely at the beginning of 1978 that of a possible twelve rigs to be ordered during the year a majority of the orders would be placed abroad. Since British prices bear no comparison with those of their competitors, the industry cannot even get a full share of North Sea orders; it is, therefore, foolish to imagine that this sector of industry is on the eve of breaking into the world offshore market. Mr Baldwin, who clearly would like to see all the construction jobs go to British firms, does not mince his words when talking of either management or unions.

The NEDO Report, referred to above, makes uneasy reading for anyone concerned with British industrial performance. It says of the comparisons between yards in the different selected countries:

Not only did the UK projects take longer in terms of elapsed years and months, but they also absorbed more man-hours on site; the difference in man-hours was proportionately greater than the difference in elapsed time because of the larger numbers employed on the UK sites.

Another sample of its findings continues to depress:

From the activity sampling surveys it is clear that under normal working conditions a greater proportion of the hours available each day is taken up by tea-breaks and walking time on the UK sites than overseas.

Planning was clearly less effective on the UK projects, judging by the results. Not only were project and construction times longer, but overrun on planned times was greater on the UK projects, and management did not demonstrate the capacity of the foreign project managements to make good lost time once a delay had been incurred.

In its comparisons of performance the report found:

1 Foreign project times were shorter.
2 Foreign projects were less prone to delays.
3 Foreign construction times were shorter.
4 Foreign projects were mostly executed with higher overall construction efficiency (as measured by the ratio of overall work content to total man-hours).
5 Productivity on specific tasks was higher abroad.
6 Manning levels were lower abroad.
7 Delays incurred in the course of foreign projects were capable of retrieval by the end.

It was not all bad for the British construction industry but sufficiently disturbing to raise some acute queries about what this— and some other industries—must do if they seriously want to capture a reasonable slice of world, as opposed to only North Sea, offshore business in the next twenty or so years.

Such bad performance also raises some acute political questions. There is a limit upon the extent to which any government can go on

promoting or shielding the inefficient, whether it is a Labour government desirous of backing the unions or ensuring work for a depressed area, or a Tory government trying to push business interests
or supporting nationalist claims to have the first bite at North Sea
related work. Furthermore, when such inefficiency stands in the way
of developments considered by the government of the day to be
crucial to the economy at large, the limit of the support that is
forthcoming will become even less.

As a result of the high level of international competition which
North Sea developments have brought to Britain's doorstep, some
at least of the skeletons in a woefully rattling industrial cupboard
are coming to light. With luck such revelations might conceivably
lead to a few cures.

The CBI has been curiously quiet about North Sea oil, though it
had a few bromide remarks to make in its report, *Britain Means
Business 1977*:

> North Sea oil will do little more than compensate for our loss of
> real national income resulting from the quadrupling of oil prices
> a few years ago. It will certainly not allow us to live comfortably
> and trouble-free for the next ten years. But if we use it sensibly, it
> can help to stop things becoming worse, and it can give us a
> breathing space during which we can re-build, and consolidate
> our position in the European Community.

This is a curious statement, to say the least. Oil will surely do
much more than compensate for the lost income as a result of the
quadrupling of oil prices: after all it means that British exports of
oil are also to be at quadrupled prices. If the best opinion the CBI
can venture on oil is that to use it sensibly will mean we can stop
things getting worse, then the country, alas, can expect little
leadership from that body.

16

Scotland and the SNP

Scotland represents the biggest single regional and political interest group or area affected by the coming of North Sea oil. As always when a small community is in close contact with a much larger one, the former is either swamped and in danger of losing its identity or manages to achieve a greater sense of identity. The latter has occurred as far as Scottish-English relations are concerned. There is a strong sense of Scottish identity which too often, unfortunately, is highlighted by English arrogance. North Sea oil has focused attention upon the economic and political problems of Scotland in a way that nothing else could: Scotland and 'Scotland's Oil' suddenly became of great significance to the rest of the United Kingdom. Just as politicians in London saw in oil a means of rescuing the country from years of economic decline, the Scottish National Party was so provoking as to make major headway in its push for independence and furthermore was importunate enough to claim that the oil was Scotland's.

Until recently approximately 40,000 Scots headed south of the border every year in search of employment. Now, for the first time since the Act of Union, the general level of unemployment in Scotland is the same as that for the United Kingdom as a whole. This is the result of two developments: oil, and the fact that for some years now governments at Westminster have been wooing Scotland with development funds. At the root of much Scottish discontent with the Union as it now exists is a long history of economic and political neglect by Westminster so that Scotland has become a depressed economic region. The SNP has derived much of its strength from this sense of economic neglect. Then came oil, almost all of which lies in Scottish waters, and with it the prospect that at last the economic balance could be redressed. This is not to say that there are no nationalist impulses other than economic ones, but economic problems have given the greatest impetus to the nationalist cause.

A higher proportion of public expenditure is allocated to Scotland than to the United Kingdom as a whole, while public revenue hardly covers current expenditure, so that the region is in receipt of capital subsidies for development purposes. Further, more than 70 per cent of Scottish trade is with England. These facts are an important background to independence considerations.

It is a Scottish complaint that economic decisions by major companies are taken in ways that damage local interests. This was the attitude in Fife, for example, when the British Sugar Corporation shut down a plant (another was opened in Lincoln) after the local farmers had geared themselves to produce beet sugar for it. The process of rationalization may lead to closures of plant in Scotland even when these are going concerns. Further, big companies from the south sometimes buy up and then close down operations which are making profits in Scotland. These are the complaints of a weak region in relation to a stronger whole; they are also grist to the SNP mill. At the same time Scotland produces 30 per cent of Britain's dollar exports, mainly engineering products.

The 1977 Report on the workings of the 1972 Industry Act revealed that Scotland took a third of government assistance to industry over the five-year period the Act had been in operation, and should get 30,000 of the 90,000 jobs resulting from the investment. On a regional basis only the Northern Area of England with even higher unemployment received more assistance than Scotland.

Scotland often resents, and has cause to resent, English or Westminster attitudes: a typical example was the siting of BNOC in Glasgow, a conciliatory gesture that meant little in terms of decision-making. As an increasing number of moderate Scots, who were certainly not members of the SNP, said in the middle 1970s, the Scottish demand for devolution needed to be taken seriously. Scotland as a whole ought to be regarded as a development area; and there was need for Scotland to get an adequate share of the oil revenue. The English, as they demonstrated elsewhere in their Empire, refuse to take nationalism seriously until faced with a crisis.

During the 1970s, however, and in part due to the pressures of the SNP whose rise threatened the interests of both the Labour and Tory parties in Scotland, Westminster did embark upon some economic policies designed to woo Scottish voters and demonstrate that the region was getting its fair share of development aid.

The issue of what to do about Scottish grievances has been starkly raised by SNP demands for independence. There are various possibilities. The creation of a strong Scottish Assembly with substantial powers and its own source of revenue derived from oil is one solution. There is—despite fierce protests from Westminster— no reason why Britain should not adopt some form of federalism: countries such as Canada, Australia, the USA, Nigeria, West

Germany, to name but five, have reasonably devolved federal systems which work effectively. At present the British system is one of the most centralized in the world. Devolution of whatever kind could not change the basic economic relationship between Scotland and England, but as a growing number of moderate Scots (who are not arguing for independence) say, a much greater crisis will develop if Westminster continues to act as though there is no crisis; feelings run deep on the nationalist issue in Scotland.

The SNP were riding high during 1977 and hoping for as many as forty seats at the next general election. The party would make any majority of Scottish seats it won the basis of a demand for independence. Once the issue of independence is broached, a number of questions which are often brushed aside or ignored have to be faced: what line would an independent Scotland take on defence? how would it fare industrially?

An independent Scotland could in fact do as well as Norway, since it would have the bulk of the North Sea oil, its existing industrial base, excellent agriculture and tourism as the four main arms of its economy. Scotland is comparable to Norway in size and population and Norway does very well as an independent state, alongside Sweden which formerly controlled it as the imperial power.

When Anthony Crosland was Foreign Secretary in 1976, he inadvertently gave the English game away when on a trip to the USA. As reported in the *Daily Telegraph* of 8 October 1976, the story was as follows:

Mr Crosland, the Foreign Secretary, asked at a Washington Press conference yesterday why Britain refused to give Scotland its independence, said in an aside heard distinctly over the microphone, 'because they have got a lot of oil'.

The SNP may or may not be a temporary phenomenon; it is undoubtedly an important one at the present time. As Christopher Harvie says in his book *Scotland and Nationalism*, 'The rise of political nationalism has been the central fact of Scottish politics since 1965.' In tracing the story of Scottish nationalism since 1945, one can see a steady progression that Westminster largely ignored until the 1970s. In 1947 a Scottish Convention held an Assembly in Glasgow and a resolution for home rule was virtually unanimous. A 1948 draft scheme for an assembly led to the Scottish Covenant of 1949 which two million people signed.

In 1962 the Tories dealt a blow to their own position in Scotland when they ended the tax concession on hydrocarbon oils and so killed off the West Lothian shale oil industry. Although the SNP contested four seats in 1964, the party had little electoral impact.

There was an SNP boom in the late 1960s although they then fared
badly at the 1970 election. This seemed all the worse after Mrs
Ewing's 1967 victory at Hamilton which had been a major blow to
Labour.

One result of these SNP advances was to make the Tories set up a
study group on devolution whose subsequent report was endorsed
by Heath and followed by the establishment of a Constitutional
Committee under Sir Alec Douglas-Home. The 1970 election was
almost an SNP disaster: its 65 candidates took 11·4 per cent of the
votes.

The SNP early saw the importance of the oil—in fact well before
either the Tories or Labour—and as Harvie says:

> 'It's Scotland's Oil!' Whatever the ethics of the proposition the
> SNP chose an opportune moment, 16 March 1973, to launch a
> sophisticated and well organized campaign.

The early oil discoveries and the boom in Aberdeen and the
Grampian region reversed the gloomy economic picture in Scot-
land. Later, however, the SNP came to regard its slogan 'It's
Scotland's Oil' as a mixed blessing.

The 1974 election saw the SNP gain up to 30 per cent of the
Scottish vote and in a strong position in the new House of Commons,
while the right of the Labour Party was silent on the issue of
devolution. Later a Labour promise to produce a white paper on
devolution in 1975 came to nothing. During 1976 the SNP won
sweeping electoral gains in local elections throughout Scotland.
Both the Labour and Tory parties were in disarray over their
Scottish policies, or lack of them, and both saw the SNP as a threat
to their own political positions in Scotland; Labour the more so,
since its majorities in general elections always depend upon Scottish
and Welsh seats, never on a majority of the English seats which the
Tories obtain. Harvie, who puts a good case for the SNP, exaggerated when he says:

> In 1977 the main question in Anglo-Scottish politics is no longer
> what to do about the Scottish National Party or about North Sea
> oil, but how to prevent a total disintegration of the relationship
> between the two peoples.

It surely had not reached quite that stage; on the other hand normal
English complacency could still allow it to do so.

The rise of Scottish nationalism needs be taken more seriously by
English politicians though not as seriously as the Scottish nationalists
would prefer. The total SNP vote in the 1964 general election was
64,053. At least by 1968 Heath had proposed a Scottish Assembly

during the Scottish Tory Conference at Perth. As Tom Wolfe says in *Scotland Lives*, 'One of the more remarkable aspects of the growth of the SNP from 1962 to 1968 was its spontaneity.' It was in part as a response to this spontaneity that Heath made his proposal. Gordon Wilson, a key member of the party and MP for Dundee East, saw an inescapable relationship between self-government for Scotland and North Sea oil. As Wolfe also said, 'The wealth of the oil destroys the myth that Scotland is too poor for self-government.' It does indeed, but only if the Scots can get their hands on it which, as Crosland foolishly but honestly gave away, the English would not allow.

The SNP leadership is young and dedicated to seriousness in its unbending pursuit of Scottish independence. The party is highly organized and produces efficient and interesting propaganda such as the series of Fletcher Papers—'North Sea Oil and the Scottish Economy', 'Scotland and Energy', 'Independence and Federalism After the Referendum', 'Norway A Model for Scotland's Future?', 'Taxation in an Independent Scotland'. At the second 1974 election of October the SNP had 840,000 votes.

According to a report, *Scotland in the 1980s*, by the Henley Centre for Forecasting, the sober facts of the rise of the SNP need to be taken seriously. There was an increase in SNP voting strength from 5·1 per cent in 1966 to 30·4 per cent in October 1974, and over the period SNP representation rose from nil to 11 seats at Westminster; on a basis of proportional representation the party ought to have won 23 seats.

As the Report suggests, given the 'first past the post' system Britain has, it is clear that somewhere between 30 per cent (producing for the SNP a seventh of the seats) and 36·3 per cent (which won over half the seats for Labour) there is a break-point at which the system begins to work in favour of a party. In other words, if the SNP could win another 3 or 4 per cent of the votes, it might capture a majority of Scottish seats. The SNP does significantly better among younger voters and this could mean that as older Labour and Tory supporters pass on, the SNP will replace them. Opponents of devolution often use dubious arguments. Thus, some claim that to give Scotland an assembly with real powers must lead on to a demand for total independence. This will not necessarily follow.

On the possibility of an SNP triumph leading Westminster to concede independence the same Report says:

This outcome only seems possible either if there is a catastrophic economic collapse leading to a breakup of the existing political alignments, or as a result of serious blundering on the part of UK politicians and unionist politicians in Scotland.

The party, from necessity, has become expert at leafletting since it was long denied outlets in the press. Their campaign, based upon Gordon Wilson's idea 'It's Scotland's Oil', produced startling results in 1971 at three by-elections at Stirling, Falkirk and Grange-mouth when the SNP share of the vote rose from 14 to 35 per cent. In 1977, however, the party had second thoughts about the 'It's Scotland's Oil' approach, which appears over-greedy and could become a vote-loser; instead the party adopted a more general approach with the slogan 'Get the strength of Scotland's wealth around you', the emphasis being on a range of natural resources, not just oil, and also including food, timber and fish.

One harsh comment upon the SNP appeared in *The Times* of March 1978:

> It [nationalism] is concerned far less with saving a culture or a language. Instead of being demanded by the people, nationalism has been gradually eased upon them by the SNP aided by the lamentable state of the Scottish economy.

There is a good deal of truth in that judgement. Possibly the greatest boon to the nationalists has been Westminster's consistent reluctance to allow a Scottish Assembly, although clearly the majority of Scots, and a substantial one at that, want one.

SNP propaganda claims that oil reserves in the Scottish Continental Shelf total 30,000 million barrels which is enough to last Scotland 400 years at its present rate of consumption; the fields off mainland Scotland are worth £100,000 million and this figure could be doubled if reserves off Shetland and off the West coast were to be included as well.

The extreme SNP case—though certainly not a view held by all the party—is that Scotland's economic ills are the result of the Union with England; the corollary of this is that independence would produce major economic benefits. The SNP has certainly enjoyed its greatest growth at the same time that North Sea oil has come on tap, and the expectations about what it might do for Britain have become a matter of public debate.

In an ingenious attempt to appear less selfish about the oil, the SNP began to argue in 1977 that Scottish and English interests are quite different: that England needs foreign exchange to settle its debts while the Scots need investment to rebuild their economy, so that some sort of equitable sharing of the benefits of oil could follow Scottish independence. One might ask, though it is a double-edged question, how much the SNP put into the finding and exploiting of North Sea oil, whose almost total benefits the party now claims for Scotland.

North Sea oil gave a great fillip to Scottish nationalism, even while focusing attention upon Scotland's economic ills. A Scotsman, who was present at the 1972 Aviemore conference on oil, commented sourly upon how London civil servants were prepared to give away the oil to the companies without adequate government control. Scottish nationalism and oil keep coming together, for nationalism means control of resources and the central fact about Scottish independence followed by an equitable division of offshore oil and gas would simply mean that two thirds of the total resources would go to Scotland. So far the only Scottish benefits from the oil, as distinct from the general benefits to the Exchequer for the country as a whole, have been additional employment. But when 55,000 Scottish jobs are compared with 200,000 American ones those benefits hardly look so great anyway.

As William Wolfe says accurately enough, 'Scottish oil can make Scotland the most prosperous country in Europe or it can provide temporary relief for the UK balance of payments. It cannot do both.' He is, of course, right and if Whitehall and the English have their way it will supply temporary, if quite long-lasting, relief for the balance of payments.

As the Mackays point out, an independent Scotland would have far greater reason to conserve the oil than would Britain and, moreover, 'It should be noted that the ratio of oil reserves to domestic income would be much higher for an independent Scotland than for Norway.' What is important to realize also, should independence become a real possibility, is that ownership of the oil would not necessarily remove the causes of Scotland's economic problems; it would provide a means to ameliorate them.

Unfortunately, once nationalism gets underway increasingly heated reactions are aroused. SNP literature, among other things, claims that Scotland has enough coal for a thousand years and 'enough oil to provide £1,800 million to a Scottish Treasury for sixty years'. Commenting upon this in *The Times*, an English writer said:

> No one doubts the urgency of the social and industrial problems facing Scotland, but it is unhelpful to link these in the public mind with a selective and distorted view of the natural resources simply because one believes that one's own country has a temporary surplus of a desirable resource such as oil.

The writer then talked of selfishness before attempting to flaw the nationalist arguments. It is, however, a fact that the SNP has risen to influence precisely because, although no one doubted the urgency of Scotland's problems, no one did much about them either.

Politicians won't do anything about problems until some form of
electoral pistol is held to their heads; this is what the SNP have done
so effectively.

Should the SNP obtain a majority in Scotland so that their
demand for independence becomes real, there will follow the
question of how to divide the oil in the North Sea. The legal position
depends upon the 1958 Geneva Convention and the normally
accepted principle of equidistance. Britain's advantage, however, in
any demand for a break-up of the United Kingdom would be that
international agreements have been with Britain and not with its
component parts. In any case there would be the complication of
Shetland and Orkney.

Shetland would probably prefer to stay with the UK in any
break-up, although in the 1974 election the SNP came second.
Shetland autonomy of the kind it now enjoys with a distant and not
too overbearing Whitehall could well seem more attractive than
more immediate domination from Edinburgh. The Shetlanders are
to have two opportunities during 1978 to vote on their future: first
on the political future of the community; and then in the Scottish
referendum. Shetland's decisions could greatly complicate any
division of the oil.

If Shetland stayed with Britain, it would probably be treated (in
terms of international arbitration) as the Channel Islands and
Scillies were in the Anglo-French dispute: that is, they would be
given a twelve-mile limit and not be used as a reference point for
subsequent demarcations. Thereafter, a North Sea division might
mean changing the median line so that some of the rich fields east
of Shetland went to Norway and not to Scotland at all. If, however,
Shetland stayed as part of Scotland, then she and Scotland could
retain the fields, provided that Shetland in relation to Scotland was
treated as Shetland in relation to the United Kingdom.

The SNP claims that waters north of latitude 55° 50′ extending
due east are Scottish, which would give Scotland virtually all the
oil fields and the largest share of the Continental Shelf: 160,000
square kilometres to Norway's 131,000 and England's 84,000.

As devolution for Scotland became an important if publicly
boring issue at the end of 1977, leaders of the Scottish Labour
Party urged Mr Callaghan to allow Scotland to decide in a referendum whether or not it wanted independence from Britain: they
preferred to bring the issue into the open. Such a move would
allow Scottish voters to support a measure of devolution while
rejecting the SNP. It had already been written into the Scotland Bill
that Scots should have a referendum on whether or not they approved
a Scottish assembly with powers devolved to Edinburgh. What the

Scottish Labour members wanted to add was a second question: whether the Scots also wanted total independence and the creation of a Scottish state. Callaghan resisted the demand. As a Labour memorandum from its Glasgow headquarters stated, this would force the Nationalists 'to defend their real objective, shared only by a minority of the Scots.' By early 1978 English nationalists were organizing to counteract the Scottish demands. The difference, however, was fundamental: while the Scottish Nationalists want independence, the English nationalists want unity which is an interesting line for 'nationalists' to take.

In sweeping demands for reform the Labour Party's annual Scottish conference of March 1978 voted against the platform and government in asking for crash programmes of public works, early retirement, a greatly expanded SDA and the nationalization of any company threatening redundancy, in other words, panic measures. Oil as a source of income was not named; it was clearly implied. Thus the Scottish Labour Party put in its bid for North Sea oil.

Curiously enough, frightened as the Labour Party had clearly become, it did far better than expected at the Garscadden by-election though with a reduced majority, while the SNP did not do as well as it had hoped, increasing its percentage of the poll from the 1974 figure of 31·2 per cent to only 32·9 per cent.

The Tory Party has hardly shown itself more imaginative in its attitudes to Scotland and the SNP than Labour. The party stands for unity as a principle; it has not, despite Heath's acceptance of the idea of a Scottish Assembly, shown much subsequent willingness to accommodate Scottish fears and economic misgivings which lie at the heart of SNP demands. The Tory Party opposes any meaningful devolution and offers little else.

The Liberals press for devolved financial powers and proportional representation. It is far from easy for the average voter to know precisely where any of these three parties stand on the issue. Mr Richard Wainwright, Liberal MP for Colne Valley, suggests a form of federal Britain, rather than separation, with elected assemblies in Scotland and Wales but not in England; there, he argues, regional assemblies must be established, for were England to be treated as Scotland and Wales, she would control 85 per cent of the population and resources through her assembly. This, he says, would be a prime recipe for deadlock.

That may be true, yet so far no one has suggested that England is not a single entity; it is therefore illogical to argue for assemblies for Wales and Scotland but not England. If there is to be devolution for Scotland, the logical outcome would seem to be devolution for everyone else; to argue for different status for England is to advance a form of imperialism which gives her a superior status to the others. None of this makes the problem easier to solve.

Recently Scotland has certainly generated some more than usually exaggerated flights of political fancy. Mr Gregor MacKenzie, Minister of State at the Scottish Office, claimed in September 1977, after a week's visit to the USA, that American industrialists were terrified of Scotland becoming independent and opting out of the EEC—a scare story if ever there was one. The SNP's Mrs Margo MacDonald took him up on it:

> What Mr MacKenzie is saying is totally at variance with what his own boss (Mr Bruce Millan) found and with what the American Ambassador said on his visit to Scotland a fortnight ago when he predicted that American investment in Scotland would continue over the next five to ten years at least.
>
> Once the Assembly is set up and politics takes its natural course, the Scots are unlikely to want to antagonize American companies who want to make worthwhile investments here.

In a final reference to the EEC she was amusing:

> As for the EEC, on the timescale of an independent Scotland's negotiations with the EEC, it would take a wise man to say what the structural framework of the EEC will be after it has been enlarged to take in Greece and Spain and has accommodated movements in the Basque country of Catalonia. Mr MacKenzie is confusing interest with fact.

Such exchanges are, no doubt, the stuff of politics, yet if they continue long enough they give rise to new climates and expectations and that is what is happening in Scotland.

As Gordon Wilson, a key member of the SNP and the architect of its oil policy, says with justice: the English can only think of Scotland as an extension of themselves. In fact, in the 1974 election SNP candidates came second in 36 of the 41 seats that Labour won in Scotland. A comparison of the parties' performance in Scotland in that election shows that 30·5 per cent of the Scottish vote gave the SNP 11 seats; 36·5 per cent gave Labour 41 seats; 25 per cent gave the Tories 16 seats; and 8 per cent of votes gave the Liberals 3 seats. On a proportional representation basis the Tories did best, getting very nearly their exact entitlement, while the SNP and Liberals did badly. Labour would be adversely affected by any change of voting pattern.

Like most of the SNP, Gordon Wilson is prepared to sidestep the issue of defence and security. This represents an emotional Tory and

British issue that the party would prefer not to stir up, although as good nationalists they ought not to leave the issue alone at all.

In a paper on oil Gordon Wilson says:

Scotland's oil resources are small on a global scale, but representing as they do one of the most prolific oil territories in any one area outside the main world oil centres, they are of utmost significance to a nation which has a population of only $5\frac{1}{4}$ million people.

Arguing that successive British governments have worked on the assumption that there should be the fastest possible build-up of oil production so as to eliminate the balance of payments deficit, an assumption that is certainly true, Wilson says:

To the achievement of this object, all other aspects of oil policy such as taxation, effective participation, downstream development, marketing of natural and other gases and long term depletion and conservation have been subordinated.

This, alas, is also true. In his engaging way Gordon Wilson disregards actuality when he makes the point that,

Scotland is now an oil exporting country (our daily production is running at an annual rate of 20m tons). It is only a matter of time before we join the OPEC production league.

Assuming that Mr Wilson means everything he says, then his main point has unpleasant implications for Britain and its oil-based economic hopes. It is:

Nevertheless there must be few Scots who can view a prospective annual production upwards of 110 to 150 million tons by a nation consuming 10 million tons as other than reckless.

This can only mean that the policy he advocates for an independent Scotland is a drastic cutback in production, so that North Sea oil neither supplies Britain's needs nor allows exports over and above those. No wonder Mr Crosland said that the government had no intention of allowing Scotland to have its independence. Similarly on gas, Wilson says:

The indications are that gas is about to be exploited at the rate of 4,000 million cubic feet per day—almost 24 times Scottish current consumption and 4 times the probable maximum Scottish consumption, even assuming a changeover to a gas-oriented energy pattern.

He suggests quite correctly that without independence Scotland will be lucky to get more than 10 per cent of the oil revenues for general expenditure while the proposed Assembly 'is to be deprived completely of oil revenue financing'.

Finally, talking of a possible division—he accepts the line of 55° 56′—Mr Wilson says:

> . . . all that will be at stake will be the small fields of Auk, Argyll and Josephine. These will represent 7 per cent of total production in the 1980s and compare with the 90 per cent overall that Scotland will lose as an integral part of the UK.

Accepting his figure and reversing the argument, Britain stands to lose control of 90 per cent of her North Sea oil bonanza in the event of Scottish independence; no wonder Tories and Labour see eye to eye on this issue.

As members of the SNP like to say, one way or another Scotland will be independent in ten years time; some even talk of seeking a majority in the UN to back their demands against Westminster. Such talk makes Scotland sound like a colony in revolt: the SNP appear to forget that an act of union took place. At the time of the Scottish Covenant in 1949, Attlee said (and in opposition Churchill agreed) that there could be home rule for Scotland if a majority of Scottish MPs voted 'national'. This Westminster would regard as a mandate. The 1978 (or possibly 1979) general election could decide this issue: should the SNP fare badly they may well have passed their peak for a generation.

Another aspect of the oil 'game' in Scotland was the parliamentary order, which came into effect on 8 July 1977, to exclude all oil installations and pipelines that lie below the low water mark from the valuation rolls of Scottish local authorities. The order was a move to thwart Scottish attempts to rate such installations. The Fife assessor, for example, had wanted a valuation of £6·5 million on the Auk and Argyll fields and the Grampian Authority wanted to rate the Forties field at £17·4 million. The next move in the rating game came in January 1978, when the Ross and Cromarty District Council began to investigate the possibility of imposing a 'throughput levy' on any oil or gas landed within its boundaries.

There are three solutions to the Scottish problem as seen from Westminster: to leave things as they are and do nothing; to go for some measure of devolution which the two major parties would both hope would be enough to defuse a situation that otherwise could get out of hand; or, in the event of an SNP majority in Scotland, concede independence. In the event of such a majority occurring, however, it is likely that Westminster-orchestrated delays would be prolonged for many years, as some Scots fear, until the oil was all used up anyway.

The arguments on both sides are not easy and less clear than may at first appear. Those who oppose any effective devolution do so on the grounds that devolution could not subsequently be denied to either Wales or Ulster, and the consequence is likely to be the break-up of the United Kingdom. Since they are opposed to any such break-up of the UK, they would prefer no form of devolution whatever to take place. Those who support devolution, with varying degrees of reluctance to, at most, lukewarm enthusiasm, argue that without devolution we may face the break-up of the UK much sooner; that devolution need not herald the break-up of the country; that a number of countries operate federal systems successfully without any question of their breaking up; and, therefore, that there is no reason why such an approach should not be adopted in this country. It might satisfy the Scots and then the Welsh, and possibly even solve the Ulster question as well, though that would appear to be a forlorn hope. There are not many ardent devolutionists.

In 1977 events forced the Labour government to propose devolution for Scotland and Wales, unfortunately less because a proper policy had been thought out than because the government could not see what else to do. Devolution is designed by Labour (and any Tory measure would have the same objective) to prevent SNP power leading to a break-up of the United Kingdom. If that is taken as the starting point, it at once becomes plain that the government will give away as little power from the centre as possible. This, of course, is the surest way of making devolution unworkable or so unsatisfying to those who most want it that it will be likely to prove counterproductive and not 'defuse' the SNP at all.

For devolution to be viable, it must include powers over some finances; to satisfy the Scottish sense of economic neglect it would be wise to concede to a Scottish assembly a portion of the oil revenues for development purposes. Neither Mr Callaghan's government nor Mrs Thatcher's opposition have any desire or intention of doing anything of the sort. It is a pity. They could, for example, take a leaf out of Nigeria's book: there oil-producing states keep a proportion of the oil revenue while the balance goes to the central exchequer. The basic Scottish complaint which has ensured the rise of the SNP is that of economic neglect. Much has been said about using the oil wealth to regenerate industry; if a modest proportion of the total government tax take during the 1980s, say £500 million a year, were made over absolutely to a Scottish Assembly to be used as capital for development purposes, this would go a long way towards rectifying long years of economic neglect.

It will be a disaster for Anglo-Scottish relations if Scotland sees—or thinks it sees—almost all the fruits of the oil wealth go southwards. An annual oil development fund of the sort proposed above would also, perhaps, do something to satisfy the claim that it is Scotland's oil.

A referendum in Scotland will at least allow the Scots to say whether they want devolution, however weak it may at first be; subsequently, through their assembly, they can demand more powers as, of course, the SNP say they will do. It is doubtful that a majority of Scots want independence; according to the SNP, however, a growing minority do.

The government's devolution measures carefully excluded anything to do with oil; even so, the major oil companies have opened offices in Scotland ready for direct dealings with a devolved assembly, should that need arise. Energy matters at present are reserved for Westminster. Similarly the government has distinguished planning decisions which affect energy—such as overland pipeline routes or installations like refineries—from other planning, and has left these in the hands of the Secretary of State for Scotland who remains in the Westminster Cabinet.

As a result a Scottish assembly as envisaged early in 1978 would have no powers over energy matters. But as Mr Gordon Wilson says, 'If the voters are interested in any subject, then you can bet that it is going to be debated.' Such a line was to be expected from the SNP, who see the assembly as merely a first step on the road to independence.

When, in the debate in January 1978, Mr Wilson proposed an amendment that would bring the oil, gas, coal and electricity industries under the control of the Scottish Assembly, Mr John Smith, Minister of State in the Privy Council Office, rejected the amendment as a separatist step. He said the energy industries were flourishing and that it would be tragic to try to divide up energy resources and have competing energy policies within the United Kingdom.

The alternative to devolution—apart from outright independence —would be for Westminster to pay far greater attention to the economic problems of the outlying regions of the United Kindom as a whole; but that is to ask more than is ever likely to happen. Apart from economic considerations there are other more genuinely nationalist ones such as culture, Scottish sense of identity and law which give to Scots a sense of nationalism quite separate from any sense of being British, and these need to be satisfied.

It is one thing to find ways of dealing with definite Scottish grievances; it is something quite different to argue for the break-up of the United Kingdom because the SNP succeed in persuading a majority of Scots to go for separation. Should the SNP get such a majority, they should be allowed to separate; but many Scots as well as a majority in Britain as a whole hope the SNP will not succeed.

For more than 270 years—over what might be described as the imperial phase of Britain's history—both Scots and English have appeared in most corners of the globe carrying with them, under various guises, what they fondly believed to be the benefits of their joint culture: political ideas, stability, trade, culture, religion. During the course of that imperial activity they were for many people and on numerous occasions insufferable in their claims to be the bearers of superior ideas. That phase of our history is now over. It would, however, be a pathetic indictment of both Scots and English, who have so often prided themselves upon their political ideas and flexibility, if they now prove so barren of understanding of each other within the small area of the United Kingdom that the only solution to their differences is separation. A nationalism that demands the break-up of a society which has become as interwoven as that of Britain must be ultimately sterile; such a break-up would bring equal dishonour to both English and Scottish politicians.

17

The Labour and Tory Parties

The second half of the 1970s saw more signs of impending changes in the overall political line-up in Britain than had been apparent for some time: Ulster Unionists, Scottish and Welsh nationalists, determined upon independent courses of their own, more than made up for the dwindling influence of the long-dying Liberal Party. As the Liberal Pact precariously maintained Mr Callaghan in power during 1977 and 1978, it was not at all clear that the 1980s would see the two major parties continue to dominate the scene at Westminster. The small regional nationalist parties have become a factor of importance that could well upset easy calculations as to the manner in which British politics will be conducted during the next decade. None the less, the two major parties will certainly remain the largest, even if they no longer quite control the situation in the manner to which they have become accustomed during the years since 1945.

On questions relating to the control of British oil resources, the two parties have broadly similar views. The Tories will not relax the tax regime on North Sea oil even if their general attitude towards the companies is more sympathetic than that of Labour. At some future date the Labour Party may decide to impose still stronger controls and higher taxes but that is only likely to occur after a spell in opposition. The Tories have said a good deal about BNOC; they are unlikely to abolish it.

Where the two parties differ, sometimes quite radically, is over the questions relating to the use of the oil revenue that will accrue to government: regeneration of industry—but how? repayment of overseas debts—but when? tax cuts—but how many and for whom? Overseas investment, investment in the social infrastructure, regional policies, these are all at the centre of British politics; the range of options and the room for argument are considerable.

The Labour Party represents a wider coalition of interests than do their more traditional Tory opponents, with the result that in opposition certainly, and in office sometimes, they are especially prone to internal divisions and arguments. As a minority government during the period 1974–78, Labour had less than its customary internal divisions largely due to the necessities of circumstance. The question of how to use the oil wealth, however, presents plenty of opportunities for dispute between the different wings of the party, so that once the 1978 or 1979 general election is over the argument is liable to break forth in a much more open and, perhaps, destructive fashion.

Western economies, and especially that of Britain, have been in trouble for a considerable time and there appears little early prospect of dramatic change. In Britain more and more hopes have been pinned upon North Sea oil as a means of salvation, and the disappointment, when it comes, is likely to be considerable. This is where argument within the Labour Party will grow. Like Orwell's farmers and pigs in the feast at the conclusion of *Animal Farm*, it is almost impossible to distinguish between Labour and Tory, with the exception of Tony Benn, which is one reason why the Tory Party so often singles him out for attack. He is about the only figure who stands for something ideologically removed from the two-party middle way.

Most members of the Labour cabinet are drawn from the right wing of the party and spend far too much of their time reassuring the City and the CBI and the oil companies that they are as good at non-intervention as the Tories. The real argument about oil revenues, both within the ranks of the Labour Party and between the Labour and Tory parties, will concern the extent to which those revenues are to be used for interventionist policies. For the first time since 1945 there is substantial unemployment accepted as the norm by both parties, something that would have been unthinkable ten years earlier. Powerful arguments can therefore be deployed for using the oil revenues to create jobs. If this is done by Labour, it will mean more, rather than less, state enterprise of one or another kind. At the present time such policies are mainly associated with the name of Mr Benn.

Tory denunciations of Mr Benn are understandable—he stands for everything they deplore; but there is more to it than that. One can detect in some denunciations an edge of fear, since continuing economic malaise could mean that even if the Tories come back to power, their approach to economic questions will not solve the country's problems. Should this turn out to be the case, then Mr Benn in opposition could well have his day and come back to power leading a far more radical Labour movement than that which now exists.

The defeat of Labour in 1978 or 1979 and a five-year period of Tory rule could mean that the mid 1980s will witness another substantial dose of state interventionist policies under a rejuvenated Labour Party, with Benn in the ascendant if not in the leadership. At present a struggle is taking place inside the party between the right wing led by Callaghan and Healey and the left wing led by Benn. Another Labour win will most likely weaken Benn's hand; a period in opposition could bring him and his supporters in the party to the fore.

When Labour came back to power in 1974, the government set about the business of obtaining a reasonable measure of control over oil. Had the Tories retained power at that time they too would have introduced their own tax and other control measures for the North Sea—certainly not as stringent as those which came under Varley and then Benn, but none the less substantial. By 1974 the size of the oil resources was becoming apparent as were the opportunities these offered to government in savings on the balance of payments and tax revenue. The Labour Party can take the credit for the control regime as it exists.

Once the scope of the North Sea oil was understood, its possible impact upon the fortunes of the Labour Party in power came to be appreciated. In negative terms oil meant that the shortcomings of the government could, perhaps, be compensated for. In positive terms the oil revenues could be used as a catalyst for change. Yet neither revenues nor the disappearance of the perennial balance of payments burden actually solve the problems which have brought British industry and the economy to a condition of more or less constant crisis. Although the beginning of 1977 must have appeared gloomy indeed to Labour in office, by the end of that year enough had happened to make the party hopeful that it might even win a general election in late 1978: the balance of payments was improving radically, reserves were increasing, government tax take was at last being boosted by oil revenue, the rate of inflation was declining. Government policies, however, were being geared more and more to North Sea oil: the aim was oil self-sufficiency if possible by mid 1978, eighteen months ahead of the original target.

There was, indeed, a short burst of euphoria at the beginning of 1978, though the realities of the weakness of Britain's economy—despite oil—had reasserted themselves when Mr Healey presented his thirteenth budget in April. Already, it seemed, Labour had come to rely upon oil too much.

Probably a majority in the Parliamentary Labour Party are against giving tax cuts a high priority, though not averse to doing so at election time. To satisfy their main constituents, the trade unions, however, they will put most emphasis upon the regeneration of industry. A large proportion of the rank and file of the Labour

Party, whatever they may say in theory, will be disappointed in practice if there are no tax cuts. The TUC wants to see industrial reconstruction and the expansion of the public services as the priorities for oil revenue use. In a debate in November 1977, on a private member's motion, both Mr Denzil Davies, Minister of State at the Treasury, and some of the Tory opposition spokesmen emphasized the need to use a proportion of the oil revenue to repay debts. By the end of 1977 the government's survival was due to the Liberals, a restrained trade union movement and oil. As the leeway which oil can provide became ever more apparent to the party, so the question of 'options' loomed larger.

Tony Benn, as he now likes to be called, has become arguably the most important man in the Labour Party; he is certainly the only major Labour figure currently producing ideas and an ideology for the future. As a result his colleagues are obliged to keep pace or at least appear to have an idea or two of their own, although most seem content simply to maintain a *status quo* which keeps them in office.

The Tory Party and many of his own party as well, intensely dislike the policies Benn advances: those of greater state intervention, more power to workers and 'open' government. In the immediate present Mr Benn's importance lies in the reactions he arouses; in the longer term, of course, he is bidding for the leadership of the Labour Party. Since much of Mr Benn's policy recommends itself to the unions, he can hardly be as far to the left as his opponents make out, a fact the Tories know only too well. Mr Benn's demands for greater planning and state intervention in industry are what make him anathema to the right. Where he does command wide popular appeal is in his nationalism; here he may find friends and sympathizers on the right as well as on the left, and could yet find himself championing an anti-EEC movement in Britain.

When the internal Labour debate on the use of oil wealth got underway in the latter half of 1977, Denis Healey and Harold Lever were on the side of those favouring tax reductions and Benn led those who wanted to go for investment in industry, better social services and repayment of external debts. The object of the green paper was not to pronounce on a single strategy so much as to examine all the possibilities. One option then considered was the deliberate policy of holding the exchange rate down by capital outflow, so as to make investment in Britain internationally competitive. By April 1978 this line had clearly won considerable backing, as the pound had been allowed to drop back very nearly to the low of two years previously.

Benn's appointment to the Department of Energy in 1977 was of enormous importance to his political career, however much it may have looked like a demotion at the time. Oil and how to use its revenues have become central to economic planning for both parties. Not only can Benn claim a large measure of credit for the control that is now exercised over the oil companies, but his position as Secretary of State at the time when oil revenues began to flow, meant he was at the heart of the debate about which options to choose.

In a speech to the annual conference of the London Co-operative Society's Political Committee in October 1977, Mr Benn warned against North Sea oil being used as 'a mask which conceals the decline of our economy' and told delegates not to imagine that oil could necessarily solve British problems. His major point was that Britain is in a process of de-industrialization and, therefore, that it is essential for oil revenues to be used for reinvestment in industry: 'I have seen industry after industry in this country upon which our living standards rest going down because of the lack of investment.' He went on to claim that public investment and ownership were critical parts of the recovery of a society whose living standards and public services rested upon manufacturers. No one can say Mr Benn does not spell out what he wants to change.

On the issue of the EEC and oil companies Benn is equally tough. Following the debate of November 1977 when the Tory MP, Dykes, revealed the contents of a cable he had received from Brussels (see Chapter 14 above), Benn subsequently put out a tough statement of his own through Transport House—that is, as a member of the party rather than as Secretary of State for Energy—in which he said:

> The Labour Government has developed its oil policy with full regard to its European obligations as I made clear in the debate, but if under Tory pressure BNOC could be dismantled or crippled, the sole beneficiaries would be the multi-national oil companies operating in the North Sea. If the Tories had their way, oil company obligations to safeguard British national interests would be removed. If that were the case Britain's North Sea oil revenues would melt away and the security of the supply of oil upon which British industrial strength rests, would disappear.

Later in the same statement he defended the controls which now exist and implied that without them 'Britain would be reduced to a mere petitioner pleading with the oil companies but unable to act to protect its interests.'

In a talk with the author about energy and other strategies Mr Benn showed two things: a determination to maintain control over oil—not an easy matter even for a powerful ministry when pitched against the multi nationals; and an equal determination to see that the oil wealth is used in the national interest—as he understands it.

On the crucial energy question of whether or not production should be maintained at approximately 100 million tons a year (that is, to cover British self-sufficiency only), he is undecided: if the price of oil increases, then production should be held down since it ought to bring in the required revenue; on the other hand if the balance of payments worsens, then sales should be increased. More generally, on the oil companies, he maintains that the Department of Energy simply does not know enough; ignorance is the main barrier to the development of a good oil policy, so the Department must know more. This is a clear justification of the role of BNOC (as a source of information for government) and, for example, of Mr Benn's appointment of Professor Odell as a consultant to the Department of Energy. Further, there is no automatic co-relation of interests between oil companies and national governments.

On the delicate issue of EEC attitudes towards Britain's oil, Mr Benn claims that our oil policy has been devised with due regard to our European obligations and he would not expect that the EEC would wish to have a head-on collision with Britain on a matter so vital to our security.

On the Scottish issue Mr Benn is explicit. To the question of how he saw the future of oil if the government were to concede Scottish independence, he replied:

I don't think that is on the agenda. I must give you a clear answer to that question. I don't think there is a majority in Scotland for separatism and therefore it doesn't arise.

On the question of how to use the oil revenues, Mr Benn starts by looking at industry which he regards as the key to most other political developments. He argues that the use of the oil revenue must be seen against a world background, and he queries whether it is any different to other government revenue:

If there is a continuing world recession for a long period and de-industrialization, then the need to develop and expand the manufacturing sector upon which we will rely when the oil runs out will become very important. Then we must ask the question: if the investment in industry leads to labour shedding through high technology, where is job creation going to come from—the service sector, public expenditure, social infrastructure or what?

These are the central questions for government. Each year government spends £50 billion while the oil revenue is £3½ billion—so it is marginal, but a factor.

Mr Benn's priorities for the use of the oil revenues are: investment and jobs; the balance of payments; for the establishment of an oil equipment industry in Britain; for downstream developments in petrochemicals and other industries; and for the international position of advantage which the oil wealth should give Britain in the EEC and elsewhere. On the question of expectations from oil he says, 'It is a steady and important accretion of strength and opportunity, but no more than that.'

Benn is a formidable man: because he does his homework, because he produces policy ideas that force others to follow or oppose, because he is one of the very few politicians in any of the parties who has a reasonable vision of where he would like to see the country go. A story about Benn told against themselves by oilmen is illuminating. He was scheduled for a morning's discussion on participation and the oilmen he was meeting agreed beforehand that each in turn, as one or other ran dry of arguments, would take him up, so as to prolong the discussion indefinitely. This they did, so that what should have been a morning's meeting stretched to late that evening, began again the next day and again lasted until late evening, obliging Mr Benn to cancel his other engagements. Throughout the proceedings Mr Benn never became ruffled, he never fluffed his arguments and he finally obtained the agreement he wanted.

During the crucial period when the oil came on tap (1974 to 1978) the Tories were in opposition. The oil 'regime' has been largely the creation of Labour and the Tories will find this difficult to change even if so inclined. A second, temporary, disadvantage to the Tory Party stems from the fact that Labour in office will manipulate the oil funds, as far as possible, to their electoral advantage, while all the Tories can do is talk of how they will manage the oil revenues when back in power. Their advantage, assuming an electoral victory, lies in the fact that though they have generalized about how to use the oil wealth, they have been careful not to make any commitments. Should the party be returned to power, largely for reasons unrelated to North Sea oil, it will enjoy the leeway conferred by oil revenues that have not already been mortgaged to party factions.

The Tories, of course, are as fascinated by the options which oil opens up as their Labour opponents. Their primary concern is to reduce the level of taxation, which is their biggest point of departure from more orthodox Labour approaches to the oil wealth, although Mr Healey is not averse to cutting taxes in the run-up to a general election. An interesting aspect of speeches by both parties' major politicians has been the extent to which they play down the oil wealth. Considering the mass of information available about the impact upon the balance of payments and upon revenue, it would appear that this tendency of the politicians is overdone. The reason is quite simple: the more oil's impact upon the economy is played down, the greater the credit for economic advances which either party can claim as the result of their policies rather than as a bonus from oil.

The difficulty about any policy of greater investment in state enterprises or the creation of new ones is the record of those industries that have in recent years come to the government for assistance. The millions which have gone to British Steel, Leyland or the shipbuilding industry, to name three such recipients of government aid, and their constant return asking for more, is not an encouraging spectacle. Nor does it argue well for the thesis that government money going into industry does anything other than encourage the industry in question to imagine that in a crisis— which seems to recur with monotonous regularity—yet more money will be available. If in twenty or thirty years time, when the oil and gas wealth runs out, the country is saddled with huge industries which are permanent loss-makers turning constantly to the government for succour, the use of oil wealth to regenerate the economy will have turned into a disaster.

One of the most able of the younger Tories, David Howell, has had a good deal to say about oil revenues. He argues that we ought not to tamper too much with these revenues but allow the bulk to flow to the taxpayer; to do so, however, would require a strong will to resist the enormous political and other pressures that are fast building up to earmark the money for other purposes.

On oil policy, as opposed to the question of how to use the revenues, there is unlikely to be any major shift in the event of a Tory electoral victory: the Tories want the revenues from the North Sea as much as Labour does and do not intend to lose them by introducing a lighter tax regime. Lord Kearton, who has an interest in seeing BNOC continue as he has created it after any change of government, does not believe there would be radical alterations in the overall approach to the North Sea, although the Tories would presumably make some inroads upon BNOC's powers.

During 1977 and 1978 Tom King, who was Tory energy spokes-man, on the whole took a remarkably similar line to Tony Benn. In a speech of November 1977 he argued strongly for conservation: by education and persuasion; by a sharp increase in price; by mandatory controls, with regulations regarding the insulation of new buildings; and by providing incentives to save—tax allowances for commercial or domestic insulation.

In the same speech—perhaps a mandatory Tory compulsion—he claimed there was no evidence BNOC was necessary to secure full rights in North Sea oil to the British people, and said that BNOC's role as a regulatory agency was incompatible with its role as an operating company. If its regulatory role were taken away it would become a state oil company—perhaps more like ENI than BP—and because of the holdings it now has in North Sea fields and its 51 per cent from the fifth round, it will be handling 50 million tons of oil a year by the 1980s, making it one of the top ten oil companies in the world. According to Tom King BNOC should be made to conform to all the commercial disciplines: it should pay PRT and have no access to the National Oil Account. Its powers, in other words, must be contained.

King, in fact, reserves his position on BNOC: a Tory government, he says, will review each of the corporation's functions when it is in power. There may be a conflict between BNOC and Britain's obligations under the Treaty of Rome. Britain, says King, will not diminish its rights over its oil and so no change will be made in BNOC that could have that effect.

Tom King differs little from his political opponents in believing that PRT is not unreasonable to the companies, especially since from the fifth round BNOC's 51 per cent equity holding in each field means that it also takes 51 per cent of the risk and puts up 51 per cent of the capital. When the time comes to work the marginal fields, there will have to be negotiations with the companies, that is, tax concessions, or such fields could be nationalized and developed entirely by BNOC. King accepts that there must be government control over company commitments to sell oil abroad: they should not be allowed to arrange ten-year re-export contracts.

On longer term oil strategies, King believes that after self-sufficiency has been achieved we should throttle back on production so as to get the maximum life out of our reserves; though energy policy must be affected by the EEC, NATO and foreign commitments generally, he opposes massive exports. The Tory party also supports the 1974 Varley guidelines; while the companies must be given as much certainty as possible they cannot be given guarantees.

On the question of attitudes towards the oil companies—an area in which the Tories are always assumed to be on the company side— Tom King says that though a Tory government would not increase taxes on the companies lightly, they might do so if it was clear that the companies were doing well; it would be a question of balance.

The party wants to maintain business confidence but, none the less, should there be a major oil price shift then they would look at the extent of company profits. He also thinks electricity generation should come from coal and nuclear power and not oil; that both oil and gas should only be used for premium purposes; and that the government should maintain good incentives for exploration and development.

Tories are as aware as Labour of the dangers of building too much hope into North Sea oil. Peter Walker, MP for Worcester and former Secretary of State for Trade and Industry, warned a Tory Reform Group at the 1977 Blackpool conference that it could become a curse rather than a blessing. Pointing out that oil should net £40,000 million for governments during the 1980s and be worth £100,000 million to the balance of payments, Mr Walker argued for wariness in the Tory Party between those on the right who wanted an orgy of tax cuts and those on the left who wanted massive public spending programmes. He said:

> The North Sea oil opportunity should be used to bring about two revolutions in British society: the regeneration of British industry so that the country will continue to prosper long after the oil runs out, and a sustained attack upon poverty and squalor and the scars which are still to be seen, particularly in our great cities.

Many would agree, but Mr Walker (whom Mrs Thatcher has excluded from her team) is not subject to the pressures of the Shadow cabinet.

As Shadow Chancellor, Sir Geoffrey Howe has been the Tory with the most to say about the use of the oil revenues. Speaking at the Oxford University Business Summer School in July 1977, Sir Geoffrey compared the opportunities offered by North Sea oil with Marshall aid and the run-down of military spending by Labour in the late 1940s. He said that Labour would be likely to waste the opportunity to stimulate growth by earmarking the funds for a big boost in government spending. He put forward five priorities: to lighten the burden of debt; to cut personal income tax; to start breaking down barriers, rigidities and controls which obstruct investment; to avoid arousing excessive expectations; and to allow the pound to rise so as to 'initiate a "virtuous spiral" of declining inflation.' Shortly thereafter in a speech delivered in Washington, Sir Geoffrey said:

> Of course the oil funds will not automatically prove to be a cure-all, but they *could* provide an unparalleled opportunity for the regeneration of our economy.

Later in the same speech he said:

> Britain's overseas debts could, of course, absorb the first five years' income from oil tax revenues. But total foreign exchange savings from North Sea oil will be about 5 per cent of GNP by early 1980s. An extra 5 or even 10 per cent will certainly not make it possible for us to give up work and 'live the life of Riley'. But it will at least afford an important opportunity for re-construction.

He repeated his Oxford priorities.

Sir Geoffrey Howe has often expressed the fear that Britain should go for a 'Dutch auction' and emphasizes that the surplus from oil is a modest one. One Tory argument is to go for overseas investments. Another frequently advanced is for less exchange control—a freer flow of funds—and a Tory government is likely to give this high priority. Most emphasis is upon transforming the present tax system, both by reducing the amount of taxes and by a shift to indirect taxation, so that people pay as they spend and, of course, keep their income longer. Sir Geoffrey stresses the need for a major simplification of the planning laws: he maintains that in Britain industrial development (for example, building a factory) takes between 1·8 and 3·5 times as long as in the countries of our competitors (the EEC or North America)—because of regulations.

David Howell, who for the first part of 1977 was in Sir Geoffrey Howe's shadow Treasury team, is opposed to oil revenues being directed into either nationalized industries or 'lame ducks' since to direct them into inadequate industries is to court inadequate returns. His first instinct is to give the revenue to the people. The revenues should be used, he maintains, either to reduce taxation or to encourage business growth rather than just higher consumption. Howell favours the possibility of some form of oil shares so as to keep the North Sea operation vivid in the public mind. He would like to change the parameters which restrict the rewards from investments; in 1977 the real rate of return on capital in Britain was below 3 per cent (the lowest of OECD countries) and he believes it should be much higher. The idea of removing restrictions, helping small companies and making it easier for people to have 'nest eggs' is, of course, orthodox Tory policy.

Britain at present has the highest level of exchange controls of any major country so that capital makes the lowest returns. Britain, Howell maintains, needs a new layer of overseas investment (she is particularly good at investing overseas anyway) on top of those of the 1880s and 1920s. Howell thinks the Treasury is obsessed with the Dutch story: a strong guilder as a result of Groningen gas while other performance has declined. He argues that Britain should work for rapid relaxation of controls on capital movements. He believes government should not be overwhelmed by the industry argument that says do not let the pound rise, since this will damage export prospects. (What seemed clear in April 1978 was that government had not ignored industry; it allowed the run on the pound, partly induced by the Bank of England anyway, to continue so as to keep the country's competitive edge strong.) With a nice turn of phrase for the hustings, Howell says he would like to see North Sea oil money used as a lubricant for new developments and not as a glue for things as they are.

A more unorthodox Tory than either Howe or Howell is John Biffen. He is a former energy spokesman and farther to the right. On energy policy he argues that as a general rule it is good to maximize areas of agreement and believes that as a whole the Tories accept the present energy policy. He would, however, like to see BNOC operating more as a commercial organization analogous to BP than as a government 'tachograph' in the oil industry. BNOC holds substantial assets for the country anyway, and should be turned into a second major like BP in which, after all, government has a majority of shares anyway. This view seems to be gathering weight in the Tory Party.

Although he claims not to hold a view on conservation, Biffen says he believes the government approach of 1977 to be approximately correct and that the decision that flaring should cease was a necessary policy regulation. Moreover, a conservation policy ought to make sense to the companies.

On the far more controversial subject of refining policy Biffen says, on the one hand, that oil ought to be refined where it makes economic sense to do so, which could mean in other EEC countries before Britain; on the other hand, he insists that Britain herself must decide where her oil is to be refined. The decision should not be willed upon her by the EEC nor should the EEC tell Britain that there has to be free movement of her oil. His might be described as a 'Gaullist' viewpoint inside the Tory Party. Biffen claims to be a nationalist first and an economic liberal second. In the first respect he is remarkably close to Benn.

Biffen thinks that a Tory government should not interfere too much in the oil business; he would expect BNOC to supply home needs so that exports would then be left largely to the commercial good sense of the companies. In the case of an emergency, any rationing or cutbacks ought to be taken in an IEA context. On depletion Biffen argues that the country should not deplete at such a rate as to unhinge the economy and so create 'British Disease'; rather, policy should be open and flexible.

The politicians—among whom Biffen includes himself—and especially the Tory party in opposition want to keep their options open. Biffen argues for an increase in overseas investment. His options preference is for the oil revenue to be used to reduce domestic debt and direct taxation; some of the revenue should go for fundamental research on alternative energy sources such as 'renewables' rather than upon nuclear energy which will have a huge and continuing appetite for public revenues. And some of the money ought to be spent upon social improvements in city centres.

On the subject of regeneration of industry, Biffen points out that it has quite different meanings to the two major parties. Labour understand regeneration to mean funds for the NEB or enterprises such as Leyland or the BSC. His Tory view would be that regeneration will best be achieved by using oil revenues to finance a switch in taxation policy. If VAT were increased to 15 per cent, for example, and direct taxes were cut, then together these changes would provide the elbow room for more real growth.

There could well be a general problem of growing restraints on resources from the 1990s onwards; North Sea oil could insulate Britain from this, for a time. The present low rate of growth in both Britain and the western world as a whole could also continue. Biffen argues that at present all British attitudes are too related to the question of economic growth. Further, the trade unions 'call the shots' in economic matters, so that those who do not belong to powerful unions are coming to see themselves as second-class citizens. There is thus a danger of the country dividing into two nations: those protected by corporate institutions and those outside their protection. John Biffen's views, though not in the mainstream of Tory thinking, are both refreshing and important as a contribution to the oil-options debate.

In a booklet (*Political Office or Political Power*) published during 1977 by the Tory Centre for Policy Studies, Biffen warned that Benn offered a much stronger challenge than the Tory leadership and rank and file assume when they treat him merely as a hate figure or bogey-man. He says, 'Tony Benn has now emerged as a major political figure in the Labour Party' and he goes on to argue that under Benn's leadership the Labour Party could become the party of national planning allied to nationalism—an aspect of politics to which Biffen is perhaps peculiarly sensitive since he is a Tory nationalist himself. 'This need not involve any substantial further nationalization. It would involve the use of national government planning agreements with multinational businesses, and the use of national import quotas and tariffs.' Certainly Biffen and Benn see eye to eye upon the need for curbing any further EEC incursions into

British political affairs; he is against its supra-nationalism or federalism and sees Benn taking on what was a more traditional Tory nationalist role. He argues:

Tony Benn is marking out a populist and radical alternative to our present economic and political arrangements. That alternative has 'national planning' as its touchstone.

It is not of itself an extremist political remedy. It need involve no expropriation of assets; it builds upon the present close relationship between government and large-scale industry, and it will capitalize on the present disillusionment with the Common Market.

Those who take refuge in mere denunciations of these policies as some wild Marxist 'redprint' are reacting in a superficial and shortsighted way. 'Bennite' socialism could become electorally popular and so requires a rather more measured and thoughtful response from the Tory Party.

Part of his subsequent message, perhaps surprisingly, is for an acceptance by the Tory Party of the mixed economy, although altering its balance; he argues that there is already a close identity between large-scale private enterprise and government as well as the public sector. He sees increasing scope for private finance to operate alongside government finance, and argues that government finance should be withheld from private industrial and commercial failure.

Looking sceptically at the EEC Biffen, who opposed entry anyway, is of the opinion that the Tories should proclaim their national objectives within the EEC and say how they will work to obtain them; too easy an acceptance of Europeanism would mean the Tories could become the party of Brussels in the public mind 'while Labour becomes the party of Britain'. Biffen and Benn, talking from the two outer wings of their respective parties, have a surprising amount in common.

Summing up the Tory approach, Sir Geoffrey Howe says that the party sees North Sea oil as a capital asset which can, if wisely managed, be used to assist a soundly-based revival of our economy. It is not, he says, a question of 'how will we spend the money' but rather 'how will we take advantage of the breathing space to take the positive steps necessary for the revival of a free economy'.

What either party does with the breathing space that oil will allow in the 1980s will lay the foundations for Britain's performance as the country embarks upon the twenty-first century.

18

Expectations and Options

Although a range of public figures have warned that oil will not cure the nation's ills, an increasing number of people have come to believe it will. What these ills might be, depends upon the viewpoint of the individual concerned. The British, in any case, are inveterate gamblers and spend a good deal of their lives calculating their chances on the pools, on the horses or scooping the big prize at bingo. Now they can add the North Sea lottery to their calculations—this time on behalf of the nation.

By the time everyone has put in a bid for a share of the oil benefits and staked a claim, it becomes clear that oil wealth is going to be over-extended. Sometimes we sound like a developing country with no industrial or other infrastructure at all, determined to use our new-found wealth to catch up with the advanced economies; more often we sound like a pools winner about to embark upon a spending spree. The more the public is told the oil resources are limited, the more each interest group demands its share of the whole.

In the early to middle 1970s a feature of North Sea developments was a persistent public scepticism, almost disbelief, that the oil bonanza could come to anything. The British tend to be collective pessimists; for years the British have been arguing that the country is in decline—though people never behave as though the decline might be their own fault—so the national hard luck story was not to be easily reversed by the coming of oil. Sufficient propaganda about oil, however, has now been dispersed to induce a reversal.

Speculation upon the extent of the oil impact on both the balance of payments and tax revenues has mounted steadily since 1975, when the first important publications on the subject appeared. Since then economic writers in the City pages of the newspapers have taken to falling back upon oil when the general outlook is gloomy, thereby producing cheering figures for the future. The public has been treated to a huge mass of figures on the thousands of millions of pounds the oil will be worth in taxes and the balance of payments, or the percentage of the GNP that oil will contribute to the economy. The figures are too large for most people to comprehend; what will oil do for the ordinary man? Oil, the British have also been told, is a once-for-all asset and therefore not to be squandered; it should be used to produce another asset against the time when it runs out. Unfortunately such preaching, if anything, has the opposite effect; if it is a once-for-all asset then everyone wants his share of it before it disappears, so that the lottery approach is enhanced.

It is sensible to argue that oil is a once-for-all asset which we ought not merely to consume. If it is to be used to create other capital assets to replace it we come to the discussion about options. If the spectre of Dutch Disease means anything, it is that we shall use the oil revenues upon a consumer spree while the de-industrialization of the country goes further. Our manufacturing sector will become less competitive and high living standards for the British could mean they price themselves still further out of world markets. The possibilities of doing something of the sort are not small.

People have forgotten North Sea gas; it saved the country an estimated £2,250 million in 1976 and a similar amount in 1977, yet this went unnoticed. The benefits were simply swallowed up by an even faster rate of consumption and imports. Twenty years, which is the average estimated lifespan of the North Sea fields at good production level, is long enough to transform the economy. It took just that time for West Germany to rebuild from the ruins of 1945 to achieve enormous industrial power. De-colonization of an empire with all its attendant problems means that Britain now also needs a rebuilding exercise; this explains both the rising oil-based expectations and the options debate.

Government expectations based upon oil-to-come led it to contract enormous debts from the IMF and elsewhere during the mid 1970s. By November 1976, for example, Britain's medium- and long-term foreign currency borrowings came to approximately $18,500 million, or about $338 per head of the population. Most of those debts were accumulated in the three years from March 1973, when Anthony Barber reintroduced the Treasury's exchange cover scheme to encourage public corporations and local authorities to borrow from the international money market. The intention was that debts should be repaid out of North Sea earnings and debt maturity has been synchronized with the estimated increased flow from the wells, so that most of the main repayments fall due in the 1980s as peak output from North Sea fields is achieved.

The White Paper published at the beginning of 1977, entitled 'The Government's Expenditure Plans', revealed the extent to which the Treasury was pinning its hopes upon North Sea oil:

North Sea oil gives us the prospect, provided that we manage our affairs prudently, of a substantial surplus in the balance of payments. It will not by itself provide significant additional employment (except in Scotland), nor in itself constitute a large continuing annual growth of resources; but, by easing the balance of payments constraints which have for so long added to the difficulty of managing the British economy, it will give us the opportunity to secure a major strengthening of the industrial base, and through this a renewed growth in employment.

The balance of payments is too often spoken of as though it is at the root of Britain's problems. It is, of course, not the cause but the result of the decreasing competitiveness of British industry and there are many reasons for that which oil is not going to cure. At least, as one sour commentator put it, the Dutch waited for the gas to flow before spending the proceeds; the British, who are ever ready to lecture upon the dangers of Dutch Disease, did not.

By the mid 1980s government revenue from oil will be between £5,000 million and £6,000 million, which at 1977 prices will represent between $3\frac{1}{2}$ and $4\frac{1}{2}$ per cent of GNP. When oil was at last beginning to have an impact upon the economy in 1977, ministers faced an increasing barrage of suggestions and demands, causing Sir Douglas Wass, head of the Treasury, to describe North Sea oil as his biggest problem.

On the one hand, some commentators have become eloquent about what might be accomplished as a result of oil; on the other, there are those who argue that it will be wasted or make little difference. Even accepting the lowest estimates of the effects of oil in terms of revenue, balance of payments, jobs and new oil-related industries, the impact will be considerable; the difficulty is that expectations are now outstripping the possibilities.

As public awareness of the oil potential increased, so there were delivered a growing number of warnings that it was not a bonanza which could do everything. In 1976, for example, Mr Leslie Pincott, the managing director of Esso Petroleum, warned that even though there might be enough oil to do all the things 'the most ambitious promoters of social improvement wanted', Britain would still face economic collapse when the oil ran out *unless* the basic performance of the manufacturing industry improved—and that, of course, has little to do with oil. Comparable warnings have been delivered frequently ever since by a variety of public figures.

City stockbrokers have developed a new industry devoted to forecasting oil results and impacts. One very optimistic analysis in 1976 was by Hoare Govett, whose economist Roger Nightingale and

Impact of N. Sea Oil and Gas on UK Balance of Payments

(£ million)

Visible Items	1975	1976	1977	1978	1979	1980	1981	1982	1983	1984	1985
Capital Expenditure—Oil Firm	-1,223	-1,444	-996	-586	-368	-199	-89	-35	-200	-200	-200
Oil Possible			-225	-358	-508	-453	-430	-300			
Gas Firm	-390	-585	-375	-265	-75	-50					
	-1,613	-2,029	-1,596	-1,209	-951	-702	-519	-335	-200	-200	-200
Oil & Gas Revenues Total	51	700	2,615	4,423	5,905	7,319	7,853	8,135	8,087	7,938	7,820
TOTAL VISIBLES	-1,562	-1,329	1,019	3,214	4,954	6,617	7,334	7,800	7,887	7,738	7,620
Cumulative Balance	-2,547	-3,876	-2,857	357	5,311	11,828	19,162	26,962	34,849	42,587	50,207
Invisible Items											
Interest Payments/Savings	-306	-385	-404	-250	141	429	774	1,153	1,545	1,935	2,148
Repatriated Overseas Companies Earnings	+20	+40	-42	-391	-500	-787	-942	-980	-985	-990	-1,000
TOTAL INVISIBLES	-286	-345	-446	-641	-359	-358	-168	173	560	945	1,148
TOTAL CURRENT ACCOUNT IMPACT	-1,848	-1,674	+573	+2,573	+4,595	+6,259	+7,166	+7,973	+8,447	+8,683	+8,768

Source: Hoare Govett.

oil analyst Douglas McGregor between them worked out that oil revenues would exceed £9 billion a year in 1985, resulting in a permanent increase in Britain's rate of growth that would continue after the oil has run out. The cumulative benefit to the country over the decade of the 1980s they put at more than £50 billion and estimated that this should raise the growth rate by $2\frac{1}{4}$ per cent a year.

One person who has warned against pinning too many hopes upon oil is Lord Watkinson, President of the CBI. Speaking in Maidenhead during 1977 Lord Watkinson said: 'It's now or never for the Promised Land'. He claimed that oil gave the chance to build something for our children's future and that after a large part had been used to pay off debts,

> . . . for the remainder, we must make sensible use of it and not use it for any kind of consumption bonanza. It must be used to help us gear up our country for the challenges of the 80s and beyond.

Oil had by now induced a seesaw of hopes and fears: if one week the economists are talking of a huge impact upon the country's overall performance, a week or so later a rival analyst is just as likely to tell us oil will prove to be a disaster. Even so, at the end of 1976 it seemed that a message of hope was penetrating to the public at large. Mr Benn said that Britain was on target to become oil self-sufficient by 1980 and added, 'I am lucky to be in a job where our major problems are ones of growth—unlike those of my colleagues.' By early 1977 even a depressed Labour Party was beginning to become hopeful, as the gathering impact of oil upon what had otherwise been dismal economic returns began to tell. So many other economic indicators were at danger level that the one bright spark of oil—becoming brighter by the month—began to be looked to for salvation. Indeed Mr Callaghan's cabinet started 1977 with renewed optimism as they talked of staying in power until 1979; the longer the party could hold on, the more likely the country would have come to feel the impact of oil and the greater the chance for Mr Healey to produce a budget, or budgets, giving a few oil-related benefits to the electorate.

By May 1977 Mr Healey could say that oil would enable the economy to be run at a higher level of activity and employment without meeting balance of payment constraints. He, too, warned that misuse of the oil resources could prove a curse rather than a blessing and that even if properly utilized they would not solve all Britain's problems. Speaking to the CBI, Mr Healey urged that oil revenues should be used to help industrial development:

> We must see that this investment is directed towards relieving

production bottlenecks in key sectors of the economy so that in future our rate of growth is less supply-constrained, and towards raising the competitive performance of manufacturing industry as a whole.

Britain's oil resources, he said, gave us time to repair the deterioration of the manufacturing base over the previous thirty years.

All are ready enough to point out that manufacturing performance has gone down, and that the country has not been investing sufficiently in industry. No one explains how, just because oil has come, it now follows that the British are going to behave in a manner fundamentally different from the one which has produced the decline. The use or misuse of the oil wealth must depend upon a change of attitude as much as any policy choice.

In their joint document, 'The Next Three Years and into the Eighties', the TUC-Labour Party Liaison Committee say:

Although the seventies have been troubled and difficult years for Britain, there are signs that the tide is beginning to turn and in the next five years we shall be reaping the full benefits of North Sea oil.

However much one is told not to bank upon North Sea oil solving Britain's problems, more and more of the political decision-makers are doing just that. In the same document the Committee also say:

The Liaison Committee calls on government and industry to take up the challenge and to find ways of financing this investment [the aim of doubling manufacturing investment between 1978 and 1988] out of offshore oil and other revenues; and a substantial part of new investment must be used to improve the economies of Scotland and Wales and other areas of the UK in need of development.

A cynic might be excused for thinking that the phrase 'and other revenues' was an afterthought; it was the oil that counted.

The reserves rose to record levels in 1977; by August they had reached the huge sum of $13,422 million (£7,725 million) although accompanied by more than $20,000 million of overseas debts. The figures were to climb higher still by the end of the year, and when at the beginning of May 1978 gold and foreign currency reserves were reported to have suffered their largest monthly fall on record (of $3,282 million), this still left a balance of $17,038 million.

Euphoria about oil reverts only too easily to pessimism again in the public mind. The news that the small Argyll field was running out more quickly than had been originally predicted produced a typically gloomy conviction that the oil was bound to come to little. Judging by some of the unstable reactions to oil news the British appear to have remarkably little confidence in themselves, with or without the oil bonus. Financial crisis has become so intrinsic a part of British life that all good news is regarded with extreme suspicion; one result, unfortunately, is to heighten the 'pools' approach, which treats oil as luck to be spent quickly before it disappears.

North Sea oil is by far the most important as well as unexpected development for Britain since the Second World War, and whatever the problems which accompany it the opportunities are very substantial indeed. Nonetheless, the Chief Secretary to the Treasury, Joel Barnett, warned an export conference at Birmingham in January 1978:

> The truth is, even with North Sea oil, if we do not improve our industrial performance we will very soon be short of resources to meet the numerous demands for cuts in taxation.

Such cautions are salutary. At the same time it is also worth remembering what the situation would be like without oil. In fact, as perversely as we doubt the oil, we also take it for granted: without it the balance of payments would by 1978 in all probability have brought us to one of our worse crises since 1945; there would be no prospects of extra government revenues, no debate about options and our position would have been unbuttressed by huge loans against oil to come. Further, we would not be able to enjoy the comforting prospect of oil self-sufficiency for the rest of the century. So quickly, in fact, have we come to accept the presence of oil and its economic benefits that despite debates and warnings we take for granted that which, ten years earlier, would have seemed an impossible economic prospect.

The government White Paper on North Sea oil revenue published in March 1978 showed a current account benefit for the year of £2,500 million, with a figure of £3,500 million given for 1979; these figures were despite an expected slowdown in production to only 55–65 million tons for the year instead of an earlier estimated 70 million tons. At the same time further revelations about Leyland and British Steel and the amounts needed to bail them out showed that little was changing on the general industrial front. Following the 1978 budget, an article in the *Sunday Times* commented, 'Denis Healey has already given away the expected North Sea oil revenue for the next two or three years in tax cuts.' If this was true, coupled with the massive international borrowing that had been made against oil for the preceding five years, then few benefits from the options, whichever were to be chosen, could be expected until well into the 1980s.

Assessments of North Sea benefits are constantly revised—upwards or downwards—according to the analyst and the approach he uses, so that it is a confusing business for anyone trying to follow the trends. A week after new advantages have been proclaimed, they will be demolished or decried. This is as much the fault of journalists as anyone else: their determination to have a different story about the same subject every week almost makes alternating gloom and euphoria mandatory; it doesn't help anyone to form a balanced judgement.

Jolts to British economic self-confidence are frequent; they do not result from North Sea oil. They occur because, despite oil, nothing as yet has changed in overall industrial performance. And this fact is, perhaps, the correct starting point for any discussion of the possible options which the oil opens up for us.

Nothing as big as oil in the industrial sense has occurred in the United Kingdom since the industrial revolution, certainly not since the railway boom of the 1840s. The Prime Minister might say, as he did in September of 1977, that 'God has given Britain her best opportunity for one hundred years in the shape of North Sea oil.' 1977 was the year in which an increasing chorus of people suggested different options and policies to be adopted; though these may be numerous, the main issue lies between the choice of present consumption or future investment. Thereafter one may examine the range of possibilities. In the end it will be a question of balance between consuming and investing. A growing majority of commentators agree that the best general use of oil wealth will be to reverse the decline of Britain's manufacturing sector, whether by using the planning favoured by the left, or by creating through tax concessions a suitable climate for private enterprise as favoured by the right. Although in theory most people agree that income derived from depleting natural assets should not be used simply or mainly for consumption purposes, in practice a good deal of consumption will be advanced as necessary: for example, to boost employment.

Another factor of immense importance which will influence the choice of options is the way the British political system works: can any option that is longer lasting than the five-year political term have much chance? As a key City banker used to dealing with government said, he would be agreeably surprised if as much as 20 per cent of the oil wealth were to be properly invested for the future.

Government obsession with the balance of payments over a long period of time has meant this issue has been given top priority: to solve her balance of payments Britain went for the most rapid development of the North Sea resources regardless of most other considerations. If as a result there is to be a comparatively long period in which the country can achieve a surplus on balance of payments, then at least that perennial problem will have been eliminated, always provided that resultant policies do not simply produce further inflation and a new imbalance.

On the occasion of his visit to the Forties Field in September 1977, the Prime Minister asked for a public debate on how the oil revenue should be spent; the debate has been in progress ever since. Repeated warnings are issued against a political auction though 1978 was to see a steadily growing auction. This is probably inevitable in the run-up to a general election; the difficulty lies in the fact that once auction-style promises have been made, they also have to be redeemed: urban renewal in the city centres; social infrastructure; reduction of unemployment; regeneration of industry; overseas investment; tax cuts; research and development of other forms of energy; repayment of debts; education; aid tied to British goods, or just aid; re-afforestation; scientific research and development. The list is long and most people can add their own particular suggestions to it. What is most important for a country that has long been in decline is the fact that North Sea oil grants time for the country to re-think and re-plan.

As an industrialized, food-importing society, Britain should give top priority to energy and food: energy replacement and the expansion of agricultural production should both receive major attention among the long-term options. Thirdly, special attention ought to be paid to improving technological skills which will provide Britain with an edge as an exporting country.

It can only be a source of gloom that—the world recession apart—almost everyone approaches North Sea oil as though it is a lifeline to save the British economy. It may be valuable that everyone knows the economy is in trouble; it is sad they should imagine oil, rather than anything else, will do the saving. One writer has suggested we should forget the endless lists of options and consider three strategies: growth through spending; planned investment; financial virtue, that is, low inflation, modest taxes, rising real income, buoyant currency and high confidence at home and abroad—a picture so startling as to be all but incomprehensible.

An examination of the options reveals huge variations in each case depending upon the source. The reduction of taxes can mean different things to different people. It could mean across the board for everyone, as Mr Healey tried in his 1978 budget, or providing incentives for small business or encouragement to new investment and top management. The much-used word 'regenerate' can mean the reduction of controls or the supply of money.

At the 1977 Labour Party conference Mr Callaghan was inspired to declare that thanks to oil, 'the next twenty years will be unlike anything Britain has seen since it first moved to become an industrial power two hundred years ago.' Visions such as this are fine but most people, including Mr Callaghan, are hazy as to how the breakthrough will be achieved, except that, somehow, they believe oil will do the trick.

There are two broad ways of approaching the subject of regeneration, either of the economy in particular or our society in general. The first is to allow the impact of the oil wealth to loosen economic restraints: to reduce taxes, increase the money flow, allow sterling to go free and remove exchange controls, in other words, to allow monetary forces to have free rein. The alternative is to control sterling and not allow it to become too strong in order not to weaken export competitiveness, and to direct money into industrial and other investment. Although public debate was inevitable and ought to be encouraged, its most likely outcome will be a growing competition by interest groups for their slice of the cake.

No neat choice of options will be possible anyway. Government and opposition may formulate policies but the British public at large, in the form of the unions for example, will also have their say in the choice of options by pressing for higher wages. When these and other pressures have been met, the government of the day will find its room to manoeuvre has in any case been further narrowed.

As part of the great debate the *Scotsman* in October 1977 invited a number of personalities to write articles on how they saw the oil revenues being used. Between them they covered the obvious ground. Invitations to such debates, however, are also invitations for exercises in the kind of eccentricity beloved of the British. One of the contributors to the series was Viscount Weir, and after dealing with the options as he saw them, he ended his article as follows:

I must finish, however, by mentioning one or two projects whose cost is negligible in terms of North Sea revenues but which could improve the quality of life out of all proportion.

I expect everyone has his own small list of this kind. Mine would include endowing the National Trust for Scotland with a £10 million capital projects fund, and with the revenue from £20 million I would replace Hampden Park; build an opera house in Edinburgh; fund the SNO; buy out Crown salmon netting rights;

build twelve more good golf courses; and generally cheer the place up in this sort of way.

Not such a small, nor cheap, list!

This drew the inevitable response from Colin Pritchard of the Church of Scotland:

> Sir, Viscount Weir's list of small projects to which to devote oil revenues exposes the true nature of his interest in the economic wealth of Scotland. Opera houses, salmon rights and golf courses are, of course, the bread and butter of that tiny sector of Scottish interests which he can claim to represent . . .

The suggestion that the government take in tax and royalties should be put into an oil development fund has received mixed reactions. Such a fund could be used to finance special projects and the public would be able to see what benefits were derived exclusively from oil. It is, in theory, a good idea. The Treasury opposes the idea. Any such fund would be liable to be raided by a government in financial trouble. There could be established a trust directly responsible to Parliament with some form of charter to regulate its activities. This variation was suggested in the *Scotsman*'s debate series by James McGuinness; he proposed that such a trust might be used just for Scotland and the Scottish Assembly be made responsible for it.

Tax cuts will naturally prove the most popular of all the uses of oil income. People may argue sensibly that this is not the way to use the money, but tax cuts affect everybody at once. Furthermore, most people are in any case convinced that they pay too much in taxes, and the politicians always like to cut taxes, especially if there is electoral advantage to be gained. The Tory Party regards cutting taxes as an article of faith at present and as the best way to stimulate real growth.

Thereafter discussion of detail follows: whose taxes? by how much? are they to be reduced for individuals or for corporations so as to make industrial investment more attractive? Tax cuts for industry, the Tories argue, would do more to stimulate growth than government investment in major industries. This approach is opposed by the Labour Party and especially those sections of it most closely associated with the Benn line. Lord Watkinson wrote to both Mr Healey and Mr Varley in the cabinet to say that the CBI 'does not in general favour increased subsidies or support schemes for trade and industry'; rather, North Sea revenues 'should not be used to increase public expenditure but to help finance necessary tax cuts.'

By January 1978 trade union leaders were calling for tax cuts and urging the government to expand the economy by at least £3,000 million in the budget in the form of reduced personal taxation, higher pensions and job creation. The unions wanted a lower rate of tax for the first £1,000 of taxable income which would cost £2,000 million in a full year.

The left wing of the Labour Party opposes such tax cuts. In March 1978 the party's Industrial Policy sub-committee, chaired by Mr Benn, said of tax cuts in their recommendations to the NEC: 'This would only lead to massive import penetration . . . it would be extremely foolish to eat our seed corn,' which was a nice way to make their point. Instead, the sub-committee emphasized the importance of using the revenue to regenerate industry. It wanted to see a major enlargement of the activities of the National Enterprise Board and extended planning agreements.

Other voices have been raised against tax cuts. Colin Pritchard of the Church of Scotland argues that, as things stand, those with the most now get the most, and lighter taxes would help *them* rather than those in greatest need.

Talk of regenerating British industry has moved to the centre of the options debate. Tony Benn has powerful support in the Labour Party for channelling the oil revenues—or a sizeable portion of them—into vital industries and the Labour Home Policy Committee supports him in opposing tax cuts. Instead they would go for a massive injection of money into the NEB and into developing alternative energy sources.

The TUC-Labour Party Liaison Committee's document, 'The Next Three Years and into the Eighties', states:

A top priority in the coming decade must be to ensure that the benefits of North Sea oil are used to regenerate our industrial structures, so that by the time the oil flow begins to lessen, the UK manufacturing sector can meet and beat the best of the world's competition.

No one would disagree with the sentiment. The question that needs be asked more brutally than the British are normally prepared to do is simply: why can't British industry do so now anyway?

The contrary City view of bankers and businessmen—though by no means all—is to say that if regeneration of British industry means 'feather-bedding', then it will not work.

Mr Benn claims, correctly, that the level of reinvestment by British industry has been hopelessly low. Industry and their Tory supporters reply that returns are inadequate, thus bringing us back full circle to the tax cuts argument. If, however, the restraints upon investment and the movement of capital were removed, would there in fact follow a big investment boom? Managers as a class say they should be taxed less as at present there are insufficient inducements for them to be managers, rather than shop-floor workers. The arguments are incompatible, but both sides have perfectly admirable points to advance.

There are those who favour reflating the economy; this, the economists are quick to point out, would be disastrous, but a moderate approach to reflation over four or five years might produce steady expansion—perhaps the first real period of expansion for industry in this country since the nineteenth century.

One of the options frequently advanced from the right is to increase overseas investment. The Labour Party and the TUC are fundamentally opposed to overseas investment as a policy option. The main reason for this opposition is their assumption that overseas investment must necessarily mean holding back on investment at home, with the subsequent effect that has upon employment. As Professor Rose of Barclays Bank argues, overseas investment does not divert funds from industry; what it does is lower reserves. He therefore supports the call for a relaxation of exchange control regulations. Overseas investment and home investment could in fact be complementary rather than in competition with each other.

Norway's Prime Minister, Odvar Nordli, said in a *Newsweek* interview in 1977:

> We have calculated that some 40 or 50 per cent of our oil revenue should be placed outside our country's borders. Our domestic economy can't absorb it all. . . . Personally I'd like to see that the capital surplus, and the investments we will make abroad, become a bank book for the economy so that we have something to fall back against on the day we run out of North Sea oil.

Of course Norway's problems are not the same as Britain's; her industrial base is tiny by comparison and she has almost no un-employment, but the philosophy should not be treated as a foolish one. Britain benefited remarkably in the years following the Second World War from the accumulated investments she already had overseas; they contributed handsomely to earnings when home performance, for whatever reasons, was inadequate.

A harsh business judgement of union opposition to overseas investment suggests that it is motivated by the desire to safeguard home inefficiency, which is often the result of union attitudes any-way. There are, on the other hand, plenty of businessmen who argue against overseas investment if this simply assists industries in Canada or Australia to compete with us.

Lack of investment in British industry is not due to lack of money; if those with the resources saw the right returns forth-coming they would invest. If, therefore, government policies deny to such investors the returns they consider to be appropriate, they will hold back and investment must come from government instead.

Another option is that of reducing overseas debts. There are two levels of debt repayment to be considered: those debts specifically secured against the coming of North Sea oil where the lenders have a right to expect liquidation as scheduled; and other longer-term debts where there is room for flexibility. If Britain is regarded internationally as a good risk, there need be no necessary com-pulsion to settle all debts at once, so that at least a part of Britain's debts should be looked at according to normal commercial criteria: the money may bring in better returns used elsewhere. As stated in 'The Next Three Years and into the Eighties', 'A second major area must be the development of plans to meet energy needs for the longer term.' On the other hand, Colin Pritchard of the Church of Scotland asks the much more interesting question: should the revenue be used to modernize the industrial structure or to move the country into a low energy economy? In the twenty-first century this will make a great deal of sense; today such a statement must sound preposterous to most planners for the future whether of left or right. An energy policy programme to develop the alternatives which will take over when oil and gas run out may well be the best way of spending a good proportion of the revenue.

As a country dependent upon food imports for an increasing proportion of its total requirements, Britain could do worse than devote a major part of oil revenues to agricultural improvements and research. By the next century with a huge world population, food is likely to have become the scarcest and most valuable of all resources. The less Britain is dependent upon imports the better. As a matter of long-term survival, therefore, she should consider transforming herself into the most advanced agricultural producer in the world.

The field of welfare—the national health service, education, new facilities in cities—could reasonably claim a substantial share of oil funds. The argument for improving the 'quality of life' is a strong one: the enjoyment of amenities and leisure is as important as efficient industry, though the one relies upon the other. As the TUC-Labour Party document also said:

The benefits of offshore oil cannot be seen in purely economic and industrial terms. A third equally important area where the Labour movement needs to set clear goals involves the creation of a compassionate society, where the new prosperity will be used to help those in need, not just the already rich, the strong and the powerful.

An argument consistently advanced from the right is that of creating incentives for management, which means more pay and less tax. A large proportion of those advancing this view happen to come from the ranks of the managerial class. As a group, of course, they have the same right to advance claims as anyone else. No one, however, has ever explained why captains of industry apparently need so much more inducement to pursue their chosen careers than do lawyers, doctors, teachers or writers, military men or even MPs. Talk of the need for better managerial inducements sometimes gives the impression of a reluctant presence in the wrong career.

A major problem Britain faces is the lack of any industrial strategy; there only exists a collection of pressures. In this connexion it is valuable now to look at questions that will affect society and its performance in the 1990s: technological education; taxation levels; and such areas of constant social concern as rent control. Perhaps what Britain needs more than anything else—and could obtain as a result of her oil wealth being wisely used—is a technological lead that would put her industry generally into the van of the advanced economies. The trouble, to use a medical metaphor, is that Britain needs a health cure rather than a dramatic operation although too many people seem to imagine that North Sea oil will provide the latter. It won't.

Lord Cromer, former Governor of the Bank of England, argued in an article in *The Times* of January 1978 that a major call upon the oil resources ought to be defence. His is about the only voice to have been publicly raised on this account. Lord Seebohm suggested that some of the money should be used to establish a world commodity centre in London; for pump priming for new 'buffer stock' schemes; in support of the Common Fund to provide developing countries with foreign currency following crop failures or other disasters; and for building up strategic stocks (he suggested copper) whose world price may be depressed.

The Labour Party's Green Paper produced at the end of 1977 presented six options: overseas investment; repayment of foreign debt; tax cuts; public services and social infrastructure; investment in manufacturing industry; and investment in energy. As a *Times* editorial eloquently expressed the dilemma:

> The range of options, however, quite simply boils down to the fact that, given substantial oil revenues, the government of the day will be able to finance a given level of expenditure with lower

general taxes; or a higher level of expenditure with a given level of general taxes; or some combination of the two.

When at last the government's White Paper on the use of the oil revenues appeared in March 1978, the idea of a Special Fund had been dropped although an annual progress report is to be made to Parliament to show how White Paper priorities are being observed. The White Paper listed four main uses for the money: investing in industry; investing in energy; reduction in the levels of personal taxation; increasing essential public services. In the debate which followed Mrs Thatcher made plain the Tory view when she said, 'We believe that the lion's share could go by cuts in taxation.'

According to a survey conducted by the *Sunday Times* during April 1978, a large majority of the British people would favour using North Sea revenues to create new jobs and seek new energy sources rather than cut taxes or raise pensions. 73 per cent of those polled wanted to see the money used to improve industrial and social conditions. In answer to the question: 'How would you most like the Government to use the money from North Sea oil?' respondents answered (given in percentages) as follows:

Create new jobs for industry	32
Invest in new energy supplies for when oil runs out	26
Spend more on public services like schools and hospitals	15
Reduce taxes	10
Repay Britain's international debts	10
Raise pensions	5

Such polls are heavily conditioned by the problems of the moment. For the four years 1974–78 inflation has given the greatest cause for concern to a majority of people; now unemployment is catching up and may soon be in top place as the political-economic worry of the majority. Should this happen it will clearly have great influence upon the choice of options people go for.

The options present us with splendid opportunities for debate and the political parties with the chance which they are likely to pursue of presenting the electorate with periodic auctions in pursuit of votes. The danger is that once the great debate is over, we shall collectively opt for our own version of Dutch Disease while paying slight and steadily diminishing attention to other possibilities.

19

Conclusions

Despite many doubts Britain has already come to take her oil for granted; not only because the country has twenty years or more of oil self-sufficiency ahead of it, but also because of the revenues which governments will have at their disposal. The more the oil is taken for granted as income for solving problems, the less likely it is that long-term planning associated with the oil as a finite asset will take place.

It is a feature of the oil world that, with the exception of Saudi Arabia, the extent of whose reserves is so vast as to preclude the possibility of claiming an early end to them, the time horizon placed by the industry upon oil reserves of most other countries round the world varies between fifteen and twenty years. Indeed, if we go backwards in time, the oil companies have long talked of such a general horizon for world supplies.

In 1967 two American brothers, the Paddocks, published a book called *Famine 1975* whose thesis was that time had already run out and the world would face the beginnings of famine in 1975. 1975 has come and gone and the world still eats—if only just, in many cases, although that is largely the result of political forces rather than any absolute world inability to produce enough food. No doubt when the fifteen-year horizon now generally given for oil expires, we shall discover that, somehow, it has been extended once more by new finds or new techniques for increasing the take from existing fields.

The main reason for attaching a deadline to the world's oil is the maintenance of the 'precious' quality of the resource. If oil is about to run out it will be considered more valuable than if resources are apparently limitless; a comparison of attitudes towards coal and its performance should make this clear. When the oil horizon has been extended (as it surely will be), we shall be told how lucky we are while the precious fluid goes on making huge profits for its producers only.

It is remarkable how quickly public excitement turns to acceptance and then indifference. The drama which surrounded the first North Sea finds and especially the largest fields—Forties, Brent, Thistle or

Ninian—is now past, yet continuing exploration is revealing new finds and steadily expanding the oil resources of the North Sea all the time. Development of the second generation of fields of medium size, often structurally complicated, farther north and in deeper waters, is now underway. These fields—Murchison, North Cormorant, Buchan, Magnus—will come on stream in the early 1980s and will average between 100,000 and 150,000 b/d at peak. In March 1978, for example, BP announced it was going ahead with the development of the Magnus field, the most northerly reservoir found to that date with 400 million barrels of reserves. Indeed, by then it was clear that another much less publicized North Sea boom was underway as this second generation of fields were developed. Tax concessions are helping this new boom, since the companies with profitable fields already in production may charge much of the exploration and appraisal drilling against tax on the existing fields and further charge the cost of new projects against corporation tax from their North Sea operations as a whole.

Early in May 1978 Mr Benn set out the terms on which the companies could compete for the sixth round of licences; some 40 to 45 blocks were to be offered in the autumn of 1978. The fourteen major fields already under development will produce more than enough oil to make the country self-sufficient by 1980. The new round, therefore, although small, means that there will be enough ongoing exploration to keep the total of finds up. Exploration continues steadily northwards, with increasing intensity west of Shetland; before long it should also reach the Western Approaches. By early 1978 government had extended the search for oil and gas into deeper waters north-west of Shetland. Phillips announced a new find in March 1978 and the prospects of a commercial find west of Shetland where the oil is the heavier crude variety seemed to have improved when BP announced it was to drill more wells. Then in April 1978 exploration appeared to indicate that large oil and gas fields may lie under the seabed of the continental shelf between the Outer Hebrides and the Rockall trough, among other things intensifying rivalry between Britain and Ireland for economic sovereignty over the area.

As far as British oil enterprise is concerned, perhaps the worst indictment of it is the fact that in the whole North Sea saga to date, more than ten years after the oil boom got underway, there are still a remarkably small number of smaller British companies involved there. Apart from BP and Shell (UK and Dutch) of the giants, Burmah got into disastrous trouble though it now appears to be making a slow, hard comeback, while of others only a handful—Tricentrol, Cluff Oil, LASMO, Thomson—have made good. 54 per cent of North Sea production was controlled by American companies as 1978 began.

Behind both exploration and production, yet steadily developing none the less, is an overall support infrastructure for the offshore operations; it will be a part of British industrial life into the foreseeable future. New developments take place all the time: the oil companies have agreed in principle, for example, to finance a helicopter-borne system for transporting injured divers to hospital in Aberdeen while still under compression. It is one of the less savoury aspects of the business that though the system was ready to operate round the clock in August 1977, it did not go into operation until March 1978 because the companies and the National Health Service were haggling as to who should foot the bill. Then UKOOA agreed that its members would pay for the scheme for a year while they continued their talks with the NHS.

Other problems constantly arise: one is the danger of explosions during the transport and storage of liquefied petroleum gas. Delays in construction at Sullom Voe meant that by March 1978 the Chevron Group was considering ordering a £15 million floating processing unit as a temporary expedient to handle oil output from the Ninian field until the plant at Sullom Voe is ready. £15 million for a temporary plant is an enormous sum; North Sea costs certainly do not diminish.

North Sea oil workers may for a time become the elite of Europe: partly because of their rates of pay, and partly as a result of the supposed romance attaching to their jobs. One of the more glamorous spin-offs from oil announced in 1978 was the luxury hotel-on-stilts to be built in the middle of the North Sea and finished by the end of the same year. The hotel is for use by men and women workers on Ekofisk in the Norwegian sector of the North Sea and has been sited almost exactly halfway between Teesside and Stavanger in Norway. It will cost $100 million and be equipped with sauna, cinema, operating theatre, clinic and laboratory, and a chapel, so it is clearly functional as well as for rest and recuperation. Guests will come and go by helicopter.

As part of a campaign to ensure the public regards oil as precious, the oil men tell us that it is too valuable a fuel to be used for certain base commercial purposes such as electrical generation. The Chairman of Shell Transport and Trading, Michael Pocock, added his voice to a growing chorus when presenting the 1977 annual report. He then said that coal and nuclear energy should provide the base load uses:

If we can achieve this there is no reason why there should not be sufficient oil for appropriate purposes well into the next century. This means, however, that alternative sources of energy must be developed now if they are to be ready when they are required and so release oil for its prime uses.

These prime uses are considered to be transportation and for chemical feedstock.

Attitudes towards emergencies are revealing. Once a disaster threatens such as the Ekofisk blowout, everyone from companies to government stir themselves, for a time, to show determination to keep such emergencies under control. An increasingly informed public is beginning to realize just how much damage an oil slick can do to beaches, to marine life, to birds. But whatever disasters occur in the North Sea—and more surely will—nothing will be allowed to stand in the way of oil extraction, so valuable is this to companies and governments alike. There is urgent need to take far more stringent precautions against such disasters than either have in fact been ready to take to date.

Emergency procedures were adopted by the five major oil-producing areas of the North Sea following the Ekofisk blowout; it is indicative of the low priority accorded disaster control that such plans took so long to mature. There could be no excuse for tight emergency regulations not existing in the southern North Sea much earlier where the gas fields have been in operation for a decade, yet only by 1978 were safety zones formally drawn round these fields. There are 61 installations in the area, 34 containing production wells. The need for permanent safety precautions was highlighted in May 1978 when a wrecked Greek oil tanker threatened to foul undersea gas pipelines off the Norfolk coast; its escaping oil did foul the coast. Problems of this kind will multiply as the North Sea network of platforms and pipelines becomes more complex requiring, among other things, periodic re-drawing of the Sea's navigation charts.

The spectacular break-up of the *Amoco Cadiz* off the French coast in March 1978 and the vast oil slick which subsequently polluted the coast of Brittany led the *Sunday Times* to produce an editorial in its issue of 7 May 1978 which began as follows:

The grounding of the *Amoco Cadiz* off Brittany two months ago was a wholly avoidable disaster. The preliminary French report on it, from which we publish extracts today, makes clear that the accident and its appalling effects occurred because of human misjudgement by a range of people: the master, the owners, the towage firms. In due course their culpability will be tested in court. What the report also conveys, however, is the anti-social and even corrupt morality of an industry: the greed of oil companies which sail under flags of convenience as a way of improving their profits, and the refusal of governments to move at more than a coracle's pace in establishing an effective international regulatory framework to curb them.

In the oil story, too often the power of the companies, the vast sums at stake and the huge profits override all other considerations. Moreover, governments constantly reveal a feebleness in their dealings with the giant companies and sometimes appear simply afraid to exercise their powers to regulate them for the benefit of the national, or international, community as a whole.

BNOC, more or less without interruption, remains a target for fierce attacks from the oil companies, so it is possibly accomplishing its purpose. The companies will go on attacking until, and if, they manage to persuade a government (possibly under Mrs Thatcher) to emasculate it.

Early in 1978 Chevron agreed to state participation in its interests in the Ninian field. Shortly thereafter it launched a bitter attack upon the state corporation. Chevron had in fact also agreed to finance BNOC's share of exploration on two North Sea blocks as part of a deal to enable the two companies to farm-in to acreage east of Shetland held by the Siebens Group, taking 57·5 per cent between them: Chevron to have a 42·5 per cent stake, BNOC a 15 per cent carried stake, with Chevron paying all BNOC's share of exploration expenses until a discovery is declared to be commercial.

There were signs in 1978 that BNOC was financially overextended; in response to criticisms from the Public Accounts Committee BNOC was given short-term financial objectives by Mr Benn for 1979. Answering a question in the House of Commons Mr Benn said:

BNOC's financial performance over the next few years is therefore heavily dependent on the success in bringing on stream fields in which BNOC has a minority interest, and nearly all of whose development decisions were taken before BNOC's creation. Profitability in the short term will also depend on the timing of the start-up of these new fields.

There was considerable criticism of BNOC in 1978. Both Chevron and Occidental attacked the state corporation in April, as did Tom King, opposition energy spokesman, and UKOOA, and its finances received some adverse scrutiny from the Public Accounts Committee. Mr George Keller of Chevron described BNOC as an 'albatross' which was slowing down development work in the North Sea; Mr Bob MacAlister of Occidental said BNOC was being used by government 'to eventually put the rest of us out of business.' BNOC's managing director, Alastair Morton, replied to these attacks: 'Just to set Mr MacAlister right, in no way is there takeover of the North Sea by the state', which seems accurate on present performance. He went on to say:

> We believe that BNOC's function should be exercised in partnership. Occasionally we shall hear noises from the industry which will indicate that we are doing our job, and trying to get it right between Government and the industry.

Lord Kearton accused the companies operating in the North Sea of attempting to influence the press and through it voters and politicians by their attacks upon BNOC's activities. Lord Kearton said that the government had been 'extraordinarily scrupulous and extraordinarily honest' in keeping the pledges given to the oil industry. He declared such oil company tactics to be their normal procedure: for example, he said, in the USA they attacked the President in advertisement campaigns, and he in turn attacked them in his press conferences.

The battle will undoubtedly go on. The oil companies would clearly prefer a Tory electoral victory soon, in the hope that BNOC's powers would be clipped; the longer it continues a itts present pace the greater its standing and influence will become.

As the huge central platform (the largest object ever moved on earth, weighing 600,000 tons) for the Ninian field was towed out to the North Sea in May 1978 at the beginning of the year's 'weather window', so the end of that particular construction job raised queries about further offshore-related employment. The concrete industry has been set back by the oil industry reverting to steel platforms, although it hopes in the long run to be back in business for the great advantage of concrete over steel is its freedom from corrosion. This may turn out to be the case eventually; immediately it meant the workforce of Howard Doris, the contractors, was cut back from a peak of 3,200 to 1,300.

There cannot be any certainty about oil-related employment in Scotland. The unemployed in Scotland are not necessarily equipped to do the work that North Sea developments have created and much of the most valuable of such work—that with a high technology content attached to it—has been clawed back by parent companies in England, the USA or the EEC. Not a great deal of new technology has been brought to Scotland as a result of the oil boom.

In the field of renewables, Britain is making great strides in work on wave energy. Apart from Salter's Ducks there is the Cockerell Raft, a multiple pontoon wave energy device invented by Sir

Christopher Cockerell. According to present calculations, a 600-mile line of wave energy machines off the south-west coast of England and the north-west coast of Scotland capturing energy from the Atlantic could supply half Britain's electricity needs.

Excitement about oil has obscured the fact that the North Sea is also one of the richest fishing grounds in the world and vital to Europe. It should remain so long after the oil is exhausted, provided an increasing scale of disasters has not permanently upset the Sea's ecology.

The North Sea is an area of enormous industrial and resource value to the countries which surround it. Apart from oil, gas and fish there are increasing prospects of other minerals being found beneath its bed. It is a vast reserve for birds. It is one of the busiest sea-lanes in the world, it provides a holiday playground for northern Europe and is used for industrial and other waste dumping. There are many calls upon it. Oil and gas, therefore, should not be extracted at such a rate or in such a manner as to cause disasters which jeopardize the other longer-term uses of the Sea.

Pressures upon North Sea oil during the remaining years of this century will be immense: to supply Britain's and Norway's needs and thereafter to supply as large a part of those of the EEC and the rest of Europe as its members can persuade Britain and Norway to produce, as well as helping meet the voracious demands for oil from the USA.

Two problems will constantly recur: the British relationship with the USA—both because a large proportion of the total North Sea resources are owned by American companies not averse to bringing to bear upon the British government the kind of pressures they employ in the USA; and because of American demands for oil imports. Second will come equally powerful pressures upon Britain from Brussels; in the years ahead the EEC is likely to argue increasingly that North Sea resources are Europe's rather than belonging to one member only.

The effects of oil upon the British economy will be profound. This will be true whether successive governments use the oil income wisely or unwisely. The role of the unions will grow in importance, particularly with respect to their policies towards manning and demarcation. So far in the North Sea story the unions have been remarkably quiet; it is unrealistic to suppose that, once production rather than exploration and development has become the main North Sea activity, the unions will not assume a much more influential role than at present. So far the companies have been only too happy to see the unions kept at a distance, as indeed has been the government. This situation will not last much longer.

Regeneration of British industry or, indeed, of the economy as a whole is clearly the talking point for the next few years. Everyone agrees that the economy is in a mess or at least in need of serious reorganization; few see that oil will not achieve this. Regeneration will only take place as a result of some fundamental changes of attitude, whether these are inspired from the political left or the political right. Oil will at most act as a catalyst, yet by 1978 more and more people were talking and acting as though oil by itself would somehow work the miracle.

Essentially regeneration of British industry is not a question of money at all. Moreover, too many people talk of regeneration of industry as though that were an end in itself. All the regeneration that reformers desire, of industry, the infrastructure, the economy as a whole, the social services, should have as its object the improvement of the lot of the British people. Though everyone at once agrees with such an obvious proposition the sad fact is that all too often this is submerged by considerations of return on investment or figures for productivity.

Oil *is* politics. It has been so for Britain ever since the government took a stake in what is now BP before the First World War, to safeguard supplies for the Royal Navy. In the period since the Second World War, oil has been the cause of many crises for Britain as for other major consumers. It involved this country in the Abadan crisis of 1951–54; it was responsible for her indecision about which side to support at the commencement of the Nigerian civil war, because of the oil stakes in what was Biafra.

Western relations with the Arab Middle East have been dominated by oil throughout the 1970s, until the oil-producing states made plain their determination to control their own resource and not allow the multinationals to do so. From now on, it is equally clear, Britain will face squabbles with her EEC partners and others as she finds herself in the happy position of enjoying self-sufficiency while they do not. On the home front oil will spark off major political rows about control, with BNOC, no doubt, at the centre; and about the use of the oil wealth, tax cuts versus government direction forming the core of that argument.

Home political arguments will be complicated by the Scottish issue and the speed, almost glee, with which the British press reacted to the relatively poor showing of the SNP in the May 1978 local elections showed that little had been learnt in the south about attitudes and feelings in Scotland. If the SNP is forced to retreat for a while—a common enough political occurrence for any party—the likelihood is that devolution or any other concessions to the special needs of Scotland will be shelved by the major political parties at Westminster.

12*

Benn's appointment of Professor Peter Odell as a consultant to his department clearly infuriated the oil companies. As the Professor commented: 'What this indicates most of all is an unpreparedness by most of the companies to face effective analysis of the industry.' Indeed, the industry as a whole is usually able to evade such analysis from outside and part of its anger at Benn, BNOC and Odell is that the three in combination bring analysis a good deal closer than otherwise might have been the case.

The oil companies represent possibly the most powerful corporate group in Britain at the present time; it is right that their actions should be under constant public scrutiny and it is perhaps worth reiterating fairly often—when debates are being conducted about private enterprise or BNOC, for example—that the oil under the North Sea is Britain's oil and not the property of any company.

The most important question relating to North Sea, or other, British oil is: what ultimately will be the benefit to the British people? By the time all the financial and political interests have had their fingers in the enormously lucrative North Sea pie, that will be a difficult one to answer. The saddest aspect of the North Sea story is the speed of development; in retrospect historians will ask why we had to be in such a hurry to exploit our greatest natural resource since the development of coal. The answer to this question is not reassuring. Britain had so mismanaged her economy that when large oil discoveries were made, the country grasped at these like a drowning man instead of approaching oil development in a more measured fashion. The fact that oil was regarded first and foremost as a means of solving the balance of payments leaves little hope that for the remainder of the century we shall either conserve or produce long-term policies for using the oil wealth for the future.

As Odell and Rosing point out in *Optimal Development of the North Sea Oil Fields*:

> . . . there is an inherent conflict of interest between oil companies and governments in respect of the profits, revenues and other benefits to be secured from the development of large North Sea oil fields.

This is true. So also is it true that there is an inherent conflict of interest between what a government in office does while considering its chances at the next election, and what it ought to do in the national interest. This applies especially to the use of North Sea revenues.

The 'state of Britain', however it is viewed, is unlikely to be cured by oil wealth, though this may certainly help any process of rejuvenation. The level of employment in the country might well become the most important guide to any choice of options to be made over the next few years. At least oil has presented the country with choices which otherwise we should not be in a position to consider at all.

The British, on the whole, are a lazy people, though they like to pretend otherwise; they enjoy spending when they get the chance and oil is about to provide them with such a chance. In the 1978 run-up to a general election, there seemed little prospect that the nation would apply to its oil wealth any of its nineteenth-century Victorian attitudes to money and, for example, invest most of it for the future.

Perhaps the last word should be given to Admiral Sir Raymond Lygo. When in January 1978 he was interviewed by Philip Howard for a *Times* profile, he assessed his countrymen accurately when he said:

> As a nation we have to live by our wits. We have never done very well by hard work.

Oil may make this process somewhat easier for us.

Appendices

APPENDIX I

Criteria governing the first four licence rounds

FIRST ROUND OF LICENSING

The five main criteria to be followed in awarding licences at the discretion of the then Minister of Power were announced by him in the House of Commons on 7 April 1964, as follows:

First, the need to encourage the most rapid and thorough exploration and economical exploitation of petroleum resources on the continental shelf.

Second, the requirement that the applicant for a licence shall be incorporated in the United Kingdom and the profits of the operation shall be taxable here.

Thirdly, in cases where the applicant is a foreign-owned concern, how far British oil companies receive equitable treatment in that country.

Fourthly, we shall look at the programme of work of the applicant and also at the ability and resources to implement it.

Fifthly, we shall look at the contribution the applicant has already made or is making towards the development of resources of our continental shelf and the development of our fuel economy generally.

SECOND ROUND OF LICENSING

Following the General Election of October 1964 the new Administration instituted a review of policy. The Ministry had earlier determined to set up a Petroleum Inspectorate to carry out its functions under the Regulations. The first member had been appointed early in 1965 and his expertise was available during the review. The review covered all aspects of policy, with particular reference to the method of allocation of licences and the extent of public enterprise participation. The Norwegian Government had invited applications for licences on their part of the continental shelf on terms similar to those used by the United Kingdom in the first round of licensing. The Dutch Government was also about to invite applications. The conclusions reached were that there was no good case to change either the method of allocation or the financial terms and conditions. In deciding to whom licences should be granted the Minister would, however, take into account certain considerations additional to those used as a basis for allocation in the first round. These were:

Any exploration work already done by or on behalf of the applicant which was relevant to the areas applied for, and his facilities for disposing, in the U.K., of any oil or gas won;

The contribution the applicant had made or was planning to make to our economic prosperity, including the strengthening of the United Kingdom balance of payments and the growth of industry and employment in the United Kingdom, with particular reference to regional considerations, and

Any proposals which may be made for facilitating participation by public enterprise in the development and exploitation of the resources of the continental shelf.

THIRD ROUND OF LICENSING

When announcing the new round of licensing in the House of Commons on 23 July 1969, Mr Roy Mason, then Minister of Power, outlined the criteria which would be taken into account in considering applications:

The applicant's programme of work and ability to carry it out.

The applicant's previous exploration work relevant to the areas applied for.

The applicant's facilities for disposal in the U.K. of any oil or gas produced.

For foreign-owned applicants, the extent to which British-owned companies receive equitable treatment in that country.

The extent to which the applicant has contributed or plans to contribute to our economic prosperity, to strengthening of U.K. balance of payments and to the growth of industry and employment in this country with particular reference to regional considerations.

The extent to which the application provided for participation by

Public Enterprise in the development and exploitation of the resources of the Continental Shelf.

In addition to these criteria which had been used in 1965, the Minister said that some added preference would be given to groups involving the Gas Council, the National Coal Board or other British interests. For Irish Sea blocks it would be a stringent criterion that applicants should provide for participation by the Gas Council or the N.C.B. through direct partnership or option or other acceptable arrangements which the parties may agree between them.

FOURTH ROUND OF LICENSING

Applications for blocks

In considering applications for non-tender blocks the Secretary of State will take the following criteria into account:

Where an applicant is foreign-owned the extent to which British owned companies receive equitable reciprocal treatment in that foreign country.

The extent to which the applicant will further the thorough and rapid exploration and exploitation of the oil and gas resources of the United Kingdom Continental Shelf; particular attention will be paid to the financial and technical capability of the applicant to carry out an acceptable programme of work.

The exploration work relevant to the area applied for which has already been carried out by or on behalf of the applicant.

If the applicant holds or has held licences, his overall performance to date.

The extent of the applicant's contribution actual or planned to the U.K. economy including the strengthening of the balance of payments and the growth of industry and employment.

Principal conditions governing tendering are:

A 20 per cent deposit is required with each tender and successful tenderers will be required to pay the balance of the tender within 14 days of the announcement of the awards.

In receiving tenders the Secretary of State reserves the right to reject the highest or any other tender either:

(i) where the tender has been submitted by a foreign owned

applicant if he is not satisfied that British owned companies receive equitable reciprocal treatment in that foreign country;

  (ii) where the applicant has not followed the rules for the submission of tenders;

(iii) if he is not satisfied that the applicant has at his disposal the technical resources necessary to carry out a work programme competently and

(iv) for any other reason; in such cases the applicant will be given the reason if he so requests.

Subject to the Secretary of State's right to reject any tender, licences will be awarded to the highest tenderers. In the event of equal highest tenders being received each applicant will be given the opportunity of accepting a joint licence each contributing an equal share of the premium offered. If a proposal to award a joint licence is not accepted within 14 days the award of the licence will be at the discretion of the Secretary of State.

APPENDIX II

Offshore Oil Fields in Production

The table below provides basic information on the nine fields in production in March 1978.

Proven Oil Fields		Extension into other UK Blocks						
Field name (Block number)	Licensees/Company interest in block (%) in 1977	Block number	Licensees	Company interest in block (%) in 1977	Date of discovery	Date of production start-up	Operator's estimate of first year of peak production	Operator's estimated peak production (million tonnes per year)	Operator's estimate of proven recoverable reserves for the field (million tonnes)[1]
Argyll (30/24)	Hamilton Brothers Oil (Great Britain) Ltd/28·8 Hamilton Brothers Petroleum (UK) Ltd/7·2 RTZ Oil & Gas Ltd/25 Blackfriars Oil Co. Ltd/12·5 The Trans-European Co. Ltd/2·5 Texaco North Sea UK Ltd/24	—	—	—	Oct. 1971	June 1975	1977	1·1	—[2]
Auk (30/16)	Shell/50 Esso/50	—	—	—	Feb. 1971	Feb. 1976	1977	2·3	7·3[3]
Beryl (9/13)	Mobil Producing North Sea Ltd/50 Amerada Exploration Ltd (Amerada)/20 Texas Eastern UK Ltd (Texas Eastern)/20 British Gas Corporation/10	—	—	—	Sept. 1972	June 1976	1978	4	75[4]
Brent (211/29)	Shell/50 Esso/50	3/4	Texaco North Sea UK Ltd	100	July 1971	Nov. 1976	1982	23[5]	220[5]

Field (block)	Participants/interest (%)	Block	Participants	Interest (%)	Discovery	Production	Year		
Claymore (14/19)	Occidental Petroleum (Caledonia) Ltd/36·5 Getty Oil International (England) Ltd/23·5 Allied Chemical (Great Britain) Ltd/20 Thomson North Sea Ltd/20	—	—	—	May 1974	Nov. 1977	1979	7·3	55
Forties (21/10)	BP Oil Development Ltd/100	22/16a	Shell UK Ltd (Shell) Esso Petroleum Co. Ltd (Esso)	50 50	Nov. 1970	Nov. 1975	1978	24	240
Montrose (22/17)	Amoco UK Petroleum Ltd (Amoco)/30·77 British Gas Corporation/30·77 Amerada/23·08 Texas Eastern/15·38	22/18	Amoco British Gas Corporation Amerada Texas Eastern	30·77 23·08 15·38	Sept. 1969	June 1976	1978	2·4	20
Piper (15/17)	Occidental Petroleum (UK) Ltd/36·5 Getty Oil International (England) Ltd/23·5 Allied Chemical (Great Britain) Ltd/20 Thomson North Sea Ltd/20	—	—	—	Jan. 1973	Dec. 1976	1979	14·6	82
Thistle (211/18)	BNOC Developments Ltd/5 Burmah Oil Exploration Ltd/8·15 BNOC (Thistle) Ltd/10·85 Deminex UK Exploration and Production/22·5 Deminex Oil & Gas (UK) Ltd/20 Santa Fe (UK) Ltd/16·9 Tricentrol Thistle Development Ltd/4·9 Charterhouse Petroleum Development Ltd/1 Ashland Oil/5·6 BNOC/5·1	211/19	Conoco Gulf BNOC (Exploration) Ltd	33⅓ 33⅓ 33⅓	July 1973	March 1978	1979	10·6	73

Approximate conversion factors 1m barrels per day = 50m tonnes per year, 1 tonne = 7·4 barrels.

[1] The reserves quoted may not be precisely comparable with each other and with other figures quoted in this report since differences exist in the procedures and assumptions adopted by different companies and by the Department of Energy.

[2] Currently under re-assessment.

[3] Total discounted reserves: that is, proven plus suitably discounted figures for probable and possible reserves.

[4] Proven plus prospective.

[5] Stabilized crude, excluding NGL for block 211/29.

Offshore Oilfields Under Development*

The table below provides basic information on the eight fields under development by the end of 1977.

Proven Oil Fields		Extension into other UK Blocks							
Field name (Block number)	Licensees/Company interest in block in 1977	Block number	Licensees	Company Interest in block in 1977	Date of discovery	Date of production start-up	Operator's estimate of first year of peak production	Operator's estimated peak production (million tonnes per year)	Operator's estimate of proven recoverable reserves for the field (million tonnes)[1]
Buchan (21/1)	BP Petroleum Development Ltd/27 1/12 Transworld Petroleum (UK) Ltd/14 CCP North Associates Ltd/10 7/12 Gas & Oil Acreage Ltd/5 City Petroleum Co./14 Candel Petroleum (UK) Ltd/14 St Joe Petroleum (UK) Ltd/14 Charter Hall Oil Ltd/1‡	20/5	Texaco	100	Aug 1974	1979	—[8]	—	—
Cormorant South (211/26)	Shell/50 Esso/50	211/21	Shell Esso	50 50	Sept. 1972	1979[6]	1981[6]	3[6]	15[3][6]
Dunlin (211/23)	Shell/50 Esso/50	211/24	Conoco Ltd (Conoco) Gulf Oil (Great Britain) Ltd (Gulf) BNOC (Exploration) Ltd	33‡ 33‡ 33‡	July 1973	1979	1982	7·5	80[3]
Heather (2/5)	Unocal Exploration & Production Co. (UK) Ltd/31·25 Skelly Oil Exploration (UK) Ltd/31·25 Tenneco Great Britain Ltd/31·25 The Norwegian Oil Co. DNO (UK) Ltd/6·25	—	—	33‡	Dec. 1973	1978	1980	2·5	20

Field (block)	Licensees / interest	Block	Companies		Discovery				
Murchison (UK) (211/19)	Conoco Ltd/33⅓ Gulf Oil (Great Britain) Ltd/33⅓ BNOC (Exploration) Ltd/33⅓	—			Sept. 1975	1980	1982	7·2	51
Ninian (3/3)	Chevron Petroleum Ltd/24 BNOC (Ninian) Ltd/30 Imperial Chemical Industries Ltd/26 Murphy Petroleum Ltd/10 Ocean Exploration Co. Ltd/10	3/8	BP Petroleum Development Ltd Ranger Oil (UK) Ltd Scottish Canadian Oil and Transportation Co. Ltd London & Scottish Marine Oil Co. Ltd	50 20 7 23	Jan. 1974	1978	1981	17·3	155
UK Statfjord (211/24)	Conoco/33⅓ Gulf/33⅓ BNOC (Exploration) Ltd/33⅓	211/25			April 1974	1979	1985	4·2	58·6[7]
Tartan (15/16)	Texaco North Sea UK Ltd/100	—			Dec. 1974	1981	1981	—[8]	—[8]

* The expression 'Oil fields under Development' covers those fields on which significant development work has occurred, indicated by the placement of major contracts for offshore equipment. It does not imply possession of a Department of Energy development consent and at the end of 1977 neither Murchison Statfjord nor Tartan had such consents. Buchan had only a consent for a seabed template.

Approximate conversion factors 1m barrels per day = 50m tonnes per year, 1 tonne = 7·4 barrels.

[1] The reserves figures quoted may not be precisely comparable with each other and with other figures quoted in this report since differences exist in the procedures and assumptions adopted by different companies and by the Department of Energy.

[2] Currently under re-assessment.

[3] Total discounted reserves: that is, proven plus suitable discounted figures for probable and possible reserves.

[4] Proven plus prospective.

[5] Stabilized crude, excluding NGL for block 211/29.

[6] These figures refer to production from block 211/26.

[7] Estimated UK sector reserves, discussions are in progress on the unitization of the field.

[8] Under assessment.

Source: Department of Energy Brown Book 1978.

APPENDIX III

Statement of the Secretary of State for Energy (Mr Varley) on Depletion Policy, 6 December 1974

In my statement to Parliament on 11th July on United Kingdom offshore policy, I said that the Government proposed to take powers to control the rate of depletion of oil. I already have power to decide on the timing, nature and extent of future licensing rounds, and in the forthcoming petroleum legislation I shall be proposing powers to control the rate of production.

How or when such powers may be used in the 1980s and 1990s will depend on the extent of the total finds, on the world oil market and on the demand for energy. On all these points great uncertainty prevails. Policy will also be influenced by our general economic situation and in particular the outlook for our balance of payments. The Government cannot, therefore, be expected to define, before any oil has come ashore, and when large parts of the sea remain unexplored, a long-term production pattern. On the other hand, these powers may be needed in the future to safeguard national interests. However much oil we find, it is limited and can only be used once. This and future governments must, therefore, ensure that this vital national resource will be used at a rate which secures the greatest long-term benefit to the nation's economy, and in particular to Scotland, Wales and other parts of the United Kingdom in need of development.

We propose, therefore, to take powers of control for use in the future, but it remains the Government's aim to ensure that oil production from the United Kingdom Continental Shelf builds up as quickly as possible over the next few years to the level set out in paragraph 4 of the White Paper [Cmnd. 5696]. This will help our balance of payments, contribute to Government revenues, stimulate our industries and make our energy supplies more secure. It will also be an important British contribution to the development of the indigenous energy resources of the industrial world. I wish, therefore, to assure the oil companies, and the banks to which they will look for finance, that our depletion policy and its implementation will not undermine the basis on which they have made plans and entered into commitments. Our future policy will be based on the following guidelines:

(a) No delays will be imposed on the development of finds already made or on any new finds made up to the end of 1975 under existing licences. If it should prove necessary to delay the development of finds made in 1976 or later, there will be full consultation with the companies so that premature investment is avoided.

(b) No cuts will be made in production from finds already made, or from new finds made before the end of 1975 under existing licences, until 1982 at the earliest, or until four years after the start of production, whichever is the later.

(c) No cuts will be made in production from any field found after 1975 under an existing licence until 150 per cent of the capital investment in the field has been recovered.

(d) If we later need to use these powers we will have full regard to the technical and commercial aspects of the fields in question and this would generally limit cuts to 20 per cent at most. We shall be consulting the industry on the period of notice to be given before any reduction in production comes into effect.

(e) In deciding on action to postpone development or limit production, the Government will also take into account the needs of the offshore supply industry in Scotland, Wales and other parts of the United Kingdom, for a continuing and stable market.

Longer-term conservation strategy is being and will be formulated as progressively more information becomes available. At this stage, the regime for depletion of any finds made in the Celtic Sea should not be regarded as settled. The British National Oil Corporation, to be established by the Petroleum Bill next year, could have an important role to play in exploring areas yet to be licensed, and in establishing potential fields whose reserves could be husbanded or developed quickly in accordance with the widest national interest. This is for the future, and does not affect present licences; but I think it right to state our more immediate intentions now.

APPENDIX IV

The authors of the *Times* article on the nuclear debate, 6 February 1978

Sir St John Elstub	Chairman of IMI and past president of the Institution of Mechanical Engineers
Sir John Atwell	Chairman (1978–79) of the Council of Engineering Institutions (CEI) and past president of the Institution of Mechanical Engineers
Sir Charles Pringle	Immediate past chairman of the CEI and past president of the Royal Aeronautical Society
Professor R. C. Coates	Vice-president of the Institution of Civil Engineers
G. Tony Dummett	Chairman of Meeting of Presidents of Professional Bodies, and past chairman of CEI and past president of the Institution of Chemical Engineers
C. Norman Thompson	Managing director, Shell Research, and president of the Royal Institute of Chemistry

SELECT BIBLIOGRAPHY

The development of British North Sea oil has been so fast that it is exceptionally difficult to keep pace with the literature on the subject, of which there is now an enormous quantity and variety. The bibliography given below consists of those books and reports or other publications which the author has found particularly informative or has relied upon for basic information on certain aspects of the wide field covered in this book. There are many omissions. Much of the information in this book comes from the huge press coverage now devoted to Britain's oil 'province'.

BOOKS

Callow, Clive, *Power from the Sea* (Gollancz 1973)
Chapman, Keith, *North Sea Oil and Gas* (David & Charles 1976)
Cooper, B. & Gaskell, T. F., *North Sea Oil—The Great Gamble* (Heinemann 1966; revised 1967)
Harvie, Christopher, *Scotland and Nationalism* (George Allen & Unwin 1977)
Jones, Mervyn & Godwin, Fay, *The Oil Rush* (Quartet 1976)
Kitchen, Jonathan, *Labour Law and Off-shore Oil* (Croom Helm 1977)
Mackay, D. I. & Mackay, G. A., *The Political Economy of North Sea Oil* (Martin Robertson 1975)
Mackay, D. I. (ed.), *Scotland 1980* (Q Press 1977)
Nicolson, James R., *Shetland and Oil* (William Luscombe 1975)
Odell, Peter R., *Oil and World Power* (Pelican 1970)
Odell, Peter R. & Rosing, Kenneth E., *Optimal Development of the North Sea's Oil Fields* (Kogan Page 1976)
Redwood, Boverton (assisted Holloway, G. T.), *Petroleum and its Products* (Charles Griffin & Co Ltd 1896)
Sampson, Anthony, *The Seven Sisters* (Hodder & Stoughton 1975)
Sibthorp, M. M. (ed.), *The North Sea: Challenge and Opportunity* (Europa Publications 1975)
Tugendhat, Christopher & Hamilton, Adrian, *Oil: The Biggest Business* (Eyre Methuen 1968; revised 1975)

WAES (Workshop on Alternative Energy Strategies), *Energy: Global Prospects 1985–2000* (McGraw Hill 1977)

Whitehead, Harry, *An A to Z of Offshore Oil & Gas* (Kogan Page 1976)

Wolfe, Billy, *Scotland Lives* (Reprographia 1973)

GOVERNMENT PUBLICATIONS

British Gas, *United Kingdom Energy Prospects and the Plans of British Gas* (British Gas 1976)

Committee of Public Accounts (First Report), *North Sea Oil and Gas* (HMSO 1973)

Department of Energy, *Development of the Oil and Gas Resources of the United Kingdom 1977 (The Brown Book)* (HMSO 1977)

    The Brown Book 1978

    OSO (HMSO 1977)

    Offshore 1976: An Analysis of Orders Placed (HMSO 1977)

    Energy Paper 7: *North Sea Costs Escalation Study* (1975)

    Energy Paper 8: *The Offshore Energy Technology Board: Strategy for Research and Development* (1976)

    Energy Paper 12: *Advisory Council on Energy Conservation* (1976)

        The Energy Commission: *Working Document on Energy Policy* (Energy Commission Paper No 1, 1977)

Other Government papers, press briefings etc. and various Acts, the most important being the Petroleum & Submarine Pipelines Act 1975.

REPORTS AND PAMPHLETS

Cairns, W. J. and Associates, Flotta Orkney Oil Handling Terminal

    Report 1 'An Environmental Assessment' (1973)

    Report 2 'Visual Impact Analysis Landscape Proposals' (1974)

    Report 3 'Marine Environment Protection' (1975)

Francis, John & Swan, Norman, *Scottish Oil Shakedown* (Church of Scotland Home Board 1975)

The Henley Centre for Forecasting, *Scotland in the 1980s* (Henley 1976)

Hill, Mark, *Oil Over Troubled Waters* (Aberdeen People's Press 1976)

Hutcheson, A. MacGregor & Hogg, Alexander (editors), *Scotland and Oil* (Oliver & Boyd 1975)

IMEG (International Management and Engineering Group of Britain Ltd.) *Study of Potential Benefits to British Industry from Offshore Oil and Gas Developments* (HMSO 1972)

Marshall, Elizabeth, *Shetland's Oil Era* (Research and Development Department of Shetland Islands Council 1977)

Ministry of Industry (Norway), Report No 30 to the Norwegian Storting (1973–74) (Ministry of Information 1977)

NEDO (National Economic Development Office), *Engineering Construction Performance* (Nedo 1976)

Nore, Petter, *Six Myths of British Oil Policies* (Thames Polytechnic 1976)

Rosie, George, *Cromarty: The Scramble for Oil* (Canongate, Edinburgh 1974)

Royal Norwegian Ministry of Finance, Parliamentary Report No 25 (1973–1974): *Petroleum Industry in Norwegian Society* (Ministry of Finance 1974)

The Sullom Voe Environmental Advisory Group, *Oil Terminal at Sullom Voe Environmental Impact Assessment* (Thuleprint Ltd 1976)

TUC-Labour Party Liaison Committee, *The Next Three Years and Into the Eighties* (The Labour Party 1977)

PAPERS AND SPEECHES

Hunt, Deirdre, 'The Sociology of Development: Its Relevance to Aberdeen', The Scottish Journal of Sociology (Vol 1, No 2) 1977
   'Organizational Strategies and Technology Diffusion: The Case of Oil-involved Engineering Companies in the City of Aberdeen 1977' (Paper privately circulated) 1977

Wilson, Gordon (MP), 'Development of the Oil Industry in Scotland' (Speech, 9 December 1976)

COMPANIES

I have drawn upon a wide range of company papers and reports of both the oil companies and various other companies whose names occur in the text. It would be impossible to list all of these.

British Petroleum Company Limited, 'Our Industry Petroleum' (BP 1977)

Shell UK Exploration and Production, 'North Sea Gas Southern Operations' (Shell 1976)

Shell International Petroleum Company Ltd, 'Information Handbook 1977–78' (Shell 1977)

MAGAZINES

There are a variety of magazines dealing with aspects of the oil industry; I have drawn upon the contents of various editions of *Petroleum Review* published by the Institute of Petroleum.

The May 1977 issue of *The Banker* published by the *Financial Times* contained a number of articles upon North Sea oil developments.

Index

Index